BIOLOGY

for OCR A

FOR SEPARATE AWARD

02-19

Byron Dawson and Ian Honeysett
Series editor: Bob McDuell

Heinemann Educational Publishers
Halley Court, Jordan Hill, Oxford, OX2 8EJ
a division of Reed Educational & Professional Publishing Ltd
Heinemann is a registered trademark of Reed Educational & Professional Publishing Ltd

OXFORD MELBOURNE AUCKLAND
JOHANNESBURG BLANTYRE GABORONE
IBADAN PORTSMOUTH NH (USA) CHICAGO

First published 2001

ISBN 0 435 58296 8

05 04 03 02 01
10 9 8 7 6 5 4 3 2

Edited by Helen Barham PhD

Designed and typeset by Oxford Designers & Illustrators

Illustrated by Oxford Designers & Illustrators

Printed and bound in Spain by Edelvives

Picture research by Elizabeth Savery

Acknowledgements
The authors and publishers would like to thank the following for permission to use photographs:
Cover photo by Science Photo Library/Eye of Science.
TB1: Fig 1, (left) CNRI/SPL. Fig 1 (middle) Microfield Scientific Ltd/SPL. Fig 1, (right) Dr Tony Brain/SPL. Fig 2, (top) Claude Nuridsany & Marie Perennou/SPL. Fig 2, (bottom) SPL/J.C. Revy. Figs 4, 5, Wellcome Library London. Fig 6, University of Zurich Nature & Science/OSF. Fig 7, Andrew Syred/SPL. Fig 18, J.C. Revy/SPL. Fig 20, Dr Jeremy Burgess/SPL. TB2: Fig 10 Quest/SPL. TB3: Fig 7, Mike Powell/Allsport. TB4: Fig 1, G.I. Bernard/NHPA. Fig 7, St Bartholomew's Hospital/SPL. Fig 11, Wellcome Library London. TB5: Fig 3 (left), Eye of Science/SPL. Fig 3 (right), Dr Jeremy Burgess/SPL. Figs 4 (left), 5, Andrew Syred/SPL. Fig 4 (right), J.C. Revy/SPL. TB7: Fig 4, Lawrence Gould/OSF. Fig 11, Art Wolfe/Stone. Fig 12, Phillip Steele/ICCE. Fig 28, Spectrum Colour Library. Fig 29, Rex Features. TB8: Fig 6, Rudie Kuiter/OSF. Fig 11, CC Studio/SPL. Fig 18, Rex Features. Fig 19, Dan Suzio/SPL. Fig 20, G.I. Bernard/OSF. TB9: Fig 1 (top), Wayne Bilenduke/Stone. Fig 1(bottom), Spectrum Colour Library. Fig 3, Biophoto Associates/SPL. TB10: Fig 1, Prof. K. Seddon & Dr. T. Evans, Queen's University Belfast/SPL. Fig 2, Phillippe Plailly/ SPL. Fig 6, SPL/CNRI. Fig 7, Stone. Fig 9, Patrisha Thomson/Stone. Fig 10 (left), N. Durrel McKenna/Panos Pictures. Fig 10 (right), Marcus Rose/Panos Pictures. Fig 12 Ennio Boga/OSF. Fig 13, SPL/Dept. of Clinical Cytogenetics, Addenbrookes Hospital. Fig 14, Gary Parker/SPL. Fig 18 (left) Harry Taylor/OSF. Fig 18 (right), Liz Eddison/Bruce Coleman. Fig 19, Derek Bromhall/OSF. Figs 28, 31, Wellcome Library London. Figs 32, 33, Peter Parks/OSF. Fig 35, David Fox/OSF.
SPL = Science Photo Library. OSF = Oxford Scientific Films

The publishers have made every effort to trace the copyright holders, but if they have inadvertently overlooked any, they will be pleased to make the necessary arrangements at the first opportunity.
P20, fig 12, Tesco Stores Ltd. p20, fig 13, Gluten Free Foods Ltd. P38, fig 10, p41, figs16, 17, p91, fig 8, Lung & Asthma Information Agency. P39, fig 12, BMJ Publishing Group (taken from *Smoking, smoking cessation and lung cancer in the UK since 1950: combination of national statistics with two case-control studies* by Richard Peto, Sarah Darby, Harz Deo, Paul Silcocks, Elise Whitely and Richard Doll 2000). P72, fig 10, Cambridge University Press (taken from *Ecology ABAL unit 9*). P78, fig 21, John Murray (Publishers) Ltd (taken from *Ecology* by Peter Chen). P101, fig 29, pbi Home and Garden Limited. P101, fig 30, LC SOLUTIONS Limited.

Introduction

This book provides coverage of OCR Biology (1980). The first examination of these specifications is in June 2003. It concentrates on Extension Block A only. Further information about the alternative Extension Block B is available from OCR.

The book has been written by examiners who have been involved in the writing of the new specifications. It is supported by other materials published by Heinemann including a Homework book, a Teacher's Resource pack and a CD-ROM.

The book is divided into two parts.

Material common to the Biology of Double Award is covered by the first ten Teaching blocks. Each Teaching block has an introductory spread. This reminds you of what you should already know from Key Stage 3. It also gives a quick Check-up test. If you feel there are things you do not remember, your teacher should have a Summary sheet to help you.

Extension A material is covered by four additional Teaching blocks, A1–A4. These also have an introductory spread so that you can check what you already know from Double award. Remember that this material can only be tested on Paper 3 or 4.

Throughout the book there are:

Key Points

Each Teaching block is split into double-page spreads. Each double-page spread starts by listing the key points it covers.

Higher tier material

If you are taking the Higher tier papers (1980/2 and 1980/4) you will be expected to know and understand all the material in this book. If, however, you are taking Foundation tier, you can miss out the parts that are shown in pink tinted boxes. This is Higher or H material.

Thinking further

At the end of each double-page spread there are questions to test your understanding. They are at two levels. The easier questions are shown by a ■ and the harder questions by a ◆.

Ideas and evidence

In the new specifications there will be questions about how scientists worked in the past and how they work today. Throughout the book there are Ideas and evidence boxes and questions.

Taking it further

Taking if further boxes include interesting facts which are not on the specification. You will not be examined on the material in these boxes.

Key words

Key words are important scientific terms that you need to know. They are emboldened in the text, listed at the end of the double-page spread and explained in the Glossary. Key words for Higher only are shown in pink.

Key facts and formulae

These are shown in blue tinted boxes throughout. It is important that you remember these.

Questions

At the end of each Teaching block there are examination-type questions. Questions with symbols ● and ■ are similar to those found on Foundation papers; those with ■ and ◆ are similar to questions found on Higher papers.

Skills sections

At the back of the book are sections to help you improve your skills in particular areas.

We hope that this book will help you throughout your course.

Contents

Teaching block 9

Homeostasis

Teaching block 10

Inheritance and evolution

Teaching block A1

Human physiology

Teaching block A2

Diversity and adaptation

Teaching block A3

Micro-organisms and food

Teaching block A4

Micro-organisms and disease

Introducing biological principles

Introduction

All living organisms are made up of cells. You have probably looked at cells under a light microscope. A microscope is needed because most cells are too small to see with the naked eye. Cells also tend to be rather transparent and so they need to be stained with a chemical that makes them more visible.

The most obvious structure seen in cells viewed under the microscope is the nucleus, which controls the actions of the cell. The nucleus is surrounded by the jelly-like cytoplasm, which contains many enzymes. It is kept in by the cell membrane which surrounds the whole cell.

Plant cells have a thick cell wall outside the cell membrane. This helps to protect the cell. Some plant cells have green structures called chloroplasts. This is where photosynthesis takes place.

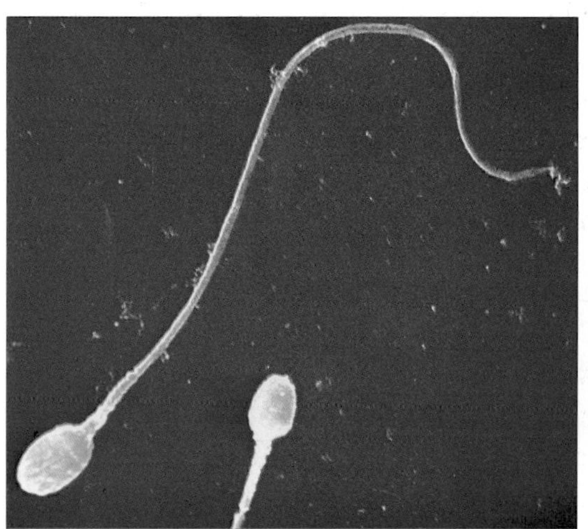
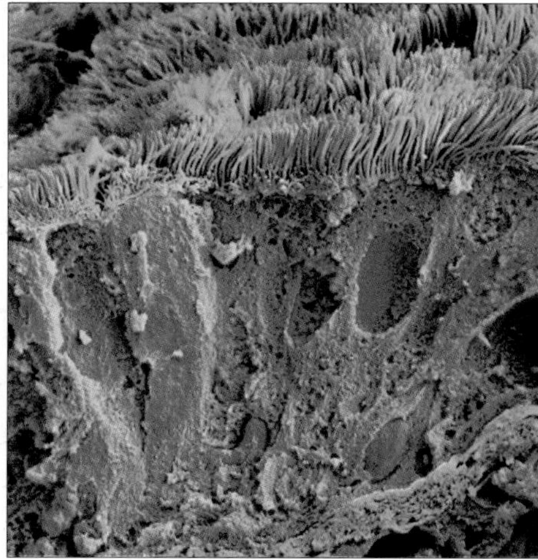
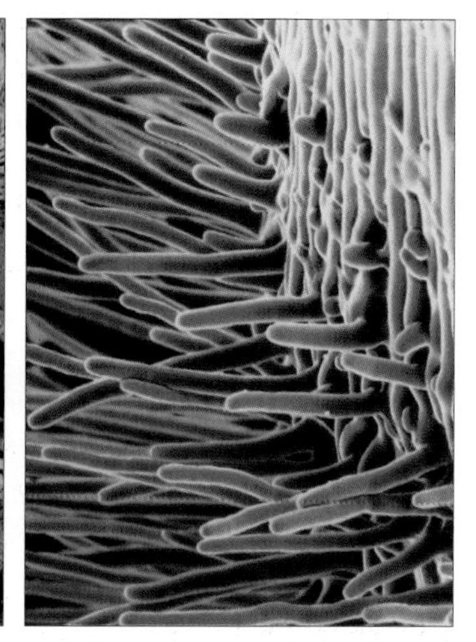

fig 1 | Coloured scanning electron micrographs of human sperm (×1700) (left), the epithelium lining the bronchi in the human lung (×1400) (middle) and root hair cells of cress roots (×200) (right)

You may have had the chance to look at different types of cells under the microscope. A selection of different cells is shown in fig 1. They all have a cell membrane, a nucleus and cytoplasm. However, they all look different. This is because they do different jobs and they are adapted to work efficiently.

Large organisms are made up of vast numbers of cells. However, the different types of cells are not just scattered about at random. Similar cells are gathered together to form tissues, and tissues are grouped together to make organs.

Check-up

Have a go at the following questions. They will remind you of what you should know about biological principles.

a Write down the functions of the following parts of the cell:
  i the nucleus
  ii the cell membrane
  iii the cytoplasm.

b What is the function of chloroplasts in plant cells?

c In which part of the plant would you find cells without chloroplasts? Explain your answer.

d Look at the sperm cell in fig 1.
  i What is the function of sperm cells?
  ii How are they adapted for their job?
  iii Explain why all the cytoplasm in a fertilised egg comes from the mother.

e Look at the root hair cells in fig 1. How are these cells adapted for their job?

If you have difficulty, ask your teacher for a Summary sheet.

Contents of the Teaching block

1.1 Cells

The development of the microscope was vital in allowing the structure of cells to be investigated. The light microscope has allowed scientists to see the differences between plant cells and animal cells. The invention of the electron microscope allowed cells to be studied in detail and smaller structures in the cytoplasm were discovered.

1.2 Life processes

This spread describes the seven processes that are characteristic of living organisms. Cells do not work individually to perform these functions, but are gathered together into tissues and work together. Different tissues make up the various organs of the body, and the organs work together in systems.

1.3 Transport and cells

Cells need to take in various substances to use for their living processes; they also need to lose waste products. These substances pass through the cell membrane by diffusion, osmosis or active transport. The first two processes rely on the passive movement of the molecules whereas active transport needs an input of energy.

1.4 Osmosis

Osmosis is a special type of diffusion: it is the diffusion of water through a membrane. The uptake of water by osmosis into plant cells is important in maintaining the support of the plant.

Links to other Teaching blocks

2.3 Absorption
4.1 Breathing
6.4 Water transport in plants
9.2 Controlling temperature
9.3 Kidneys and lungs
10.1 Genes and chromosomes – 1
10.2 Genes and chromosomes – 2

1.1 Cells

Key points

- All cells have certain structures in common, no matter what type of organism they come from.
- There are some differences between animal cells and plant cells.

Cell structure

Using your eyes, you can see detail down to the size of about 0.1 mm. This is not small enough to see most of the individual cells that make up living organisms. Fig 2 shows the appearance of cells seen under a **light microscope** at high power. Fig 3 shows an animal cell and a plant cell drawn diagrammatically.

Each of these cells has a **cell membrane**, a **nucleus** and **cytoplasm**. The cytoplasm contains enzymes that control all the chemical reactions in the cell.

a Although the cytoplasm contains enzymes, about 90% of cytoplasm is made of another substance. What is this?

The cell membrane controls the movement of substances into and out of the cell. Fat-soluble substances can pass through the cell membrane more easily than can water-soluble substances.

b What does this tell you about what the cell membrane is made of?

The nucleus contains the genetic material that codes for all the proteins that the cell makes.

In addition to the cell membrane, nucleus and cytoplasm, plant cells have other features that are only found in plant cells.
These are:

- the **cell wall**, which is made of cellulose and helps to support the cell
- **chloroplasts**, which contain chlorophyll to trap light for photosynthesis
- a large permanent **vacuole**, which contains cell sap for storage and support.

c Vacuoles are also found in animal cells. How are these different from those found in animal cells?

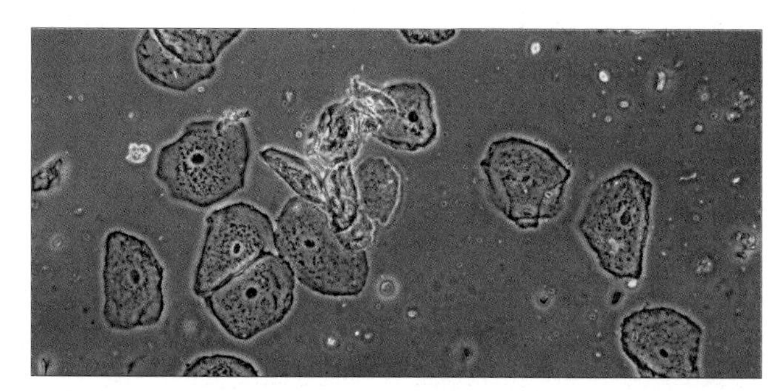

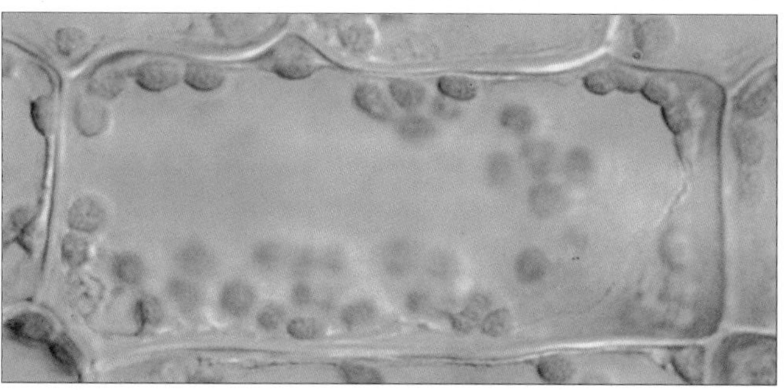

fig 2 | Light micrographs of epithelial cells from a human mouth (×240) (top), and a cell from the leaf of Canadian pondweed (×3150) (bottom)

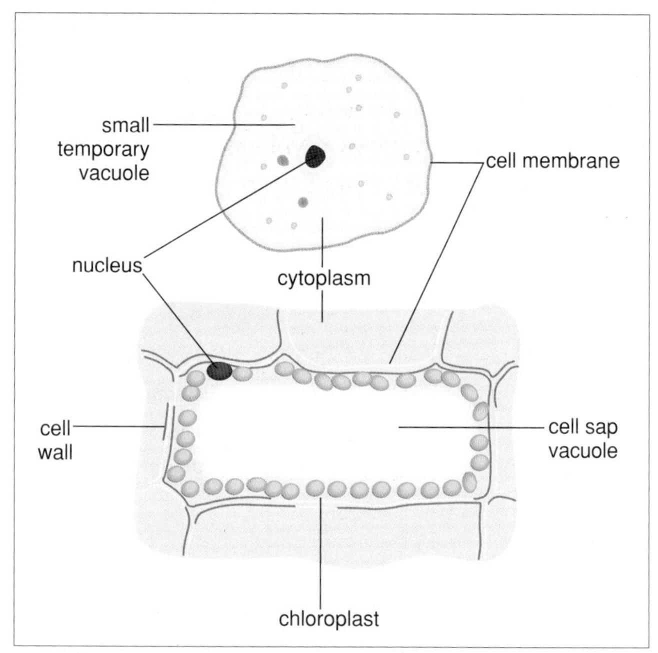

fig 3 | Diagrams of an animal cell (top) and a plant cell (bottom)

IDEAS AND EVIDENCE

The first person to see cells was a British scientist called Robert Hooke in 1665. He invented the kind of microscope that we use today and used it to look at a thin slice of cork.

He saw many little box shapes (fig 5) which he called cells because they reminded him of the small rooms or cells in which monks lived.

It was not until 1930 that the electron microscope was invented. This uses a beam of electrons instead of light to view specimens.

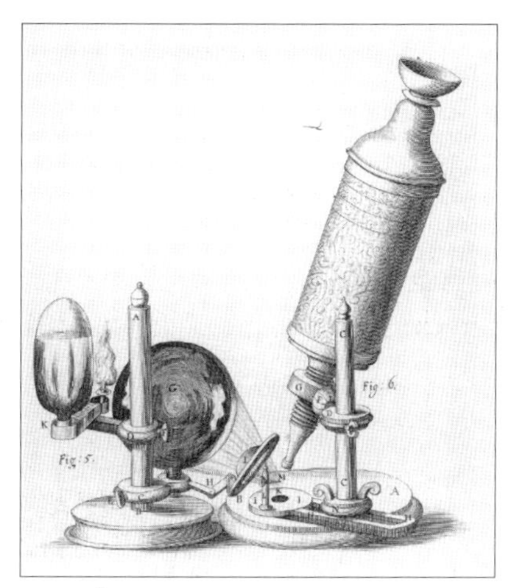

fig 4 | Hooke's microscope

These microscopes allowed cells to be studied in far more detail than is possible using a light microscope.

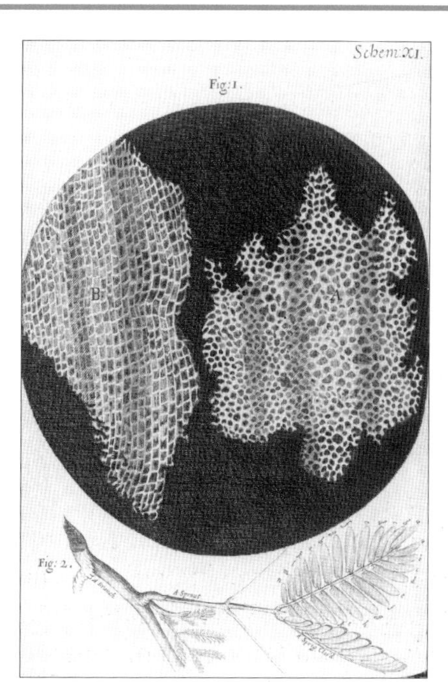

fig 5

Looking more closely at cells

The best light microscopes can magnify cells so that objects as small as 0.002 mm can be seen clearly. At this magnification other structures in the cell start to become visible but they cannot be seen clearly.

If an electron microscope is used then objects as small as 0.000002 mm – two thousand thousandths of a millimetre – can be seen! Many other structures in the cell can therefore be seen using an **electron microscope**. A cell as seen using the electron microscope is shown in fig 6.

Some of the most important of the structures seen are called **mitochondria**. This is where many of the reactions of respiration that release energy from food take place. This energy can then be used by the cell for all its functions.

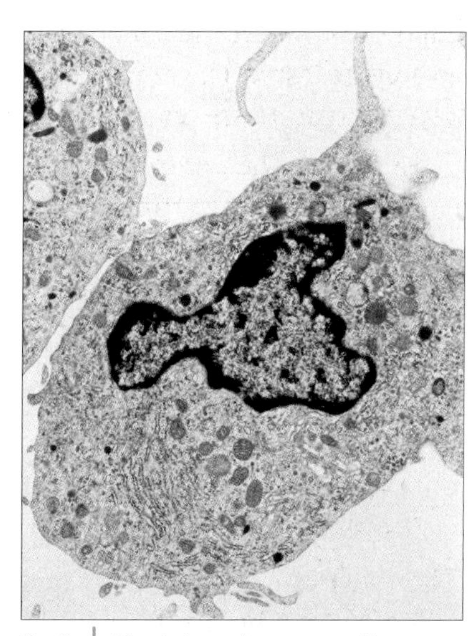

fig 6 | The electron microscope enables many of the cell's structures to be seen

Thinking further

1 Make a table to show the similarities and differences between plant and animal cells.

2 The animal cell in fig 3 is 0.03 mm wide in real life. How many times larger than real life has this cell been drawn?

3 Cells like sperm cells and muscle cells have large numbers of mitochondria. Explain why this is.

KEY WORDS

cell membrane • cell wall • chloroplasts • cytoplasm • electron microscope • light microscope • mitochondria • nucleus • vacuole

1.2 Life processes

Key points

- Organisms need to carry out certain life processes in order to stay alive.
- Cells working together as tissues, organs and systems carry out these processes.

Life processes

You have already seen that cells help organisms to carry out a number of processes that are vital to life. Scientists usually list seven processes that are needed for life. They are:

- movement
- excretion
- respiration
- reproduction
- sensitivity
- feeding
- growth

a How do plants move?

b What is the difference between feeding in animals and feeding in plants?

fig 7 | Coloured scanning electron micrograph of an *Amoeba*

In single-celled animals such as the amoeba (fig 7) these processes are all carried out by the one cell.

In organisms that have more than one cell (multicellular organisms), certain cells perform certain roles. This is called **specialisation** and it makes organisms more efficient. You should have looked at some of these specialised cells, such as sperm and root hair cells.

Grouping cells together

Similar cells that do similar jobs are usually gathered together into **tissues.** For example, nerve cells are gathered together into nerve tissue. Some simple multicellular organisms such as sea anemones are made up completely of tissues but have no distinct organs.

In more complicated organisms, different tissues are gathered together into **organs** to perform a particular job. For example, the brain is responsible for co-ordinating the body's actions and is made up of blood, nerves and connective tissue.

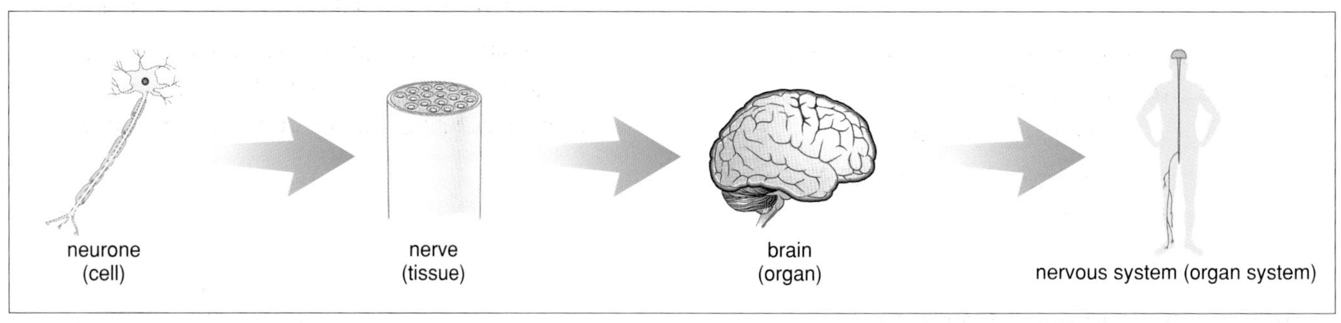

fig 8 | Levels of organisation in the nervous system

Groups of organs often work together in **systems** to carry out certain functions. For example, the brain, spinal cord and nerves make up the nervous system (fig 8).

Different types of biologist

Biology is such a large subject that it is difficult to study the whole subject in real detail.

Like cells, scientists tend to specialise. A particular type of scientist will study organisms at different levels. Fig 9 shows some examples.

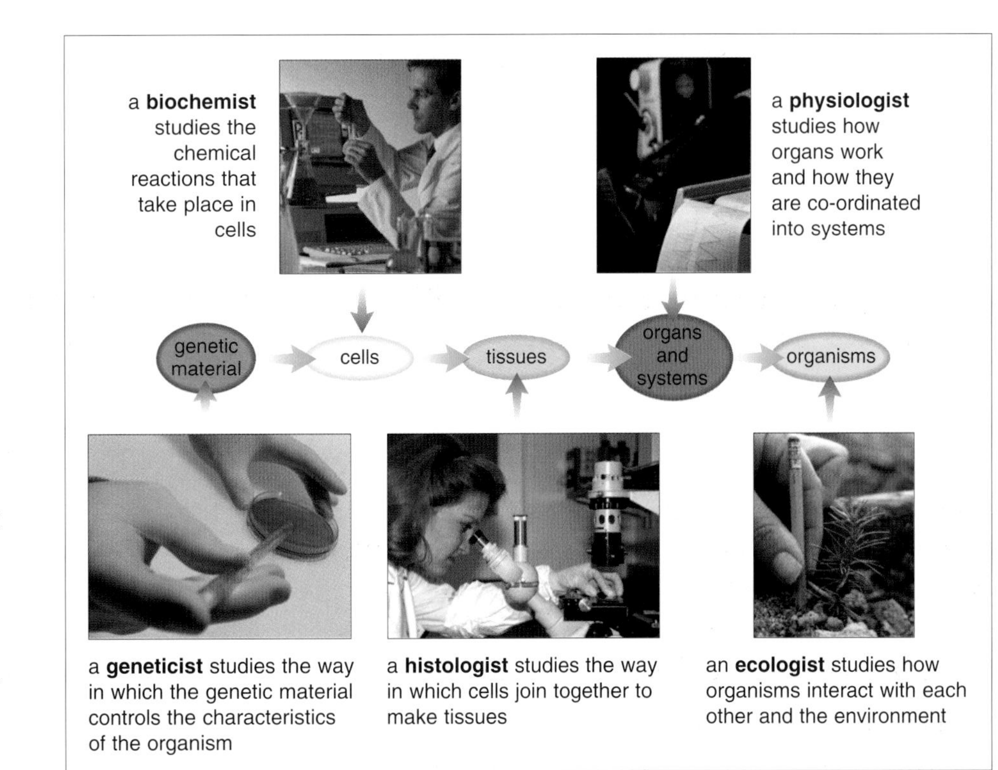

fig 9 | Different scientists specialise at different levels of organisation

Taking it further

Single-celled organisms seem to be limited in size. Individual cells cannot be too large because the nucleus would not be able to retain control of the cell. Multicellular organisms can become much larger. Look at the 'organisms' in fig 10.

By becoming larger, organism B has increased its volume eight times but its surface area has increased only four times compared with organism A. Because of the ratio between volume and surface area, larger organisms have difficulty taking up all the necessary chemicals and releasing waste products into the environment. They need special systems to help. Having many cells allows the cells to specialise.

Large organisms also find it easier to keep warm in cold conditions than do smaller organisms.

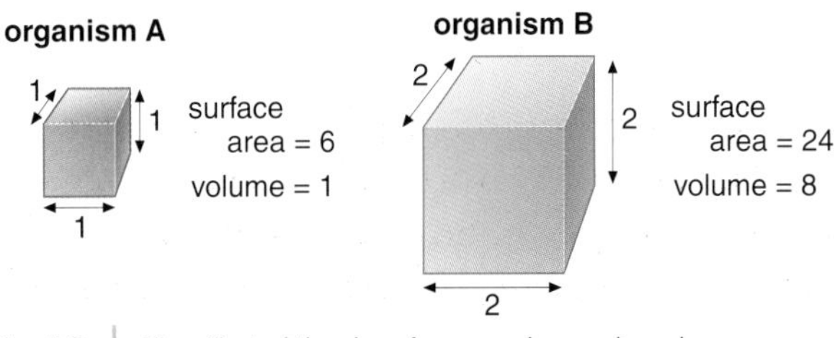

fig 10 | The effect of the size of an organism on its volume and surface area

Thinking further

1 State whether the following structures are cells, tissues or organs:

a ova **b** heart **c** muscle **d** a muscle.

2 State which system each of the following organs is part of:

a the testes **b** the bladder **c** the lungs.

3 If cells become specialised they often lose the ability to perform other jobs. What are the likely disadvantages of this to the organism?

KEY WORDS

organ • specialisation • system • tissue

1.3 Transport and cells

Key points

- Different substances need to enter and leave a cell across the cell membrane.
- Molecules move across the membrane by one of three processes: diffusion, osmosis or active transport.

What needs to move?

The processes that take place inside cells need various substances, including raw materials for respiration and growth. The processes produce waste products that need to be removed from cells. Some of these substances are shown in fig 11.

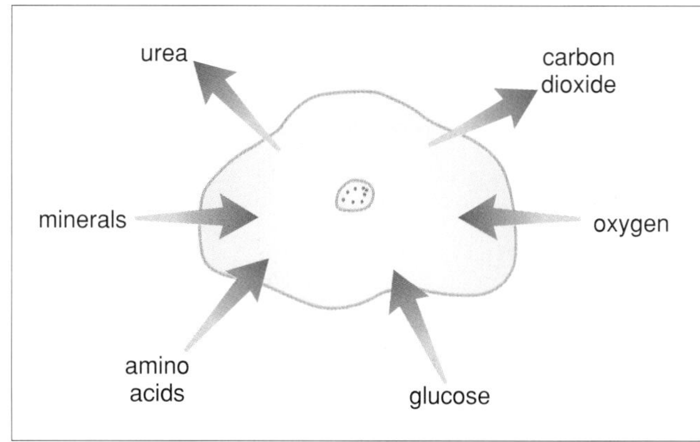

fig 11 | Substances needed and wastes produced by a cell

How do these substances move?

Molecules of a substance will move from an area where there are a lot of molecules to an area where there are few molecules (fig 12). This is movement down the **concentration gradient**. It is really just a case of the molecules spreading out – it is a **passive** process. This process is called **diffusion**. The proper definition is:

> the movement of a substance from an area of high concentration to an area of low concentration.

Diffusion works because molecules are constantly moving about in a random way. Large molecules move more slowly than smaller ones and so they tend to diffuse more slowly. It is also harder for larger molecules to get through the cell membrane. Small molecules such as oxygen, carbon dioxide and water can diffuse in and out of cells very quickly.

Osmosis is really a special type of diffusion. It involves the movement of water molecules across a membrane. This is important in enabling plants to support themselves.

A third method of transporting substances across the cell membrane is active transport.

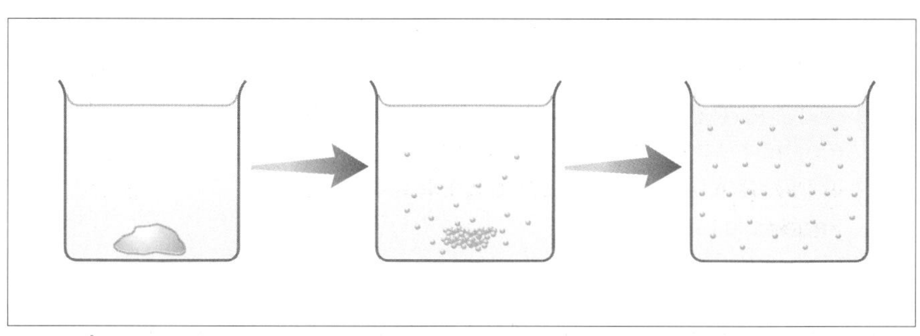

fig 12 | A crystal of copper(II) sulphate dissolves and diffuses throughout the water in a beaker

Active transport

Sometimes substances need to be transported from an area where they are in a low concentration to an area of high concentration. This is called **active transport.** This is movement in the opposite direction to diffusion – it is *against* the concentration gradient.

Moving substances in this direction does not rely just on the energy of the particles but needs an external supply of energy. This energy comes from respiration.

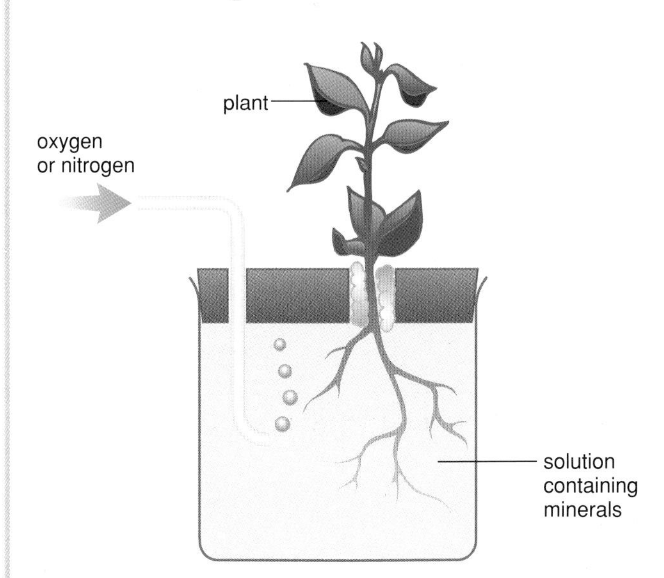

fig 13 | Apparatus used to investigate mineral uptake by plant roots

There are many examples of situations in animals and plants in which substances need to be moved against a concentration gradient. One of these is the uptake of minerals into the roots of plants.

The uptake of minerals into plant roots can be studied using the apparatus shown in fig 13. Fig 14 shows the uptake when oxygen is bubbled through the solution and when nitrogen is used instead.

a What does the plant use the oxygen for?

b What is the difference between the uptake with oxygen and that with nitrogen? Explain this difference.

Active transport works because there are protein molecules in the cell membrane which pick up the molecules and move them across the membrane.

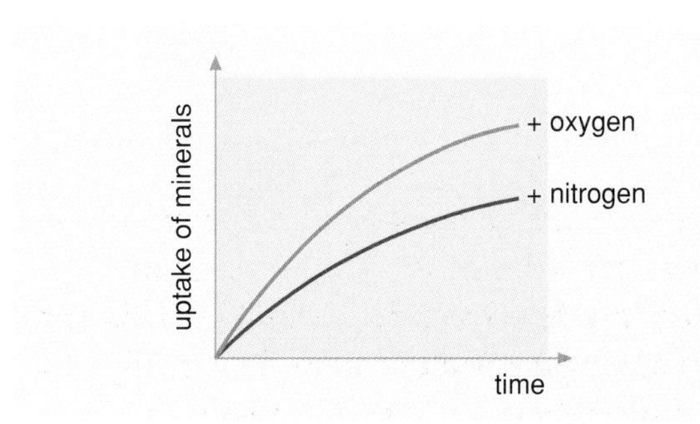

fig 14 | A graph to show the rate of mineral uptake with oxygen or nitrogen bubbled through the solution

Thinking further

1 A drop of ink is put on to the surface of the water in a glass beaker. Explain the following observations.

a All the water turns blue.

b The water turns blue without being stirred.

c The water turns blue more quickly when it is hot than when it is cold

2 Oxygen diffuses across the placenta from the mother to the baby and carbon dioxide diffuses in the other direction. Explain what makes this happen.

◆ **3** Look at fig 15 and explain why cells can only transfer particular molecules by active transport.

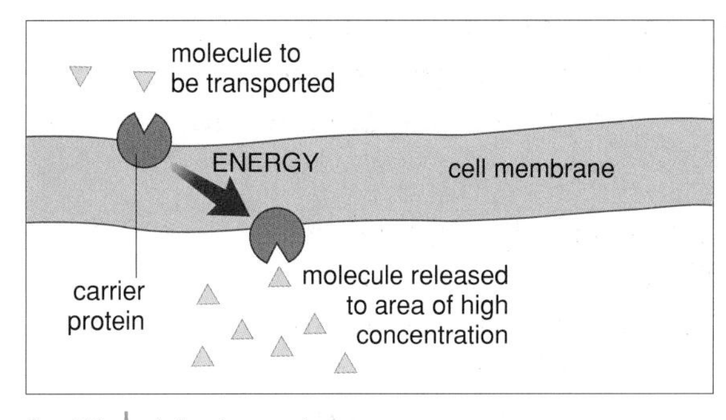

fig 15 | Active transport

KEY WORDS

active transport • concentration gradient • diffusion • passive

 *Diffusion of potassium manganate(VII).*

1.4 Osmosis

Key points

- Water can go in or out of cells by osmosis, which is a special type of diffusion.
- Osmosis can occur because cell membranes are partially permeable.
- Osmosis is a very important process that enables plants to support themselves.

What is osmosis?

A very simple apparatus can be used to demonstrate osmosis. It uses dialysis or visking tubing. This is a plastic film that acts rather like the cell membrane. The apparatus is shown in fig 16.

When the apparatus is set up, the level of the sugar solution in the funnel rises. This is because water is moving into the concentrated sugar solution from the weaker solution, trying to even out the concentrations. This movement of water is called **osmosis**.

Osmosis is really a special type of diffusion. It is the diffusion of water from where there is a high concentration of water molecules (the weaker sugar solution) to where there is a low concentration of water molecules (the stronger sugar solution).

a Why does the solution in the funnel stop rising after a while?

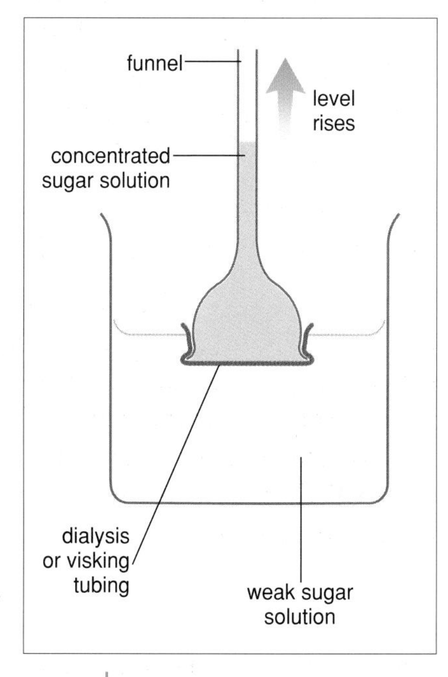

fig 16 | Demonstration of osmosis using visking tubing

Why does osmosis happen?

The dialysis tubing is like the cell membrane in that it only allows certain molecules through. It is said to be **partially permeable**. The sugar molecules are too large to pass through the membrane but the water molecules are small enough to diffuse through it.

Osmosis can therefore be defined as:

> the diffusion of water molecules from a high water concentration to a lower water concentration through a partially permeable membrane.

Biologists often use the term **water potential** to describe how likely a solution is to lose or gain water by osmosis. Water will move from a solution that has a high water potential to one that has a low water potential.

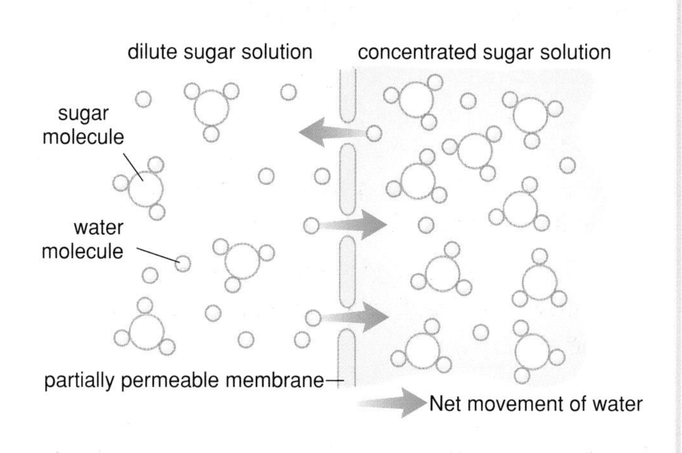

fig 17 | Osmosis

Osmosis in cells

A thin layer of plant cells can be obtained by peeling a strip from an onion. Solutions of different concentrations can then be dropped onto the cells and the effect on the cells observed using a microscope.

Cells placed in distilled water take up water by osmosis. This happens because the cell contains dissolved chemicals and therefore has a higher water potential than the surrounding fluid. Eventually the cell stops taking up water even though the concentrations inside and outside are not even. This is because the cell wall becomes stretched and prevents any more water entering. The cell is said to be **turgid** (fig 18).

b The cell wall is made of a strong material that stops the cell from bursting. What is the name of this material?

c Why would animal cells burst if they were used in this experiment?

In concentrated sugar solution, the cell loses water by osmosis and the cell becomes limp or **flaccid** (fig 18).

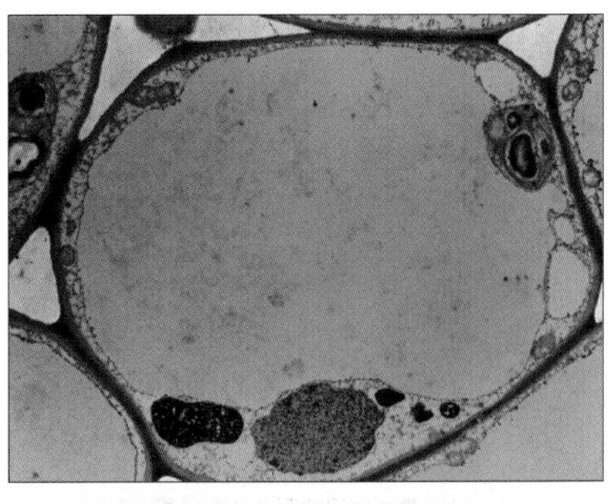

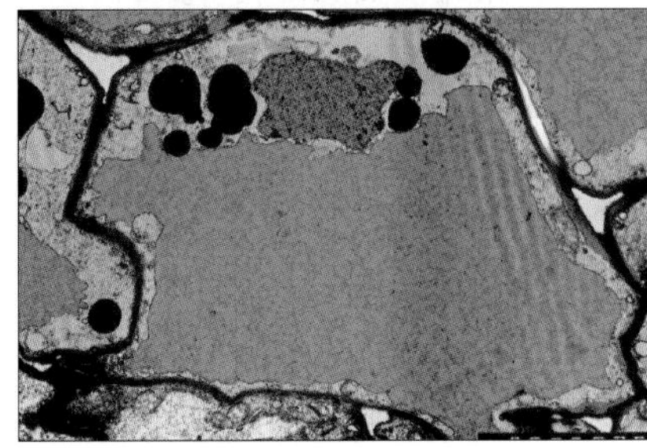

fig 18 Coloured transmission electron micrographs of a turgid plant cell (top) and a flaccid plant cell (bottom)

These changes can also be demonstrated by cutting chips out of potato tubers and soaking them in sugar solutions of different concentrations. In concentrated solutions, the potato cells lose water and the chips get shorter. In distilled water, the chips gain water and get longer (fig 19).

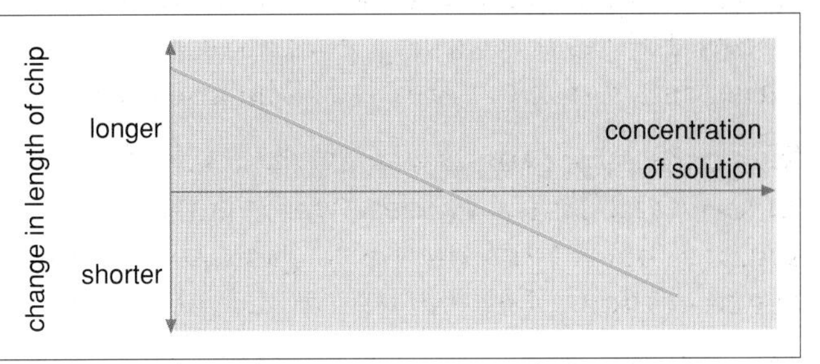

fig 19 Change in chip length with solution concentration

Support in cells

Turgid cells are very important for supporting plants. This is particularly the case in plants that do not contain much woody tissue. The turgid cells in the plant push against each other and this helps to keep the plant upright. If the plant loses water faster than it gains it from the soil, the cells will become flaccid. This can cause the plant to droop or **wilt** (fig 20).

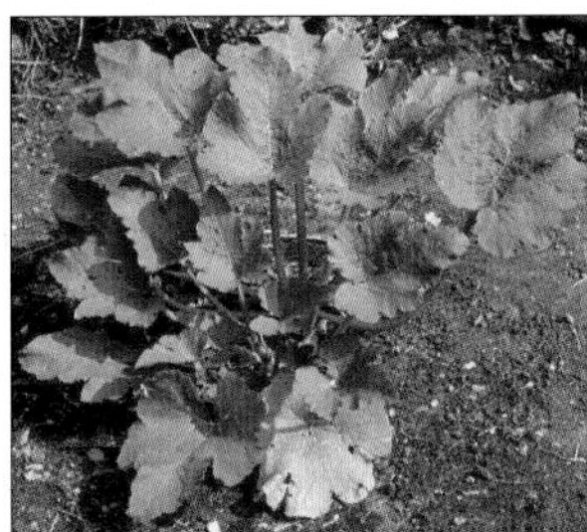

fig 20 A courgette plant which has wilted after several weeks without rain (left), and the same plant 4 hours after being watered (right). Some plants wilt after only a short period without water.

Thinking further

1 Explain why eating salted peanuts makes the inside of the mouth feel dry.

2 The Romans used to put salt on the crops of their enemies. Explain why the plants wilted and died.

3 In fig 19, the chips do not change length at a certain concentration. Why is this?

4 Why is measuring length a rather inaccurate way of telling how much water the chip has lost or gained? Suggest a better way of measuring any change.

KEY WORDS

flaccid • **osmosis** • partially permeable • **turgid** • water potential • **wilt**

 *Osmosis in onion skins.*  *Osmosis with potato chips.*

Questions on biological principles

● **1** Copy fig 21 and write the following structures in the correct columns. *(6)*

cell membrane • cell sap vacuole • cell wall • cytoplasm • nucleus • temporary vacuole

structure found in:		
plant cells only	animal cells only	animal cells and plants cells

fig 21

● **2** Copy the paragraph below, using words from the following list to fill the gaps. You may use each word once, more than once or not at all. *(8)*

cell wall • cytoplasm • distilled water • flaccid • osmosis • sugar solution • turgid • wilt

When plant tissue is placed in __________ the cells take in water by __________ . The tissue continues to take up water until the __________ pushes against the __________ . The cells are now said to be __________ . If placed in __________ the cells may lose water and become __________ . This could cause a living plant to __________ .

■ **3** The following extract is from a science-fiction novel *The War of the Worlds*. The Earth has been invaded by creatures from Mars. The narrator describes one of the creatures:

> A big greyish, rounded bulk, the size of perhaps a bear, was rising slowly and painfully out of the cylinder. As it bulged up and caught the light, it glistened like wet leather. Two large dark-coloured eyes were regarding me steadfastly.

He goes on to describe:

> … the peculiar V-shaped mouth with its pointed upper lip, the absence of brow ridges, the absence of a chin beneath the wedge-like lower lip, the incessant quivering of this mouth, the group of tentacles, the tumultuous breathing of the lungs …

a What clues in the extract tell you that the creature was sensitive to its surroundings? *(2)*

b What indication is there that the creature showed the characteristic of respiration? *(1)*

c What other characteristic of living organisms did the creature show? *(1)*

d Name four other characteristics that the creature must have for a scientist to classify it as a living organism. *(4)*

■ **4** Explain the following observations.

a In a dessert made from two different coloured jellies, the colours were gradually mixing where they met. *(2)*

b Parsnips placed in a saucepan of cold water increased in size. *(2)*

c When making jam, adding large amounts of sugar to fruit stops bacteria from rotting the fruit. *(2)*

■ **5** Fig 22 shows a bag made from dialysis tubing tied over the end of a glass tube. The bag was filled with solution A and the beaker was filled with solution B.

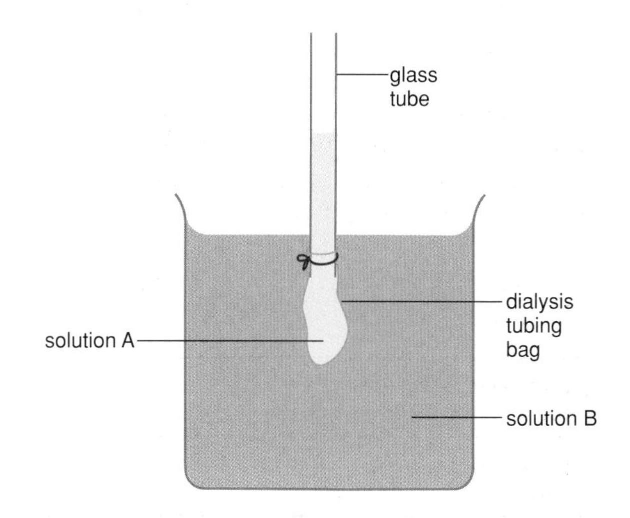

fig 22

Describe what would happen to the bag and the level in the glass tube in each of the following cases.

a Solution A = distilled water;
solution B = 100 g/dm^3 sugar solution. *(2)*

b Solution A = 100 g/dm^3 sugar solution;
solution B = 100 g/dm^3 sugar solution. *(2)*

c Solution A = 100 g/dm^3 sugar solution;
solution B = 80 g/dm^3 sugar solution. *(2)*

◆ **6** Fig 23 shows the concentration of various substances in the blood of two different species of fish and in sea water. The table also gives the total concentration of the blood and sea water.

	concentration in arbitrary units		
	sodium ions	urea	total
sea water	450	0	1000
dogfish	290	350	1000
salmon	180	1	340

fig 23

a Explain why the salmon loses water even though it lives in the sea. *(2)*

b The salmon has to drink sea water to replace lost water but has to remove the sodium ions from its body. Why does the pumping out of sodium need energy? *(2)*

c The dogfish has a different approach to surviving in sea water. Use the information in fig 23 to suggest how it achieves this. *(3)*

d The salmon moves from the sea and swims up freshwater rivers in order to breed. Explain what problems this might pose to the fish. *(3)*

7 An experiment to demonstrate osmosis was done using potato chips. Potato chips were weighed and then soaked for 30 minutes in sugar solutions of different concentrations. The potato chips were then re-weighed and the percentage change in mass calculated. The results are shown in fig 24.

concentration of sugar solution in g per dm^3	0	70	140	210	280
percentage change in mass	12.4	8.5	1.0	−2.9	−7.5

fig 24

■ **a** **i** Plot the results of the experiment on a graph. *(2)*

ii Draw the best straight line through the points. *(1)*

iii Explain what happens to the potato chips in distilled water. *(3)*

◆ **b** From your graph estimate the sugar concentration inside potato cells. Explain how you obtained your answer. *(3)*

◆ **c** A student found a test tube that did not have a label so they did not know the concentration of the sugar solution it contained. The potato chip in this solution showed a percentage change of +5%.

Use your graph to find out what concentration of sugar solution must have been in the tube. *(1)*

IDEAS AND EVIDENCE

■ **8** Read the following passage and answer the questions that follow:

Aristotle lived in Athens about 2400 years ago and is often considered to have been the first real biologist. He made detailed studies on more than 500 different species of animal. He was the first person to use detailed diagrams to illustrate his observations.

He did however make a number of errors. His methods often ignored the importance of measuring times and distances accurately. He also believed in 'spontaneous generation' whereby organisms were thought to appear from dead material.

Soon after Robert Hooke developed the microscope in the seventeenth century, the idea of spontaneous generation was proved to be incorrect.

a Explain why the development of the microscope helped to disprove the idea of spontaneous generation. *(3)*

b What other developments had been made by the seventeenth century that made it easier to take accurate measurements? *(2)*

Digestion

Introduction

The food that animals eat is made up of seven important types of molecules which are needed by the body. These are carbohydrates, proteins, fats, minerals, vitamins, fibre and water.

These food molecules are needed in different amounts, and different foods vary in the molecules that they contain. A balanced diet contains the correct amount of each of the types of food molecule.

Some of the food molecules are a rich supply of energy that the body can release in respiration. Others are used as the raw materials for growth. Vitamins are not used for either of these functions but are important in various reactions and processes in the body.

A person who does not eat a balanced diet may develop certain diseases. This may be the result of too much of a certain substance or too little (a deficiency). Examples that you may have studied include tooth decay and anaemia.

Many of the chemicals in food are large molecules such as starch, proteins and fats. These molecules need to be broken down into small soluble molecules so that they can pass into the bloodstream. This breakdown process is called digestion and it is controlled by enzymes.

You may have used a model of the digestive system in an experiment to demonstrate digestion and absorption. Visking or dialysis tubing is used to represent the lining of the digestive system and various food chemicals can be placed inside the tubing.

fig 1

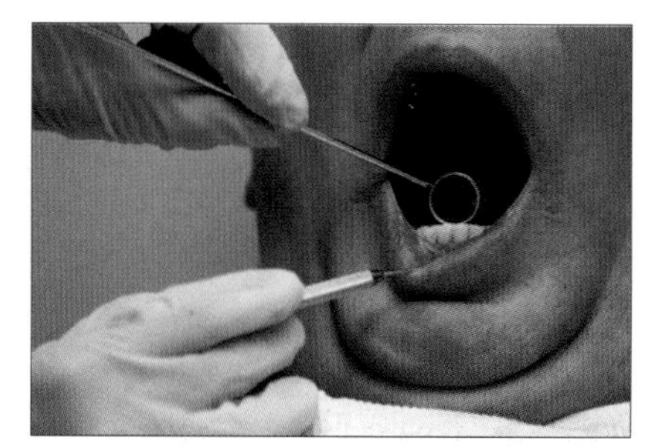

fig 2

Check-up

Have a go at the following questions. They will remind you of what you should know about digestion.

a Food molecules can be classed as one of seven different types. Write down which of the seven types of food molecules each of these examples belongs to.

calcium • cholesterol • haemoglobin • iron • starch • sugar

b A person eats a meal of steak and chips, with a drink of orange juice. Make a list of the main food molecules in each of these foods.

c Fig 3 shows the recommended daily amounts of different food molecules and energy required by different groups of people.

person	protein in g	iron in mg	calcium in mg	energy in kJ
1-year-old child	14.9	7.8	525	3850
15-year-old boy	55.2	11.3	1000	11 500
15-year-old girl	45.0	14.8	800	8830
woman	45.0	14.8	700	8100
breast-feeding woman	56.0	14.8	1250	11 000

fig 3

Check-up (continued)

i Explain why the need for calcium goes down after the age of about 15 years.

ii The 1-year-old child may be a tenth of the size of an adult but needs as much as a third of the protein that an adult needs. Why?

iii Why does the 15-year-old girl need more iron than the 15-year-old boy?

iv Explain the changes in requirements when a woman starts to breast-feed.

d Fig 4 shows an experiment to demonstrate the need for digestion in the digestive system.

i What does the water in the boiling tube represent?

ii After some time the water in the boiling tube is tested for starch and sugar. What results would you expect? Give reasons for your prediction.

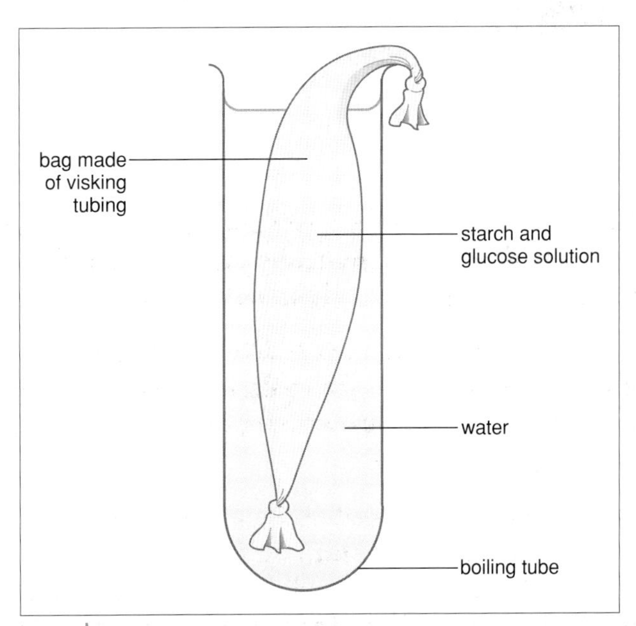

fig 4 | Experimental demonstration of the need for digestion

If you have difficulty, ask your teacher for a Summary sheet.

Contents of the Teaching block

2.1 Enzymes

You discussed the importance of enzymes at Key Stage 3. We now use food tests to follow the course of enzyme reactions, and discuss some of their properties.

2.2 Digestion

You should know about the importance of digestion. This spread traces the movement of food down the digestive system and looks at how it is digested.

2.3 Absorption

Once the food molecules have been digested, they are small enough to be absorbed into the blood stream. This occurs in the small intestine.

Links to other Teaching blocks

1.3 Transport and cells
3.1 Aerobic respiration
9.1 Controlling glucose levels
Chemistry 4.4 Enzymes

2.1 Enzymes

Key points

- The digestive system produces enzymes that break down the components of our food.
- This digestion can be demonstrated using various food tests.

How do enzymes work?

Most enzymes are located in the cytoplasm of cells. Here they control the chemical reactions occurring inside the cell. The enzymes of the digestive system are unusual in that they are released outside cells. Like all enzymes, they are **specific**. This means that one type of enzyme will only break down one particular type of food substance. The three main types of food molecules that need to be digested are shown in fig 5, together with the enzymes that digest them. These enzymes are produced in different parts of the digestive system.

type of food molecule	type of enzyme needed for digestion	example of an enzyme
starch	**amylase**	salivary amylase
lipids (fats)	**lipase**	pancreatic lipase
protein	**protease**	pepsin

fig 5

The enzymes break down the food molecules into molecules that are small enough to pass into the blood stream. The actions of these enzymes are shown in fig 6.

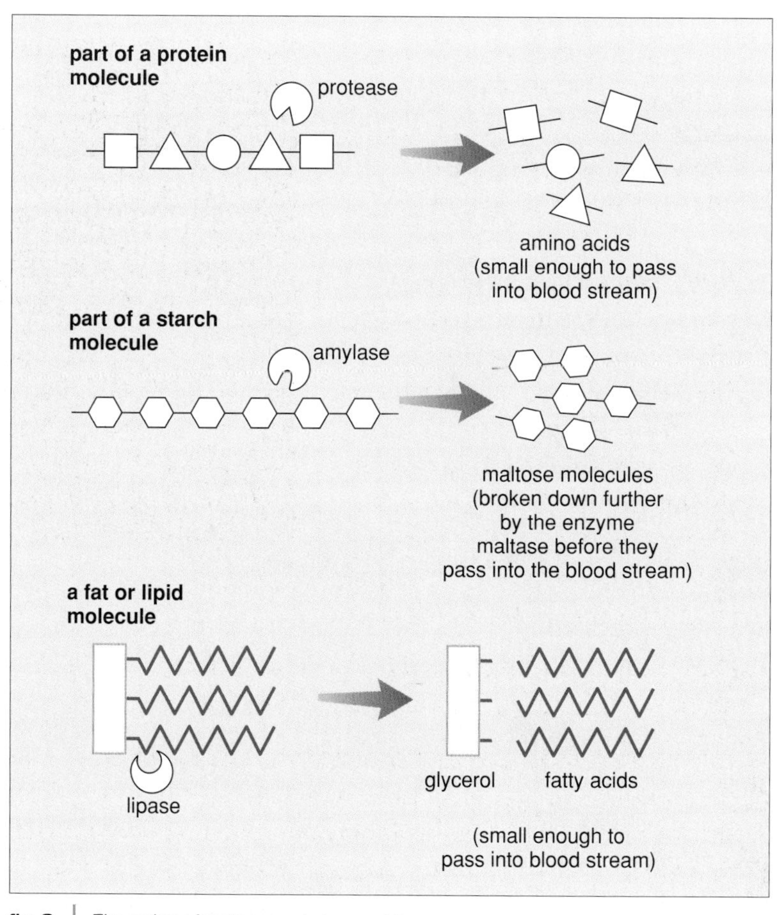

fig 6 | The action of protease, amylase and lipase

a Which food molecules do not need to be digested?

Demonstrating the action of enzymes

If a digestive enzyme is working, it should be possible to show that the food molecule that is being broken down disappears and that the product appears. For example, starch can be mixed with amylase and kept at a suitable temperature. By taking samples at regular intervals, it can be shown that the starch disappears and sugars appear.

b What do you think would be a suitable temperature?

The starch or sugar can be tested for using the food tests shown in fig 7.

food molecule	substance used for test	details of test	sign of a positive result
starch	**iodine solution**	drop iodine solution into the solution to be tested	solution turns blue–black
simple sugars	**Benedict's solution**	add Benedict's solution to the solution and boil in a water bath for 2 minutes	solution turns orange–red
protein	sodium hydroxide and copper(II) sulphate **(Biuret test)**	add several drops of dilute sodium hydroxide solution followed by several drops of copper(II) sulphate solution	solution turns purple

fig 7

Where are the enzymes produced?

As it passes down the digestive system, food passes through different structures and organs. Substances from other organs are added to the mixture in the digestive system via tubes or ducts. It is now known that different enzymes are produced in different areas of the digestive system. This has been investigated in a number of different ways. One of the first investigations was done by Dr William Beaumont.

IDEAS AND EVIDENCE

A number of famous scientists have investigated the production of enzymes in the stomach. The first to make major discoveries was William Beaumont. He was a young American army doctor who was stationed in the country. He treated a young man called Alexis St Martin who had been shot accidentally in the stomach. Beaumont managed to save the man's life. However, when the wound healed, there was a hole in the abdomen, leaving the stomach open to the outside.

fig 8

Beaumont realised the scientific value of this and made a number of observations on St Martin.

Up until then people had thought that the stomach 'cooked' the food. By taking samples from St Martin's stomach, Beaumont showed that food was broken down chemically. He found that meat was broken down particularly well. He also found that the liquid produced in the stomach killed bacteria.

Thinking further

■ **1** The liquid from St Martin's stomach broke down meat. What is the main food molecule in meat?

■ **2** What enzyme must be produced by the stomach in order to break down the meat?

■ **3** How could Beaumont have tested to see if this substance had been broken down?

◆ **4** William Beaumont was surprised that St Martin did not die because of the wound becoming infected. Why are people less likely to die from wound infections nowadays?

KEY WORDS

amylase • Benedict's solution • Biuret test • iodine solution • lipase • protease • specific

 *Enzyme action.*  *Food test.*

2.2 Digestion

Key points

- The enzymes produced by the organs of the digestive system break down the food molecules.
- This process of digestion is assisted by the production of chemicals from other organs.

The digestive system

The human digestive system (fig 9) stretches from mouth to anus and is about 9 metres long. It is divided into a number of organs and structures. These are responsible for digestion and absorption of the products into the bloodstream as food passes along the gut.

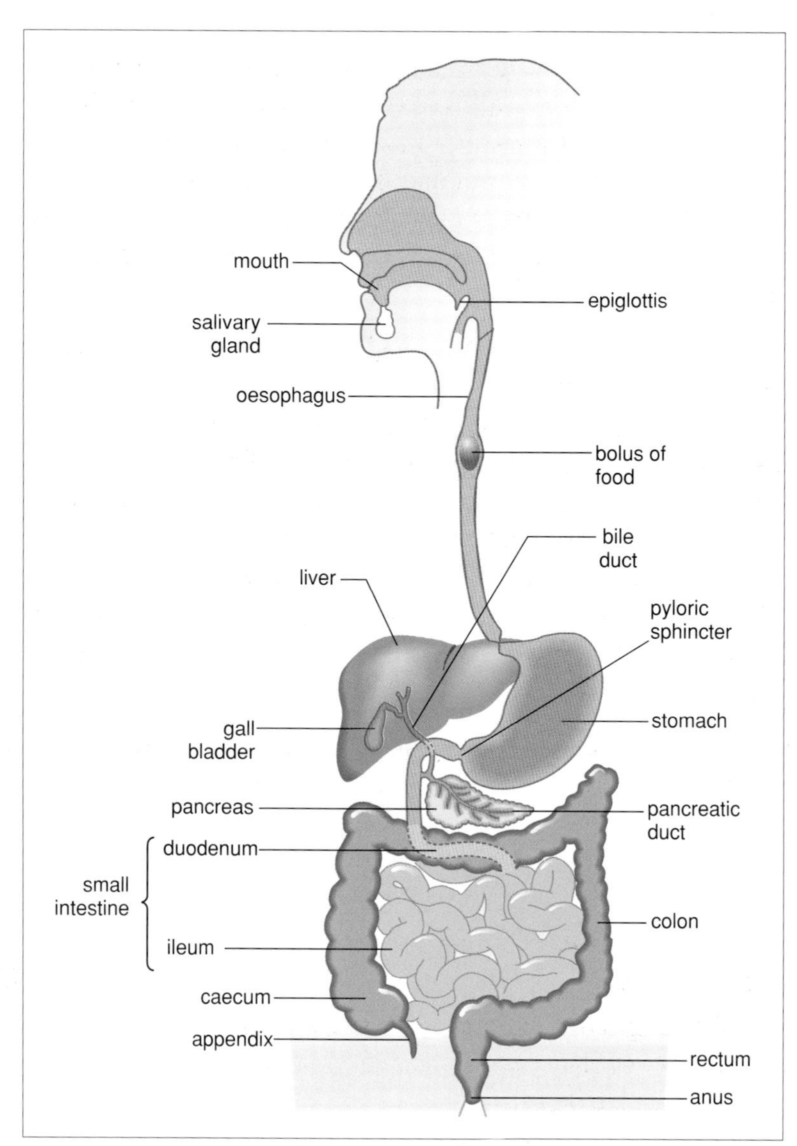

fig 9 | The human digestive system

Digestion in the mouth

The food is physically digested in the mouth by the action of the teeth and tongue. This breaks the food into smaller pieces.

a This physical breakdown means that enzymes can digest the food faster. Why is this?

The salivary glands release saliva into the mouth. Saliva contains mucus to lubricate the food and stick it together. It also contains amylase which breaks down starch into the sugar maltose.

Digestion in the stomach

Food enters the stomach from the oesophagus. Physical digestion of the food continues as the stomach churns the food. Pits in the wall of the stomach (fig 10) release **gastric juice.** (It was this that William Beaumont collected.) Gastric juice contains hydrochloric acid and a protease called pepsin. Pepsin works best at a low pH – the acid provides this environment.

b William Beaumont found that gastric juice protects the body from infection. Explain how it does this.

After the food has been in the stomach for several hours, it is squeezed into the first part of the small intestine, the duodenum.

fig 10 | Coloured scanning electron micrograph of the surface of the stomach lining (mucosa) showing gastric pits (×125)

Digestion in the small intestine

Three different liquids are added to the food in the small intestine. They come from the liver, the pancreas and the wall of the small intestine itself.

- The liver produces a yellow–green liquid called **bile**. This is stored in the gall bladder and passes into the duodenum (the upper part of the small intestine) through the bile duct. Bile does not contain enzymes but contains **bile salts**. These bile salts break down large fat droplets into smaller droplets. This process is called **emulsification**; it increases the surface area for the enzyme lipase to work on.

c Bile also contains a weak alkali – sodium hydrogencarbonate. What is the purpose of this?

- The pancreas produces a liquid that passes into the upper part of the small intestine via the pancreatic duct. This liquid contains more alkali and a number of enzymes. They include additional amylase, protease and some lipase.
- The wall of the small intestine also produces enzymes. These include enzymes to break down carbohydrates other than starch, for example maltase to break down maltose and lactase to break down lactose.

The food molecules are now small enough to pass into the bloodstream.

Thinking further

■ **1** Why does bread start to taste sweet after being chewed for a while?

■ **2** The flow diagram in fig 11 shows how starch is digested. Draw similar flow diagrams to show how protein and fats are digested.

◆ **3** Small stones can develop in the gall bladder and the gall bladder has to be removed. Why might someone who's gall bladder has been removed be advised not to eat meals that contain large quantities of fat?

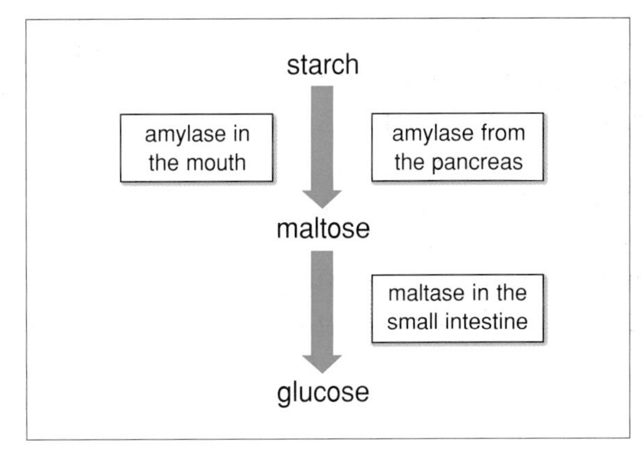

fig 11

KEY WORDS
bile • bile salts • emulsification • gastric juice

 *Digestion of fat.*

2.3 Absorption

Key points

- After digestion, food molecules are absorbed from the small intestine into the bloodstream.
- The small intestine has many features that allow rapid absorption to take place.

Where does absorption occur?

The second part of the small intestine is called the **ileum**. By the time the food reaches the ileum, the food molecules have been digested into small soluble molecules. These molecules can then pass through the lining of the small intestine into the bloodstream. This is called **absorption**.

The dissolved molecules pass into blood vessels which join together to form the **hepatic portal vein**. This takes the food molecules to the liver to be processed.

How small do the food molecules need to be?

Amino acids, fatty acids, glycerol, and sugars that are made up from one sugar unit (e.g. glucose) are all small enough to be absorbed into the bloodstream. Other sugars such as maltose, lactose and sucrose that are made of two sugar units need to be digested first.

Taking it further

fig 12 People with lactose intolerance often drink soya milk

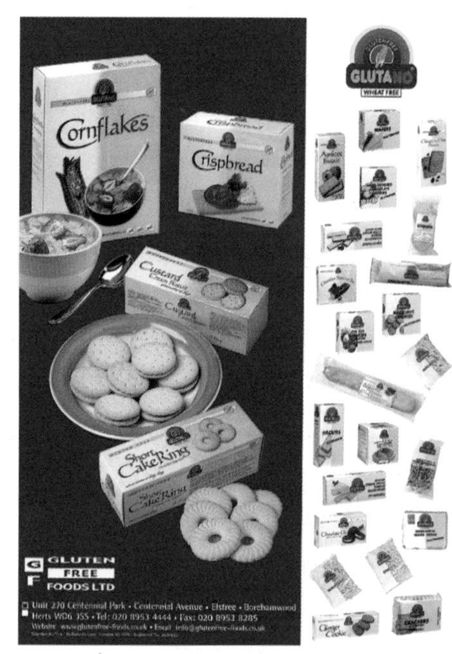

fig 13 Foods which are marked to show that they do not contain gluten are suitable for people with coeliac disease

Two common conditions show how important it is for food molecules to be digested so that they are small enough to be absorbed.

- Many people are lactose intolerant. This means that they cannot digest lactose, the main sugar in dairy products. Lactose is too large to be absorbed and so stays in the intestine where it is used by bacteria. Gases and acids produced by the bacteria can cause considerable discomfort.
- A rarer condition is coeliac disease. People with this disease cannot digest the protein present in gluten, which is found in wheat and some other cereals. The protein therefore cannot be absorbed properly. This irritates the lining of the intestine, preventing other food from being absorbed.

Structure of the small intestine

The small intestine is specially adapted to absorb the dissolved food molecules (fig 14). It has a large surface area over which absorption can take place. This increases the rate of absorption enormously. A number of factors provide a large surface area.

- **Long length** – the human small intestine is over 5 metres long, most of which is the ileum.
- **Folds** – the inner lining is not smooth but is folded, particularly in the higher regions. The folds increase the surface area by about three times.

- **Villi** – The folds are covered in finger-like projections called **villi.** The many villi increase the surface area by about ten times. The cells lining the villi have small projections called **microvilli.** These may increase the surface area by another twenty times.

a How many times larger is the surface area of the small intestine compared with a simple straight tube of the same length?

The small intestine also has many small blood vessels. These capillaries pass into every villus so that there is a only a short distance for the food molecules to diffuse.

b Which blood vessel do these capillaries join to form?

Villi also contain tubes called **lacteals** or lymph vessels. These tubes absorb the products of fat digestion. They all join together and empty their contents into the bloodstream near the heart.

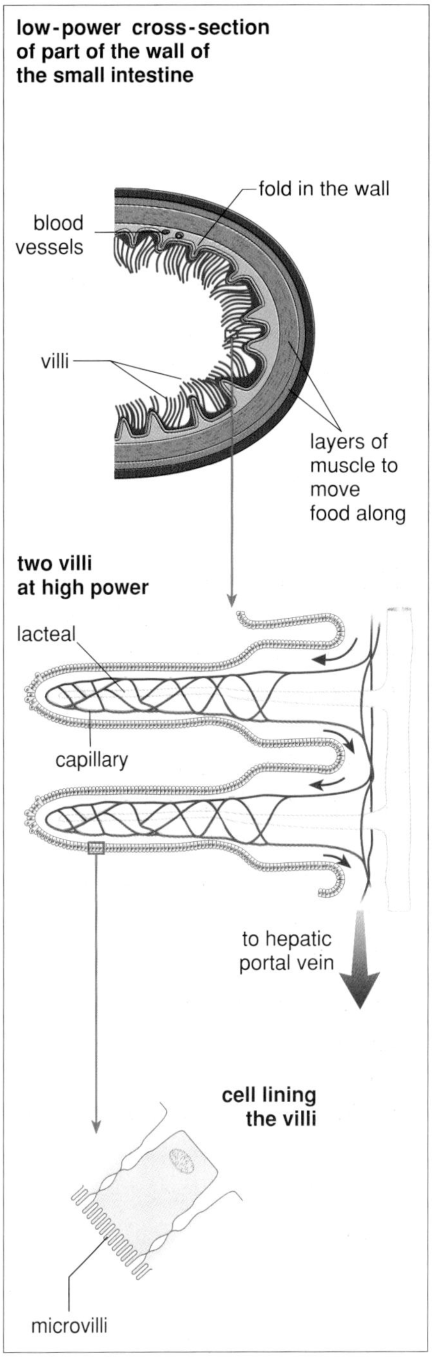

fig 14 | The structure of the small intestine provides a large surface area for absorption

Thinking further

1 What is meant by the term absorption?

2 Why do athletes often eat sweets containing glucose rather than sucrose just before they compete?

3 The liver breaks down poisons in the blood and regulates the composition of the blood. Why is it important that the hepatic portal vein takes blood from the intestine straight to the liver?

KEY WORDS
absorption • hepatic portal vein • ileum • lacteals • microvilli • villi

Absorption of food.

Questions on digestion

1 Copy the paragraph, using words from the following list to fill the gaps. You may use each word once, more than once or not at all. *(4)*

amino acids • amylase • blue • denatured • lipase • protease • purple • red • specific • sugars

Proteins in our diet are broken down by the enzyme __________ into small soluble molecules called __________ . Before the protein has been digested it will give a __________ colour when tested with the Biuret test. The enzyme lipase will not break down proteins because enzymes are __________ .

2 Fig 15 shows the human digestive system.

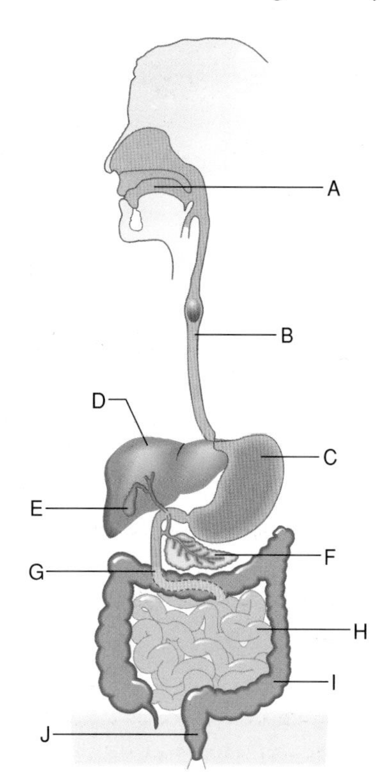

fig 15

Choose letters from the diagram to fit the following descriptions. *(5)*

a An acidic region

b An alkaline region

c The region where starch is first digested

d The site of bile production

e The main area where food is absorbed into the bloodstream

3 A student performed an experiment using amylase to digest starch solution. He repeated the experiment with the solutions at six different temperatures and timed how long it took for the starch to be digested. The results are shown in fig 16.

temperature in °C	time taken for starch digestion in minutes	rate $\frac{1}{\text{time}}$
10	5.0	
25	1.7	0.59
30	1.2	0.77
40	1.0	1.00
55	2.0	
65	10.0	

fig 16

a How would the student tell when the starch had been digested? *(2)*

b The student worked out the rate of starch breakdown for three of the temperatures. Work out the rate of reaction for the other three temperatures. *(3)*

c Plot a graph of the results, plotting temperature on the x axis and rate on the y axis. Join the points with the best curve. *(4)*

d At which temperature is the starch broken down the fastest? *(1)*

e Use your graph to estimate the rate of starch breakdown if the experiment had been carried out at 45°C. *(1)*

f Name two variables that the student should have kept constant in order to make the experiment a fair test. *(2)*

4 Read the following sentences and write down the missing words. *(10)*

A person eats a boiled egg. This contains mainly protein and fat. The protein is first digested in the __________ by the enzyme __________ . This breaks the protein down to __________ . This enzyme works best at a __________ pH and so __________ is produced to provide this pH. The droplets of fat are __________ into smaller droplets by __________ .

The fats are then digested by __________ , which is produced in the __________ . The products of the protein and fat digestion are absorbed into the bloodstream in the __________ .

5 Rosie's teacher gave her four solutions labelled A, B, C and D. The teacher told Rosie that two were carbohydrates and two were proteins. Rosie did tests on the solutions. Her results are shown in fig 17.

	colour of solution after:		
solution	**Benedict's test**	**Biuret test**	**iodine test**
A	blue	purple	brown
B	red	blue	brown
C	blue	blue	black
D	blue	purple	brown

fig 17

■ **a** Describe how Rosie did the Biuret test. *(2)*

■ **b** Which two solutions are carbohydrates and which two are proteins? *(2)*

■ **c** Identify the two carbohydrates as closely as you can. *(2)*

◆ **d** Rosie was told that one of the proteins was amylase. Explain how she would find out which solution it was. *(3)*

◆ **6** Cubes made from a jelly-like protein called gelatin can be coloured by including a red dye.

a When a cube is placed in a solution of pepsin, the solution gradually turns red. Why is this? *(2)*

b Describe how you could use these cubes to find out the pH at which pepsin works best. *(4)*

c What results would you expect from your experiment? *(1)*

7 Read the section *Taking it further* on spread 2.3. Use this information and your knowledge of biology to answer the following questions.

■ **a** Lactose cannot pass into the bloodstream. Explain why. *(1)*

■ **b** What must happen to lactose before it can pass into the bloodstream? *(1)*

◆ **c** Suggest why some people cannot digest lactose. *(1)*

◆ **d** The irritation caused by coeliac disease often destroys the villi in the small intestine. People with coeliac disease have stunted growth and diseases such as anaemia. Explain why. *(3)*

◆ **e** How can people who have coeliac disease or who are lactose intolerant prevent themselves from suffering? *(2)*

IDEAS AND EVIDENCE

◆ **8** In the early 1900s, a scientist called Ivan Pavlov carried out an important set of experiments to investigate the production of enzymes.
He anaesthetised a dog and performed an operation to divert the oesophagus so that it opened to the outside (fig 18). He also operated on the stomach so that he could sample the gastric juice produced.

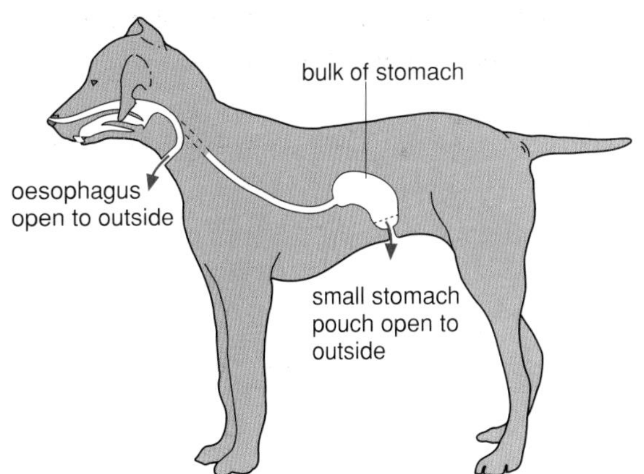

fig 18

a When the dog ate, the food passed out of the hole in the neck and did not enter the stomach. Pavlov found that the dog still produced gastric juice. Suggest how this is brought about. *(2)*

b When Pavlov just showed food to the dog, it again produced gastric juice. Suggest why. *(1)*

c Pavlov placed food directly into the dog's stomach every day, even when not experimenting. Explain why. *(2)*

d Compare Pavlov's experiment with that of William Beaumont's (spread 2.1) in terms of planning and experimental set up. *(2)*

e Pavlov's experiments were done almost 100 years after Beaumont's work. How might Pavlov have found out about William Beaumont's discoveries? *(2)*

f News of Pavlov's discoveries spread more quickly than did news of Beaumont's discoveries. Suggest why this might have been. *(3)*

g Some people today may object to Pavlov's experiment. Suggest why they might object and explain how a scientist might justify this type of experiment. *(3)*

Respiration

Introduction

We all know that cars use petrol as fuel. We would not be surprised to find that the car soon came to a stop if we did not put petrol in the fuel tank. The petrol provides the energy that the car needs to move.

fig 1

In just the same way, all living organisms require energy if they are to move and carry out the complex processes of living. The fuel that provides this energy is called food, and every day, just like filling the tank with petrol, we have to eat food to provide us with energy to live.

In a car, the energy is released from the petrol by burning it in the engine. You may have noticed that the engine gets very hot after the car has been running for a short time. In our bodies the energy contained in food is released in a chemical process that is similar to the burning of petrol in a car's engine. However, it would not be very healthy if each time we ate food it burst into flames inside our bodies!

fig 2

To prevent this happening, our body produces enzymes. These are proteins that control the rate at which the energy trapped in the food is released. This happens in a series of steps, so that only a small amount of energy is released at any one time. In this way our bodies can use the energy released from the food without being damaged by excessive heat.

Although we do not burst into flames when we eat food, our bodies still get warm. Our normal body temperature is 37 °C, which is much hotter than the normal room temperature of about 20 °C. This heat in our bodies comes from the release of energy from the food that we eat.

The process of releasing this energy in our bodies is called cellular respiration. We will be looking at how it works in this Teaching block.

Check-up

Have a go at the following questions. They will remind you of what you should know about respiration.

a Copy out the paragraph below and use the following words to fill in the gaps. You may use the words once, more than once, or not at all.

glucose • water • carbon dioxide • oxygen • energy

Respiration occurs when the __________ that we eat combines with __________ to form the gas __________ and __________. The process releases __________ which the body uses.

b Write a word equation to summarise respiration. Use the words from the list in question **a** to help you.

Check-up (continued)

c The lungs absorb oxygen and excrete carbon dioxide. Explain how the oxygen gets from the lungs to the cells of the body, and how carbon dioxide gets from the cells to the lungs.

If you have difficulty, ask your teacher for a Summary sheet.

Contents of the Teaching block

3.1 Aerobic respiration

This is the kind of respiration that you studied at Key Stage 3, in which glucose in the food we eat is broken down using oxygen to release energy. Most organisms use aerobic respiration to release energy from food. The oxygen that we need for aerobic respiration is supplied to our bodies by our heart and lungs. During exercise the lungs and heart have to work hard to provide enough oxygen for the working muscles, and we become short of breath. This is sometimes called aerobic exercise. It improves our fitness.

3.2 Anaerobic respiration

This is a different kind of respiration which occurs when there is not enough oxygen for aerobic respiration. In most organisms anaerobic respiration can only be performed for short periods of time. In humans it occurs during periods of intense muscular activity.

Respiring without oxygen may sound like a good idea, but it is not very efficient, and causes muscle fatigue. Some organisms, however, are much better at anaerobic respiration than are humans.

Links to other Teaching blocks

1.2 Life processes
2.3 Absorption
4.2 Breathing rate and depth
5.1 The green machine
7.4 Food chains and energy
7.5 Decomposition and recycling
9.1 Controlling glucose levels
Chemistry 1.7 Energy transfer
Chemistry 7.4 Carbon dioxide

3.1 Aerobic respiration

Key points

- Respiration provides energy for all life processes.
- Our metabolic rate can be calculated from the rate at which we consume oxygen.
- Aerobic respiration is a very similar chemical process to burning.
- We can calculate the amount of energy in food by finding how much heat it gives out when burned.

Respiration versus photosynthesis

Respiration is virtually the opposite of **photosynthesis**. Photosynthesis traps energy from sunlight and stores it in food. Respiration releases the energy that has been trapped in the food.

A good tip ...

If you can remember the equation for respiration, all you have to do is write it backwards and you have the equation for photosynthesis.

Respiration: glucose + oxygen → water + carbon dioxide

Photosynthesis: carbon dioxide + water → oxygen + glucose

a Write out the equations for respiration and photosynthesis and indicate where energy is absorbed or released.

The symbol equation for respiration is:

$$C_6H_{12}O_6 + 6O_2 \rightarrow 6H_2O + 6CO_2 + \text{energy}$$

b Write down the symbol equation for photosynthesis.

All living things respire

Respiration occurs in all living things, including plants. When you study photosynthesis, it is easy to think that plants photosynthesise, and animals respire ... however, this isn't the whole story!

Just like animals, plants respire 24 hours a day in order to provide energy for living. However, during the hours of daylight they also photosynthesise. Photosynthesis occurs at a faster rate than respiration, so respiration is difficult to measure.

c Look at the fig 3. State how many times a day the rate of respiration equals the rate of photosynthesis.

d Explain what is happening to the production of oxygen and carbon dioxide at these times.

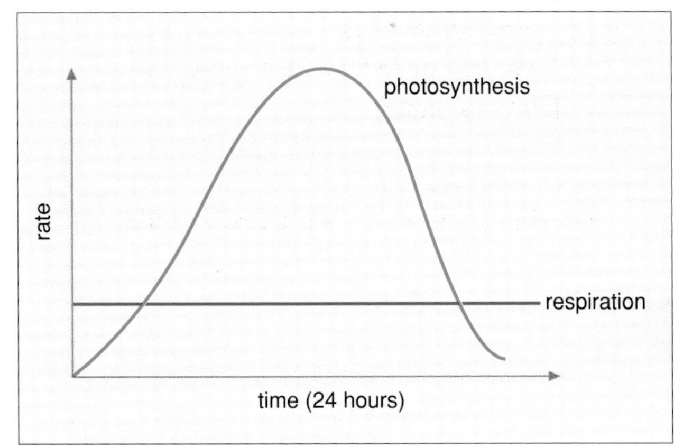

fig 3 | Comparison of the rates of photosynthesis and respiration over a 24-hour period

Energy in food

Different foods contain different amounts of **energy.**

Fat contains almost twice the amount of energy as carbohydrates like **glucose.** Protein contains almost the same amount of energy as carbohydrates.

e Explain why the body stores surplus energy as fat, rather than as carbohydrates.

We can measure the amount of energy in food using a **calorimeter** (fig 4). It is called a calorimeter because energy used to be measured in calories although it is now measured in **joules.** In a calorimeter food is burned in oxygen and the heat given off is calculated by measuring the temperature rise in a known volume of water.

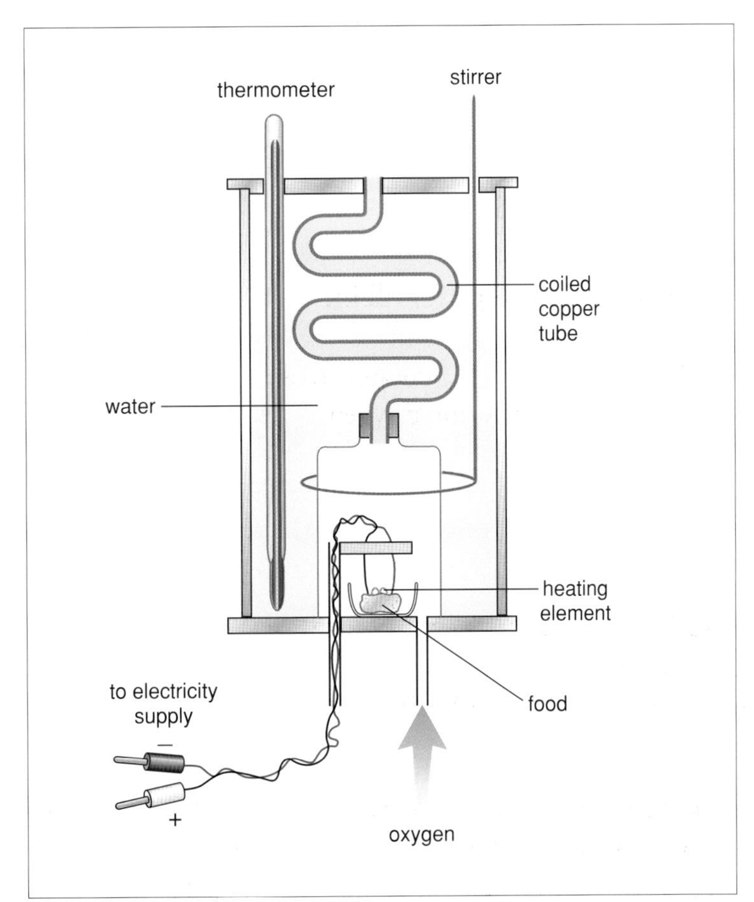

fig 4 | A calorimeter is used to determine the amount of energy in a sample of food

You can do a similar experiment by burning a potato-crisp snack under a boiling tube of water and measuring the temperature rise of the water (fig 5).

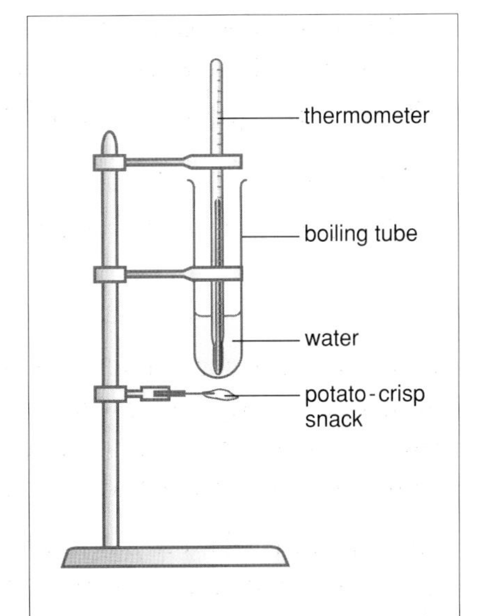

fig 5 | In this experiment a potato-crisp snack is burned to find out how much energy it contains

Thinking further

■ **1** Respiration is a very similar process to burning. State three similarities and three differences between the two processes. Give your answers in the form of a table.

◆ **2** Describe how you would carry out the potato-crisp-snack-burning experiment (fig 5) so that your results would be as accurate as possible.

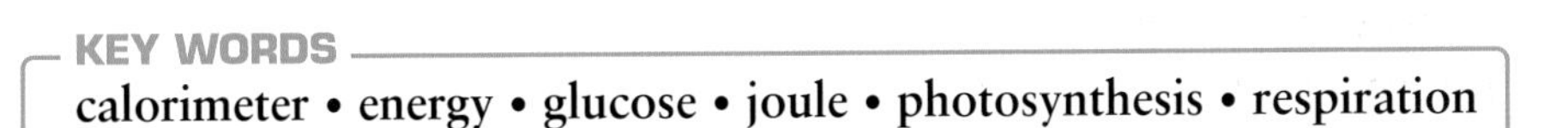
KEY WORDS
calorimeter • energy • glucose • joule • photosynthesis • respiration

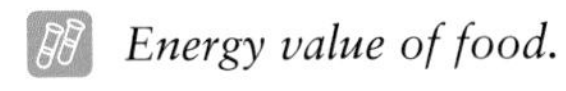
Energy value of food.

3.2 Anaerobic respiration

Key points

- Anaerobic respiration does not require oxygen.
- Different products are formed in aerobic and anaerobic respiration.
- Anaerobic respiration releases less energy than aerobic respiration.

Making alcohol

When oxygen is in short supply, some organisms such as yeast can respire **anaerobically** to produce an **alcohol**, called ethanol:

glucose → carbon dioxide + ethanol + energy

This process is called **fermentation** and is used for making wine and beer. This is shown in fig 6.

a State three similarities and three differences between aerobic and anaerobic respiration. Write your answers in the form of a table.

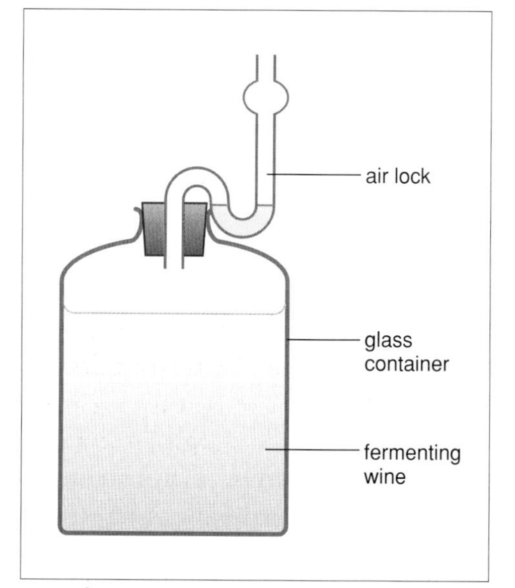

fig 6 | Equipment used to make wine at home

What happens in humans?

Humans can also respire anaerobically. However, the process of anaerobic respiration in humans is different to that in yeast. This is quite a good thing – if we respired in the same way as yeast we would get drunk every time we took part in any strenuous activity. Just imagine what school sports day would be like!

Instead of producing carbon dioxide and ethanol during anaerobic respiration, humans produce a substance called **lactic acid:**

glucose → lactic acid + energy

b State the differences between anaerobic respiration in yeast and that in humans.

Anaerobic respiration – too good to be true?

Anaerobic respiration may sound too good to be true. If we can respire without oxygen, why can't we hold our breaths for several hours and live underwater like a fish? The problem is that anaerobic respiration can only be used for short periods of time. It is used only when there is insufficient oxygen to support aerobic respiration. It has several major disadvantages compared with aerobic respiration.

The disadvantages of anaerobic respiration

- It releases less than half the energy from each molecule of glucose. It is therefore much less efficient than aerobic respiration.
- It produces lactic acid. Lactic acid is toxic and causes muscle fatigue.
- It produces an **oxygen debt** that has to be repaid to break down the lactic acid.

The oxygen debt

Have you ever wondered why you remain out of breath for several minutes after you have stopped running? If you think about it, you would surely expect that when exercise stops, so would the need for obtaining more oxygen. It is reasonable to assume that breathing would immediately return to its resting rate. Clearly this does not happen.

The reason is that during anaerobic respiration lactic acid builds up in the muscles. As the level rises, the muscles get more and more fatigued. Eventually exercise has to stop but the lactic acid is still there. The body then needs a supply of oxygen to break down all the lactic acid. This is called the oxygen debt. We remain out of breath until we have obtained sufficient oxygen to break down the lactic acid. The fitter we are, the quicker this happens.

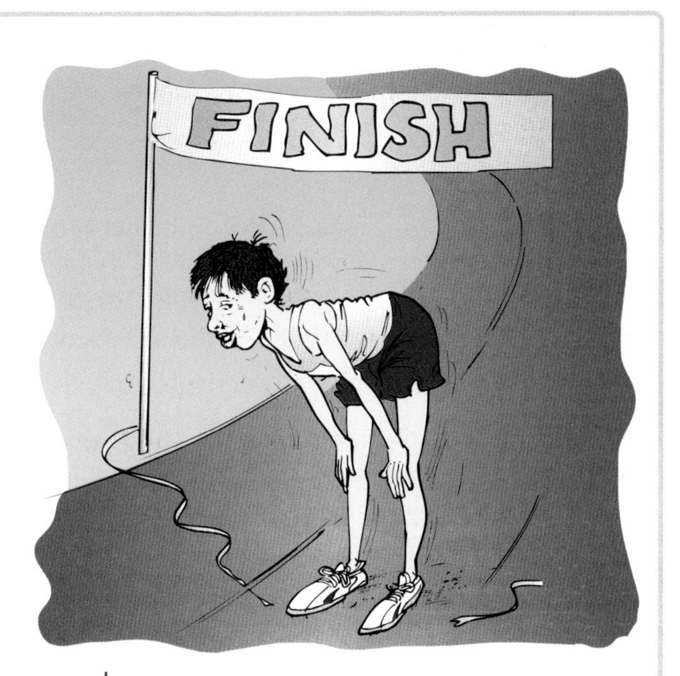

fig 7 | Repaying the oxygen debt

Silage making is a good example of anaerobic respiration. The farmer cuts the grass and leaves it for 24 hours to wilt. It is then packed into plastic bags to keep out the oxygen and is left for 10–14 days. The lack of oxygen encourages anaerobic respiration in bacteria. The bacteria break down the carbohydrates into lactic acid. Black bags are usually used by farmers in the United Kingdom but green or colourless bags are used in other countries. Absence of light is not essential.

Thinking further

■ **1** Joy sprints in the 100-metre race at school sports day.

a Explain why she can run the whole distance without actually breathing.

b Explain why she is out of breath after she finishes the race.

◆ **2** John runs in the marathon. Explain why the oxygen debt does not stop John running such a long distance.

KEY WORDS

alcohol • anaerobic • fermentation • lactic acid • oxygen debt

 *Measuring the rate of fermentation in food.*

Questions on respiration

1 Quorn is a vegetarian food made from single-cell protein. The single-cell protein is grown in fermenters. Fig 8 shows what goes into a fermenter to make the protein.

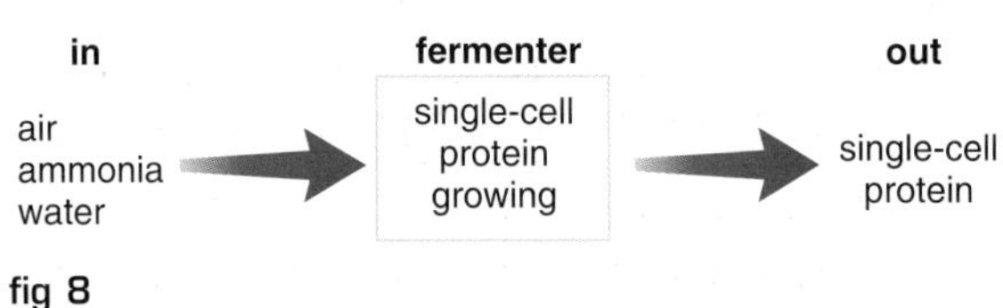

fig 8

● **a** What other substances need to be put into the fermenter? Choose from the following list. *(1)*

alcohol • carbon dioxide • protein • sugar

■ **b** Explain why air is put into the fermenter. *(2)*

■ **2** A calorimeter is used to find the amount of energy in a sample of food. *(4)*

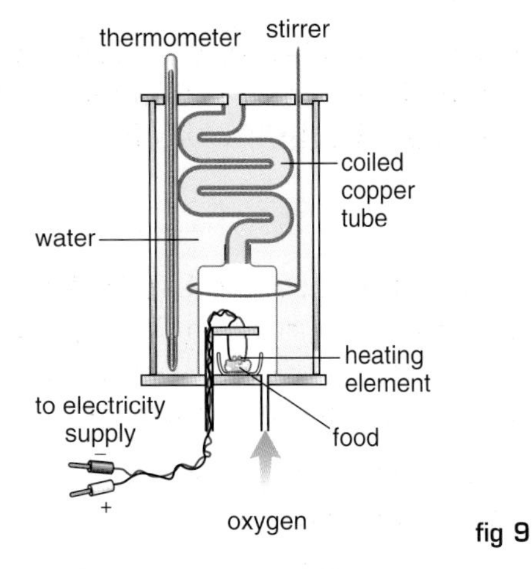

fig 9

Explain the purpose of the following items in the calorimeter:

a oxygen

b water

c the heating element

d the stirrer.

3 Joy baked a cake using a recipe that uses yeast. She knows that the yeast needs sugar as food and oxygen from the air, and will produce carbon dioxide which makes the cake rise.

● **a** Write a word equation to show what the yeast should do. *(2)*

■ **b** Having mixed the ingredients, Joy immediately put the cake in the oven at a temperature of 160 °C. Explain why the cake did not rise. *(2)*

4 Joy's father also uses yeast to make wine.

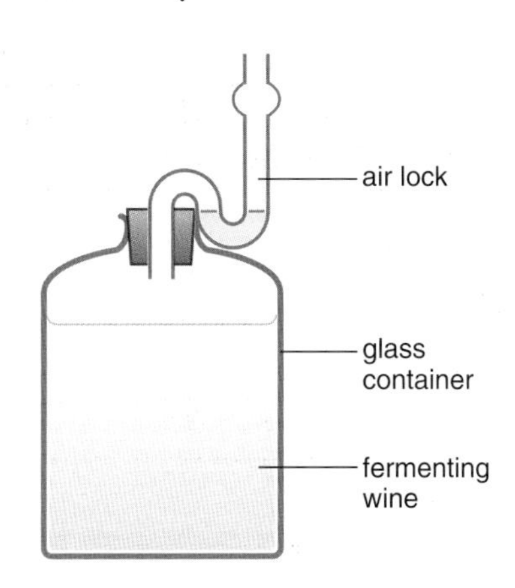

fig 10

● **a** State which substances are produced by the yeast when making wine. *(2)*

■ **b** Copy and complete the following sentence:

The wine-making process is an example of __________ respiration, and the process is called __________ *(2)*

■ **c** One function of the air lock is to keep out unwanted bacteria. State two other functions of the air lock. *(2)*

■ **d** Explain why sugar is used in wine making. *(1)*

● **e** Joy's father knew that all was going well when he saw bubbles of gas coming through the air lock. State the name of this gas. *(1)*

◆ **f** After several weeks, the number of bubbles of gas decreased. Suggest two reasons for this decrease. *(2)*

5 Joy's father decided to try making wine at two different temperatures to see which would work the best.

■ **a** State what he would have to do to ensure that he carried out a fair test. *(2)*

◆ **b** Suggest what he could measure to find out which temperature worked the best. *(1)*

6 Neil knows that an increasing level of carbon dioxide in the atmosphere leads to global warming.

■ **a** Write down the names of two processes that increase the amount of carbon dioxide in the atmosphere. *(2)*

■ **b** Write down the name of one process that decreases the amount of carbon dioxide in the atmosphere. *(1)*

■ **c** Since 1850 there has been a gradual increase in the amount of carbon dioxide in the atmosphere. Plot the information in fig 11 on a grid and draw a curve of best fit. *(3)*

year	carbon dioxide concentration in parts per million
1850	270
1900	285
1960	315
1980	335
2030	Estimated 600

fig 11

■ **d** From your graph estimate the amount of carbon dioxide in the atmosphere in 2000. *(1)*

◆ **e** Explain how human activity is leading to global warming. *(2)*

7 Anita planted some seeds. The seeds germinated and started to grow.

● **a** State the process that provides the energy needed for the seeds to grow. *(1)*

■ **b** The seedlings grow but have not yet turned green or started to photosynthesise. Explain what is happening to the dry mass of the seedlings. *(2)*

■ **c** Eventually the seedlings turn green and start to photosynthesise. Explain what is happening to the dry mass of the seedlings now. *(1)*

■ **d** Fig 12 shows the rate of oxygen consumption by the seedlings during respiration and the rate of carbon dioxide consumption by photosynthesis. Plot a graph of the two sets of figures. *(3)*

time in hours	oxygen consumed by respiration in arbitrary units	carbon dioxide consumed by photosynthesis in arbitrary units
3	2.2	0
6	2.3	2.0
9	2.6	3.5
12	2.9	9.2
15	2.8	10.5
18	2.4	6.3
21	2.3	2.5
24	2.2	0

fig 12

■ **e** State at which times of day the rates of respiration and photosynthesis are equal. *(2)*

◆ **f** State what will be happening to the mass of the plant at those times. *(1)*

8 Bobby and his friend were late for school. They ran to catch the bus. As they ran they noticed that it took a short while before they became short of breath.

● **a** State what type of respiration was going on in Bobby's cells as he started to run. *(1)*

■ **b** He soon became short of breath. State what type of respiration was now going on in Bobby's cells. *(1)*

◆ **c** It was not long before the muscles in his legs began to ache. Explain what was happening to cause the pain in Bobby's leg muscles. *(1)*

◆ **d** Bobby and his friend just managed to catch the bus. They were still out of breath when they sat down. Explain why they were still out of breath when they had stopped running. *(3)*

◆ **e** Bobby got his breath back before his friend. State and explain what this tells you about Bobby and his friend. *(1)*

IDEAS AND EVIDENCE

9 Bobby wants to be an athlete. He knows that a lot of training is required in order to get as fit as possible. He also knows that some athletes take muscle-building drugs to improve their performance.

■ **a** Suggest why it would not be a good idea for Bobby to take drugs. *(3)*

◆ **b** Some people think that drug testing is unreliable and that false accusations have been made against top athletes. State and explain whether you think drug testing should continue if the results may not always be reliable. *(3)*

Breathing

Introduction

The aerobic respiration discussed in Teaching block 3 requires oxygen and produces carbon dioxide. The taking in of oxygen and the removal of carbon dioxide is called gaseous exchange. In some animals this occurs over the whole of the body but larger animals have special structures for gaseous exchange. Examples of these are the gills of fish (fig 1) and the lungs of mammals.

fig 1 | Salmon gills

You should have studied the structure of the lungs to see how they are adapted for gaseous exchange (fig 2). The two lungs are made up of about 700 million air sacs which give a total surface area that is about the size of a tennis court. The air sacs have a thin wall, and a rich network of thin blood vessels surrounds them. These features allow oxygen to diffuse into the blood and carbon dioxide to diffuse in the opposite direction.

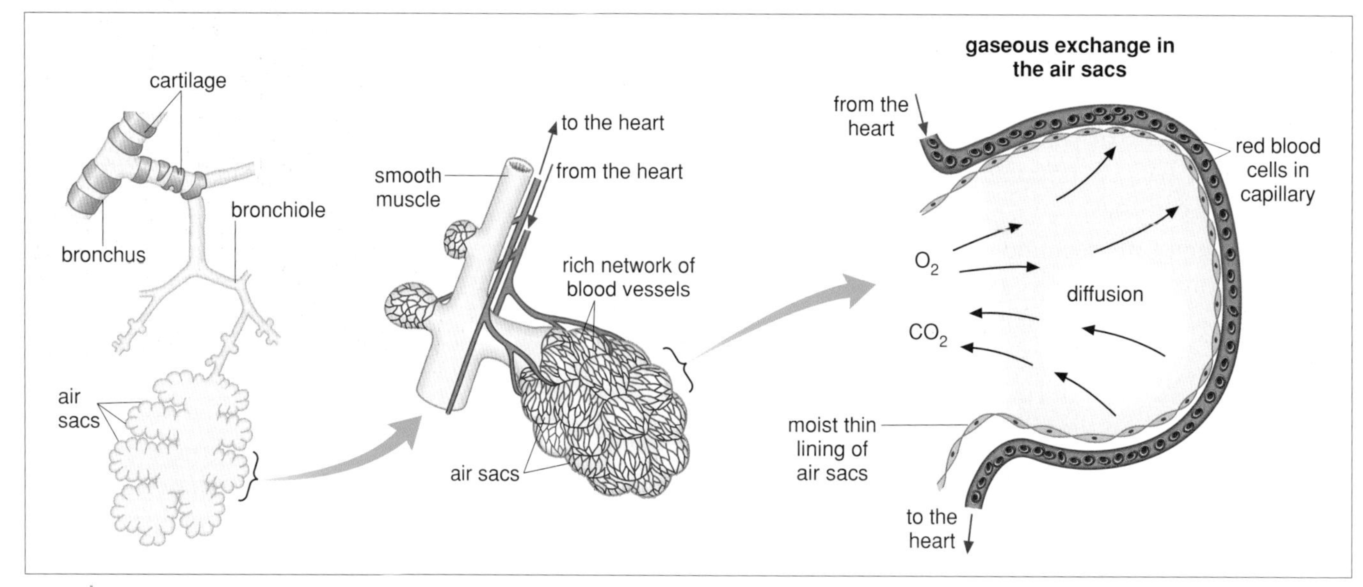

fig 2 | The air sacs (alveoli) of the lungs are specialised for gaseous exchange

Small inactive organisms can obtain enough oxygen by diffusion. However, we would not receive enough oxygen by simply allowing air to diffuse in and out of the lungs. Mammals, like many other animals, draw air in and out of the lungs by muscular contractions. This is called breathing and it speeds up the rate of gaseous exchange.

You should also be aware that the lungs are delicate structures that can be easily affected by cigarette smoke, pollution or other impurities in the air such as pollen grains.

Check-up

Have a go at the following questions. They will remind you of what you should know about breathing.

- a Write down the name of the gas that is needed for respiration and the waste gas that is produced.
- b Explain the differences between the processes of respiration, breathing and gaseous exchange.
- c The lungs are specially adapted for efficient gaseous exchange. Describe three of these adaptations.
- d Write down the name of one disease that may be caused by cigarette smoking and one that may be caused by inhaling pollen grains.
- e Explain why a polar bear needs to breathe whereas an oak tree does not, even though they both need to respire.

If you have difficulty, ask your teacher for a Summary sheet.

Contents of the Teaching block

4.1 Breathing

The actions of the ribs, intercostal muscles and diaphragm cause pressure changes in the lungs which draw in air. These structures are specially adapted for this function.

4.2 Breathing rate and depth

Normal quiet breathing provides enough oxygen for a person at rest but when exercising, more oxygen is required and more carbon dioxide is produced. The body therefore has to increase the rate and depth of breathing.

4.3 Keeping the lungs clean

The lungs have an in-built system to keep themselves clean. Unfortunately, this cannot always cope with impurities such as cigarette smoke.

fig 3

Links to other Teaching blocks

1.3 Transport and cells
3.1 Aerobic respiration
9.3 Kidneys and lungs

4.1 Breathing

Key points

- The lungs are associated with a number of other structures that allow them to inflate and deflate.
- These structures are specialised for this particular function.

The respiratory system

The structure of the respiratory system is shown in fig 4.
The lungs are found in the **thorax,** which contains a number of other organs, including the heart. Surrounding these organs is the ribcage. This is made up of twelve pairs of ribs.

a What material are the ribs made of?

b Write down another function of the ribs, apart from breathing.

Attached between the ribs are **intercostal muscles**. Stretched across under the ribs, forming the base of the thorax, is the **diaphragm**. This is a sheet of muscle.

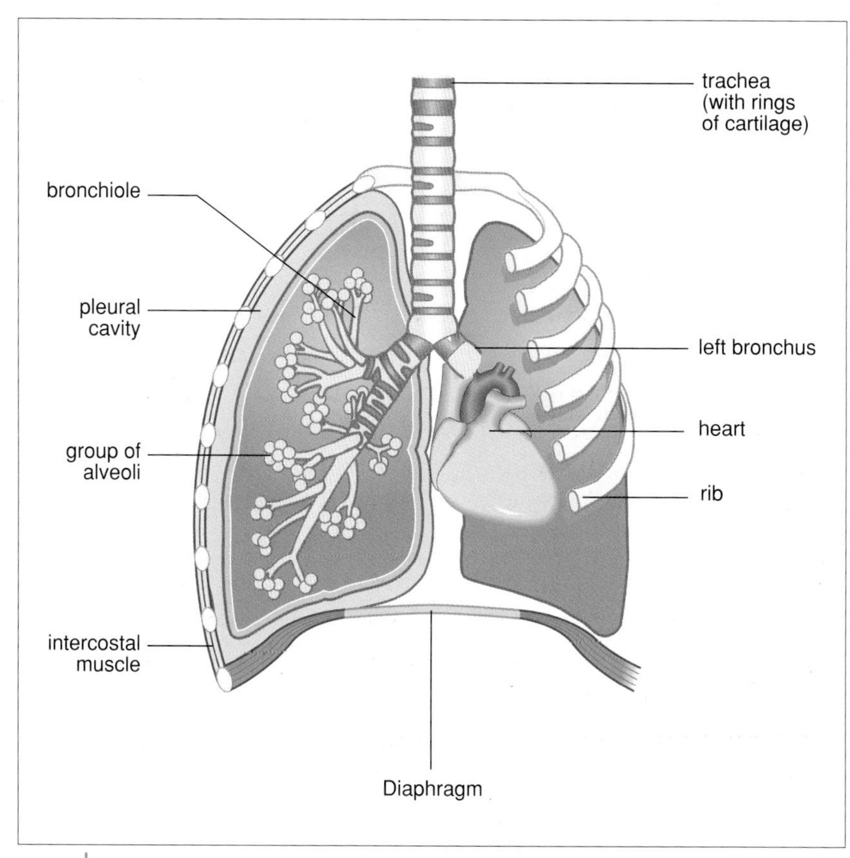

fig 4 | The human respiratory system

The millions of air sacs or **alveoli** in the lungs are connected to the outside by a series of tubes.
The smallest tubes are the **bronchioles.** These join together to form the two **bronchi** and these merge to form the **trachea** (windpipe).

Breathing

The millions of alveoli of the lungs act like tiny elastic balloons. To make a balloon inflate, the air pressure inside must be higher than the pressure outside the balloon. The function of the ribs, intercostal muscles and diaphragm is to change the pressure inside the lungs. This is shown in fig 5.

In order to breathe in, the intercostal muscles contract. This makes the ribs move upwards and outwards. The diaphragm contracts and so flattens out. Both of these actions increase the volume of the lungs and so decrease the pressure. The pressure inside the lungs is now less than the outside air pressure so air is drawn into the lungs.

The air passes into the mouth, down the trachea and into the bronchi and some of the bronchioles. It then passes into the alveoli by diffusion.

To breathe out, the diaphragm and the intercostal muscles relax. The diaphragm returns to the original position of curving upwards, and the ribs move downwards and inwards. Both of these actions decrease the volume and so increase the pressure in the lungs. This forces air out of the lungs.

c Why does moving the ribs upwards and outwards need more energy and muscle contraction than moving them downwards?

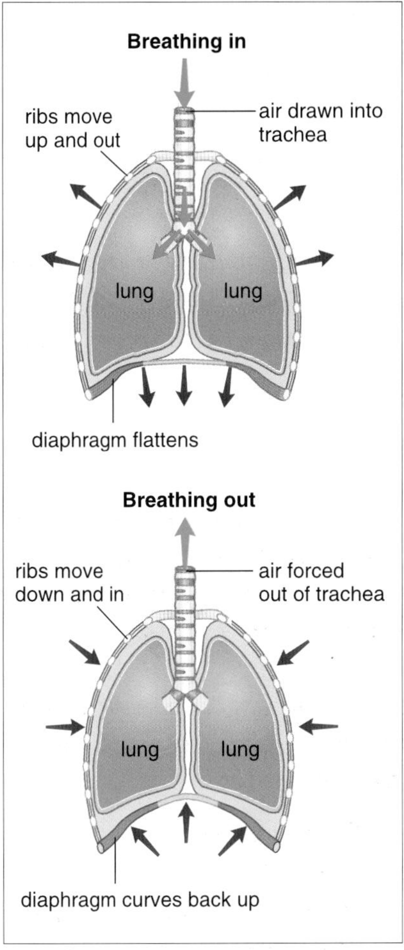

fig 5 Movements of the ribs, diaphragm and chest during breathing

Structure and function of the lungs

The structures of the breathing system have a number of adaptations that enable them to work efficiently:

- **Movement of the ribs and diaphragm** – the ribs are not joined rigidly to the vertebral column but can tilt up and down. At the front they are joined to the sternum by cartilage. This allows some flexibility. The diaphragm is curved upwards so that when it contracts it will flatten out, increasing the volume of the thorax.
- **Cartilage in the trachea** – the trachea contains C-shaped rings of cartilage that help to prevent the trachea collapsing inwards.
- **Airtight pleural membranes** – the lungs are surrounded by two thin pleural membranes with a gap between them called the pleural cavity. This is airtight and so when the volume increases, the pressure in the lungs decreases.

Thinking further

■ 1 A candidate wrote the following description of breathing.

> Air is drawn into the lungs by the lungs inflating. This pushes the ribs upwards and outwards and makes the diaphragm flatten.

Explain the mistakes made by the candidate.

■ 2 When and why would the trachea be most likely to collapse without the rings of cartilage?

◆ 3 The pleural cavity contains a thin film of moisture. Suggest a function for this fluid.

KEY WORDS
alveoli • bronchi • bronchioles • diaphragm • intercostal muscles • thorax • trachea

4.2 Breathing rate and depth

Key points

- In the alveoli of the lungs, a certain amount of oxygen is removed from the inhaled air and replaced with carbon dioxide.
- This process can be adjusted according to the body's needs by altering the rate and depth of breathing.

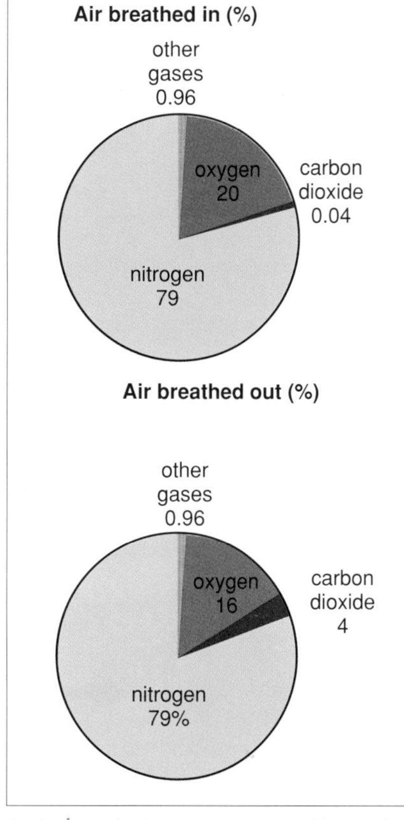

fig 6 | Typical percentage composition of air breathed in and air breathed out

Composition of the air

The percentage of the different gases in the air does not vary very much from one place to another. These percentages are shown in a pie chart in fig 6.

a Suggest a place where the percentage of carbon dioxide may be:
  i slightly lower than the value in fig 6 for inhaled air
  ii slightly higher than the value in fig 6 for inhaled air.

The percentages of the different gases in the air breathed out are also shown in fig 6. It is important to realise that the oxygen is not totally removed from the air in the alveoli – air that is breathed out is about 16% oxygen. One reason for this is that the alveoli are not emptied of air when we breathe out. The gases in the alveoli can only be exchanged by diffusion into and out of the bronchioles.

b How do these facts make artificial respiration possible?

Measuring breathing

Breathing can be measured in a number of different ways. The **breathing rate** is the number of breaths per minute and is easy to count.

c Count your breaths per minute whilst sitting quietly.

The depth of each breath, which is the volume of air breathed in or out, is harder to measure. The air can be collected in a bag and the volume measured. Alternatively, machines such as a **spirometer** can give a

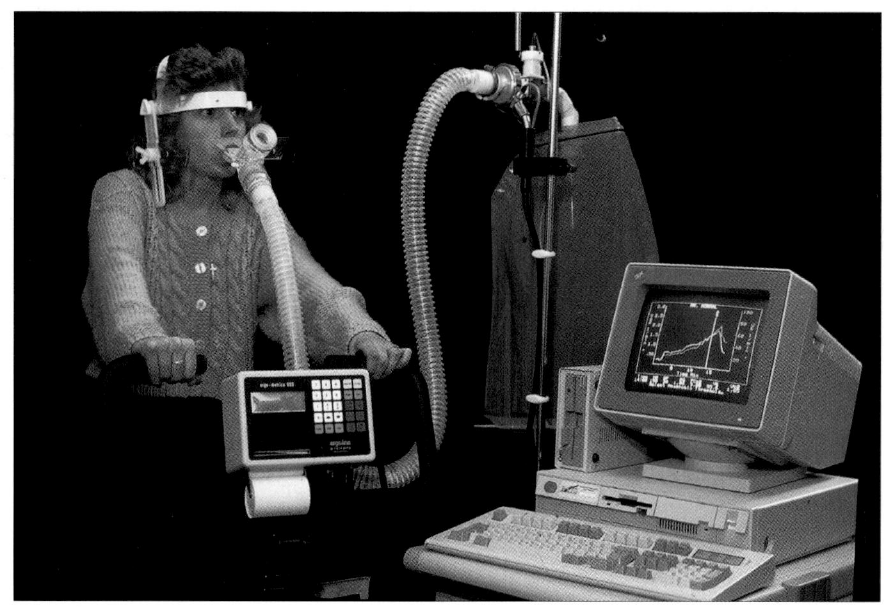

fig 7 | The computer monitors the woman's breathing as she pedals the exercise bike. The exhaled air is collected in the bag and can be analysed.

print-out of the pattern of breathing. One of these is shown in fig 7. Fig 8 shows the volume of air that is exchanged whilst breathing quietly (the **tidal volume**). If a person breathes in and out as deeply as possible then much more air can be exchanged. The maximum is the **vital capacity.** There is always some air left in the lungs that cannot be exchanged.

During exercise, more oxygen is needed for respiration and more carbon dioxide is produced. The rate and depth of breathing are both increased. This removes the excess carbon dioxide and takes in extra oxygen.

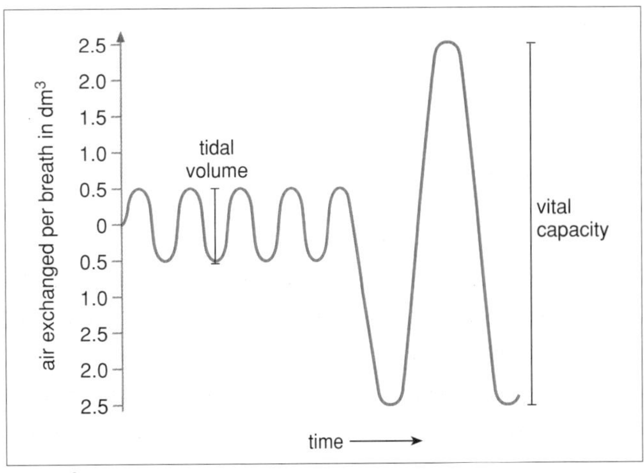

fig 8 | An example of a spirometer trace

▷▷ Taking it further ▷▷

Control of breathing

The intercostal muscles and diaphragm are controlled by an area of the brain called the medulla. The medulla sends impulses along nerves to make these structures contract.

During exercise the extra carbon dioxide or lactic acid in the blood is detected by special receptors called chemoreceptors. This information is sent to the medulla, which instructs the intercostal muscles and diaphragm to contract harder and more frequently. This increases the depth and rate of breathing.

Thinking further

■ **1** Use the pie charts in fig 6 to construct a table to show the differences between air breathed in and air breathed out.

■ **2** From fig 8 estimate
  a the tidal volume
  b the vital capacity.

■ **3** From the breathing rate that you measured in question **c** opposite, work out how much air you exchange in one minute. (Assume that your tidal volume is the same as in fig 8.)

◆ **4** Hyperventilation occurs if a person breathes very heavily for a while when they are not exercising. This may cause their breathing to stop briefly.

  a Suggest why breathing may stop following hyperventilation.

  b Women sometimes hyperventilate while in labour. To prevent this happening, the woman is asked to breathe in and out of a paper bag for a while. Explain why this helps to prevent hyperventilation.

KEY WORDS
breathing rate • spirometer • tidal volume • vital capacity

 *Oxygen in different samples of exhaled air.*

4.3 Keeping the lungs clean

Key points

- The lungs have an in-built system for filtering the air and preventing infection.
- This system can be damaged by smoking tobacco.

Mucus and cilia

Hairs in the nostrils help to filter out large particles from the air as it is breathed in. The nose also contains blood vessels which are close to the skin to warm the air.

The trachea and bronchi are lined with cells called **epithelia** (fig 9). They have a covering of fine hairs called **cilia.** Mixed in with these epithelial cells are **goblet cells.** These produce and release a sticky liquid called **mucus.** Dust and micro-organisms in the air are trapped in the mucus and are then wafted up to the mouth by the beating of the cilia. The mucus is then swallowed.

a What happens to the micro-organisms once they have been swallowed?

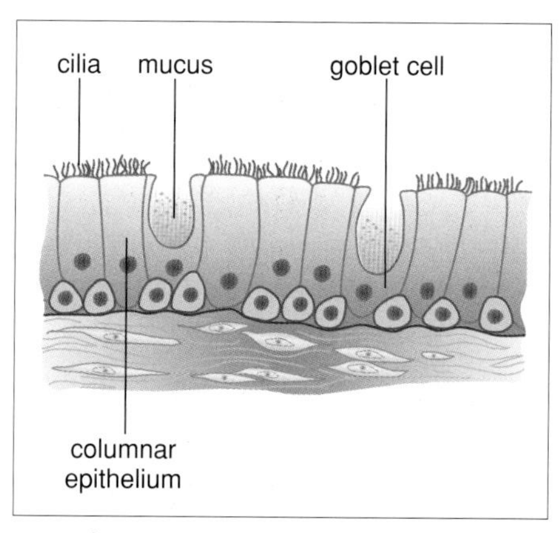

fig 9 | The cells lining the trachea and bronchi

Smoking and the lungs

The smoking of manufactured cigarettes started to become popular in the late 1890s. The number of cigarettes smoked each year in the United Kingdom is shown in fig 10.

b Suggest reasons for the peaks marked A and B on the graph.

c Compare the pattern of smoking shown for men and women.

It has been known for some time that the smoking of tobacco has a number of effects on the lungs and increases the chances of developing certain diseases.

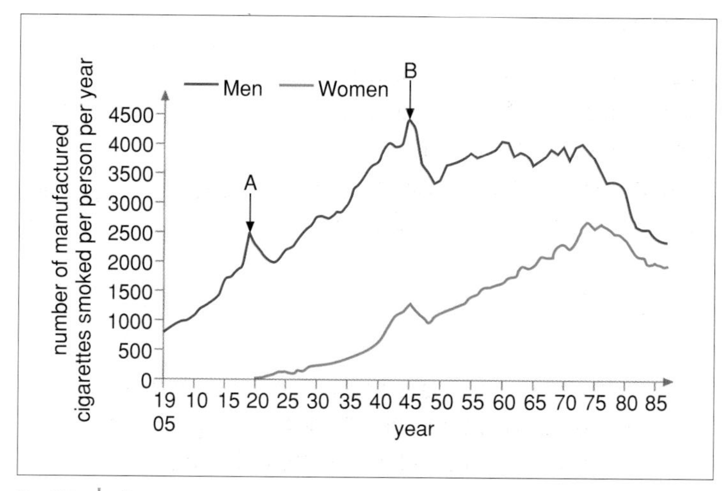

fig 10 | Annual consumption of manufactured cigarettes per person in the United Kingdom from 1905 to 1987

Bronchitis

Various chemicals in tobacco smoke stimulate the goblet cells to produce more mucus. The cilia are also destroyed or prevented from moving. These two actions mean that large amounts of mucus build up in the bronchioles and alveoli, reducing gaseous exchange. This results in coughing and shortage of breath.

The accumulated mucus may also become infected. These are the symptoms of **bronchitis.**

Emphysema

Over a period of time, infections of the alveoli can cause the walls of the alveoli to break down. This results in few large air spaces rather than many small alveoli and reduces gaseous exchange. Fig 11 shows damaged lung tissue.

d Explain why having fewer large air spaces reduces gaseous exchange.

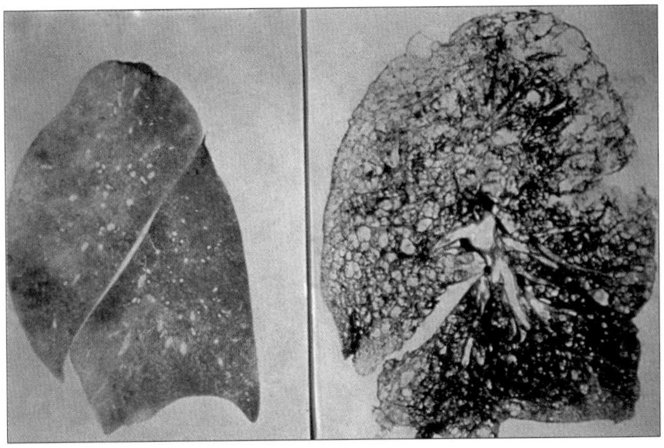

fig 11 | A normal lung (left) and a lung from someone with emphysema (right)

Lung cancer

Various chemicals in the tar contained in tobacco smoke can stimulate the epithelia to divide. They multiply in a fast uncontrolled way and form a tumour or lung cancer. This may continue to grow, or cells may break off and pass to other organs before they start to divide again. This may result in death.

About 90% of all deaths from lung cancer are smoking related. The chance of getting cancer depends on the number of cigarettes smoked. If a person stops smoking then the risk of getting cancer gradually decreases.

Fig 12 shows the percentage of middle-aged women and men that smoke and the number of deaths from lung cancer in this group between 1950 and 1998.

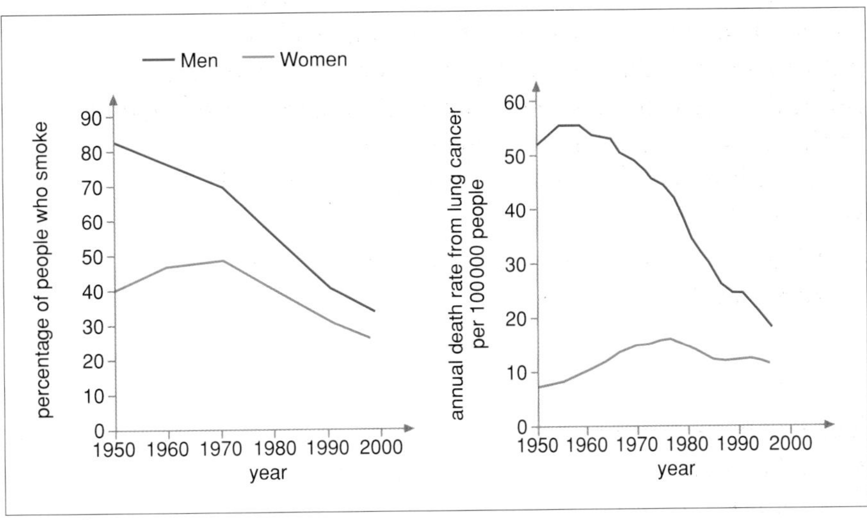

fig 12 | Changes in the percentage of middle-aged people who smoke and the annual death rate from lung cancer between 1950 and 1998

Thinking further

■ **1** Compare the data shown for the percentage of men who smoke (fig 12) with the total number of cigarettes smoked since 1950 (fig 10).

■ **2** What is the difference between the percentage of males who smoked in 1950 compared with 1998?

■ **3** What evidence is there from fig 12 that smoking causes lung cancer?

◆ **4** In which year was the percentage of women who smoked the highest? How did this differ from the year in which most women died of lung cancer? Suggest a reason for this difference.

◆ **5** Discuss why the percentage of people who smoke has changed over this period.

KEY WORDS

bronchitis • cilia • emphysema • epithelia • goblet cells • lung cancer • mucus

Questions on breathing

● **1** Arrange the following structures in the order in which air enters them during breathing: *(3)*

alveoli • bronchi • trachea • bronchioles

● **2** Fig 13 shows an experiment set up as a demonstration of breathing.

a What do the following represent:

i the balloons
ii the glass tube
iii the rubber sheet
iv the glass jar
v the two rubber tubes? *(5)*

b Explain what happens when the rubber sheet is pulled down. *(2)*

c Why would this not happen if there was a hole in the rubber sheet? *(1)*

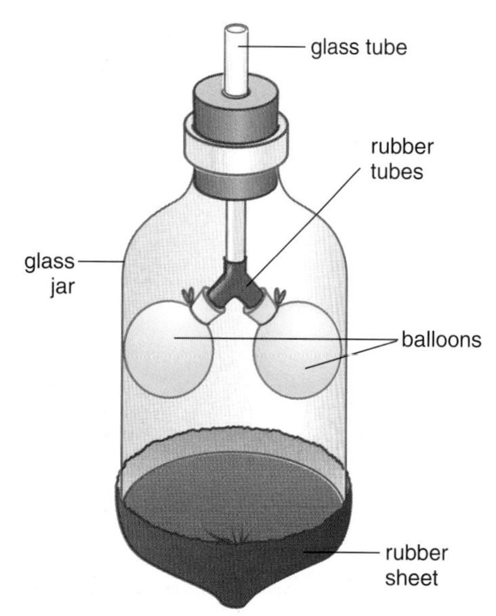

fig 13

■ **3** Explain how air is drawn into the lungs. Use the following words in your explanation: *(4)*

ribs • intercostal muscles • diaphragm • pressure • volume

■ **4** Fig 14 shows apparatus that can be used to demonstrate the difference between air breathed in and the air breathed out.

a Describe what would happen when a person breathes in and out of the glass tube while sitting down. Explain your answer. *(2)*

b What differences would you expect if the person breathed in and out of the tube whilst jogging on the spot? *(2)*

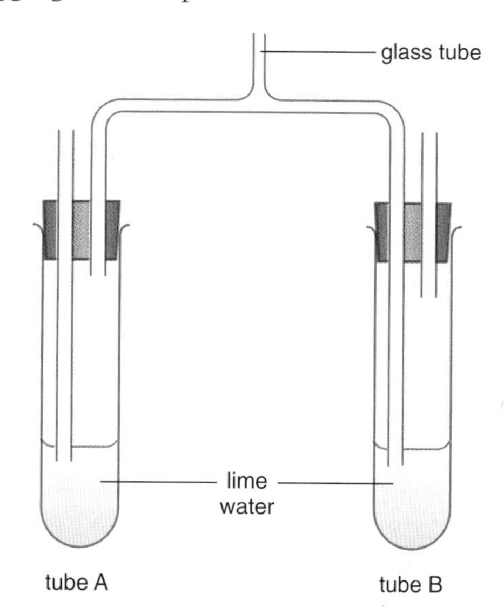

fig 14

5 Read the following passage and answer the questions that follow:

In a small single-celled animal, the intake of oxygen presents no problem but when an animal grows beyond a certain size, the volume of protoplasm demanding oxygen outstrips the surface area that can provide it. It is a purely mathematical misfortune that as the volume of a solid body increases its surface does not expand at the same rate. Consequently, as an animal grows larger it runs the risk of being asphyxiated by its own bulk. This means that there has to be an additional surface with the specific purpose of supplying all the oxygen such a large creature requires. Since this surface has to be many times greater than the overall area of the body, it poses an elaborate packaging problem.

◆ **a** Explain why the intake of oxygen presents no problem in a small single-celled animal. *(2)*

◆ **b** What does 'asphyxiated by its own bulk' mean? *(2)*

■ **c** What are the 'additional surfaces' found in fish and mammals? *(2)*

◆ **d** How do mammals solve the 'elaborate packaging problem'? *(2)*

6 Fig 15 shows a spirometer trace of a person's breathing.

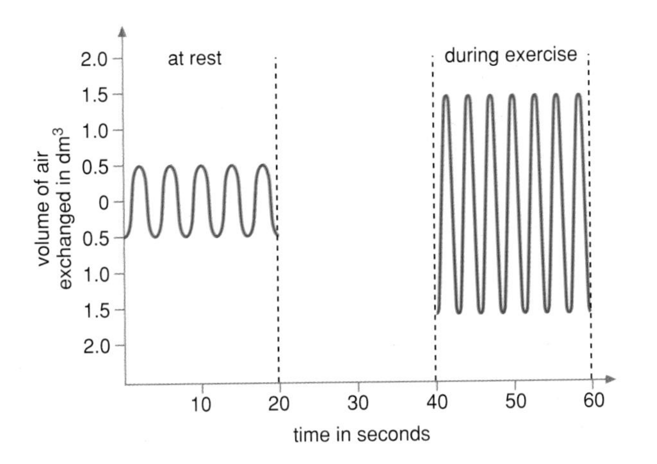

fig 15

- **a** What is the person's resting tidal volume? *(1)*
- **b** What is the person's breathing rate at rest? *(1)*
- ◆ **c** Use the values from parts **a** and **b** to work out the volume of air that the person exchanges per minute at rest. *(2)*
- ◆ **d** Perform similar calculations to find out how much air is exchanged per minute during exercise. *(3)*
- ◆ **e** Work out the percentage change in air exchange between rest and exercise. *(2)*
- ◆ **f** How does the body bring about this change in the amount of air exchanged? *(4)*

IDEAS AND EVIDENCE

7 Asthma is a very common condition. It is caused when the walls of the bronchioles go into spasm and contract. Various triggers such as dust, pollen, animal hair or cold weather may bring on an attack.

- ◆ **a** Explain why a person's breathing rate increases during an asthma attack. *(2)*
- ◆ **b** Why is smoking likely to make the effects of an asthma attack worse? *(2)*
- ◆ **c** Suggest why different people are likely to suffer attacks at different times of the year. *(2)*
- **d** Fig 16 shows the number of patients of different ages with asthma in 1996.

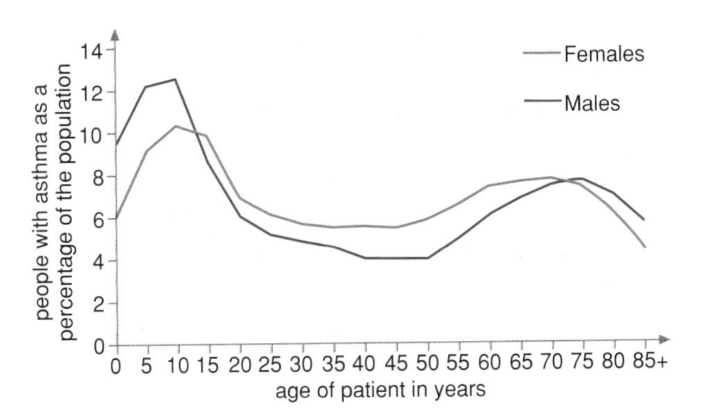

fig 16 Number of people with asthma in England and Wales in 1996

- **i** Which type of person is most likely to suffer from asthma? *(2)*
- ◆ **ii** Children are often told that they will grow out of asthma. Does this data give any evidence for this claim? *(3)*

e Fig 17 shows the number of patients receiving drugs for the treatment of asthma in three consecutive years.

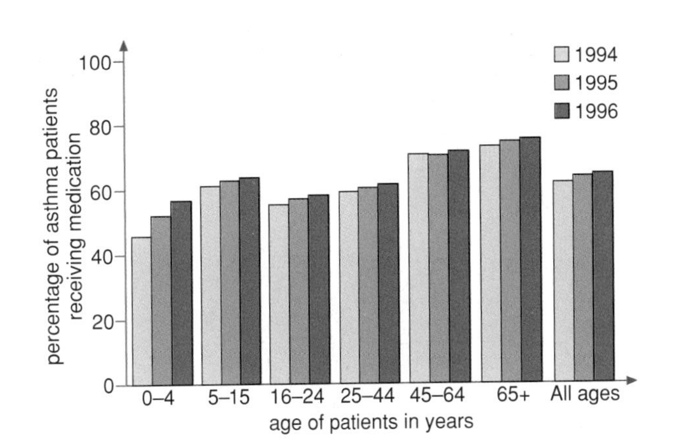

fig 17

- **i** Which group is prescribed the most drugs? *(1)*
- ◆ **ii** Is this the group that contains the highest number of asthma sufferers? Suggest why they are prescribed most drugs. *(2)*
- ◆ **iii** Many people think that the incidence of asthma is increasing. How far is this claim supported by the data in the graph? *(3)*

Photosynthesis

Introduction

Have you ever wondered why, even after millions of years, we have never run out of food or used up all the oxygen in the air? There are billions people on Earth, and every day we are eating food and breathing air. Logically we would think that, eventually, it must all be used up.

Fortunately for us, green plants also live on this planet. If it were not for the plants, we would be in serious trouble. They actually produce the oxygen that we need to breathe, and as they grow, they produce the food that we eat. What is even more amazing is that they do this by converting our waste products, such as carbon dioxide, into the food and oxygen that we need to survive. They do this chemical magic by a process called photosynthesis.

fig 1 | The chemical magic of photosynthesis

Photosynthesis is a truly amazing process. Plants use a green pigment called chlorophyll to trap the energy from sunlight. They use the energy to manufacture complex molecules like sugars, starches and proteins, which we can then use for food. Plants release oxygen into the atmosphere as a byproduct of photosynthesis.

Animals have never learnt how to do this chemical magic, which is why there are no green chlorophyll-containing animals. Just imagine if we were green and contained chlorophyll – every time we went out in the Sun we would grow bigger and fatter! There is no doubt that although humans cannot photosynthesise, it is a process that is responsible for keeping us alive and well.

fig 2 | If humans could photosynthesise ...

This Teaching block explains some of the mysteries of photosynthesis, and how green plants perform this chemical magic.

Check-up

Have a go at the following questions. They will remind you of what you should know about photosynthesis.

a Use the following words to make a word equation for photosynthesis. You may use the words once, more than once, or not at all.

oxygen • glucose • water • light • carbon dioxide

__________ + __________ → __________ + __________

b Name two elements that are required for plant growth in addition to carbon, oxygen and hydrogen.

c Draw a diagram of a root hair and explain how it absorbs minerals from the soil.

d Name the process that is used by a root hair to absorb water from the soil.

e Suggest why fungi are unable to manufacture food by the process of photosynthesis.

If you have difficulty, ask your teacher for a Summary sheet.

Contents of the Teaching block

5.1 The green machine

The leaf is the factory of the plant. It is here that photosynthesis takes place, and the leaf is designed to make this process as efficient as possible. The leaf is adapted to absorb gases from the atmosphere and to have as large a surface area as possible to trap the maximum amount of light.

5.2 Limiting factors

The rate of photosynthesis is controlled by limiting factors. These include temperature, light and the availability of raw materials.

5.3 Photosynthesis and beyond

One of the products of photosynthesis is glucose. Glucose is the starting point for a whole series of reactions that turn it into other substances such as starch and protein. These can then be used for other purposes.

Links with other Teaching blocks

1.1 Cells
3.1 Aerobic respiration
7.4 Food chains and energy
7.6 Food production
Chemistry 7.3 The oceans
Chemistry 7.4 Carbon dioxide
Chemistry 8.3 Fertilisers
Chemistry 8.4 Fertiliser problems

5.1 The green machine

Key points

- Photosynthesis takes place inside green leaves.
- It produces carbohydrates and oxygen and removes carbon dioxide from the atmosphere.
- The leaf's structure is highly adapted to carry out itsfunction of photosynthesis.

The importance of photosynthesis

Photosynthesis not only provides food through plant growth but also releases oxygen into and removes carbon dioxide from the atmosphere. All green plants, but particularly the tropical rain forests and the huge amount of green phytoplankton near the surface of the sea, carry out this process.

Photosynthesis versus respiration

Photosynthesis is virtually the opposite of respiration.

$$\text{carbon dioxide} + \text{water} \xrightarrow[\text{chlorophyll}]{\text{light}} \text{oxygen} + \text{glucose}$$

Photosynthesis traps the **energy** from sunlight and converts it into food. Respiration is the process by which this energy is released and allows us to live.

If you can remember the formula for respiration, all you have to do is write it backwards and you have the formula for photosynthesis.

The balanced equation for photosynthesis is:

$$6CO_2 + 6H_2O \xrightarrow[\text{chlorophyll}]{\text{light}} 6O_2 + C_6H_{12}O_6$$

a Write down the balanced equation for respiration.

Inside the machine

Fig 3 shows a cross-section of a **leaf**. The **leaf** has developed through millions of years of evolution to carry out the job of photosynthesis. It is a very specialised organ. Leaves are usually very thin and provide the plant with a very large surface area to trap as much sunlight as possible.

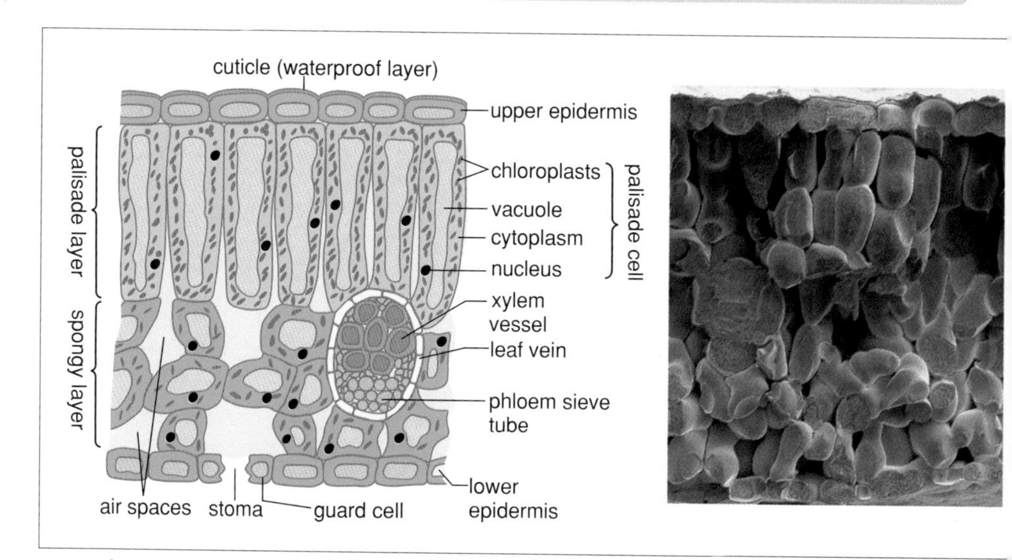

fig 3 | A cross-section of a leaf and a scanning electron micrograph of a fractured spinach leaf (×200)

b Imagine you are a design engineer. Make a list of all the jobs a leaf has to do.

c State how the leaf has evolved to carry out each of the jobs you listed in **b**.

What does what?

Xylem and phloem

The **xylem** and **phloem** (fig 4) are transport vessels. They go from the roots all the way to the leaves. Photosynthesis requires water and produces glucose. The xylem transports water up from the roots to the leaves, and the phloem transports glucose away from the leaf for storage.

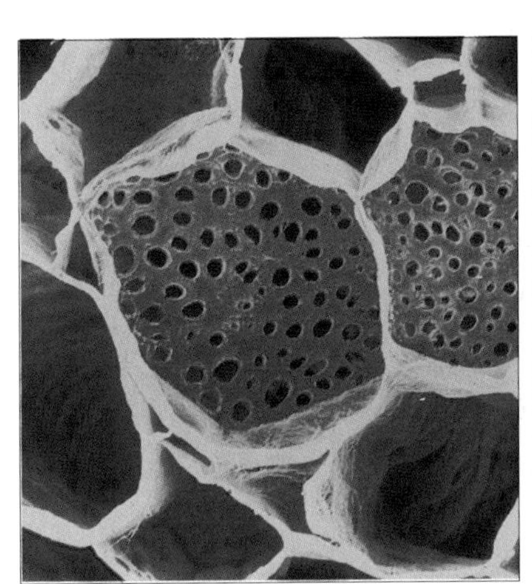

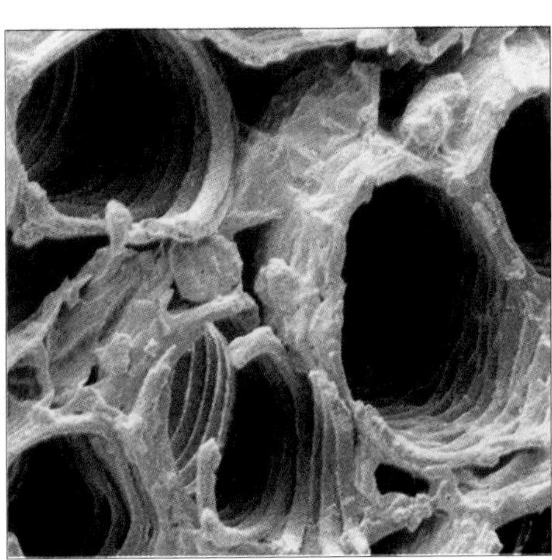

fig 4 | The veins contain the phloem sieve tubes (×770) (left) and the xylem vessels (×600) (right)

Chloroplasts

Chloroplasts are small packets of a green pigment called **chlorophyll.** They are found mainly near the upper surface of the leaf in the palisade layer (fig 5). The chlorophyll absorbs the sunlight energy for photosynthesis.

d Explain why chloroplasts are found near the upper surface of the leaf.

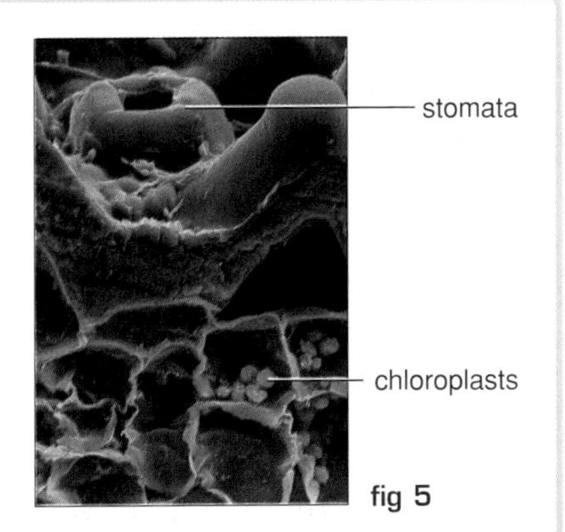

fig 5

Stomata and air spaces

Leaves need to absorb carbon dioxide from the air and get rid of oxygen to the air. They do this through small openings on the underside of the leaf, called **stomata** (fig 5 and fig 16 on spread 6.4). The gases diffuse through the leaf via the **air spaces** between the cells. In order to prevent loss of valuable water, the stomata can close when photosynthesis is not taking place, for example at night.

Thinking further

1 Think about the job that a leaf does and explain why it is thin and green with a large surface area.

2 Explain why the stomata open during the day and close during the night.

KEY WORDS

air spaces • chloroplast • chlorophyll •energy • leaf • phloem • photosynthesis • stomata • xylem

 *Gas production during photosynthesis.* *Gas exchange in leaves.*

5.2 Limiting factors

Key points

- The rate of photosynthesis is affected by changes in light intensity, temperature and carbon dioxide concentration.
- The rate of photosynthesis may be limited by conditions such as light intensity, temperature and carbon dioxide concentration.

How fast can you go?

Photosynthesis is a chemical reaction. This means that, like all chemical reactions, the **rate** or speed of the reaction depends on physical conditions such as **temperature**, and the availability of the reactants, such as **carbon dioxide**.

a State one other reactant that might affect the rate of photosynthesis.

Light intensity has a more immediate effect on the rate of photosynthesis than any other factor. During the hours of darkness, photosynthesis stops completely, only starting again at sunrise. The rate of photosynthesis will be at its greatest at about midday when light intensity is highest.

Other factors that can affect the rate of photosynthesis are temperature and carbon dioxide concentration.

b Look at the three graphs in fig 6. Suggest why the graph for temperature is a different shape from the other two graphs.

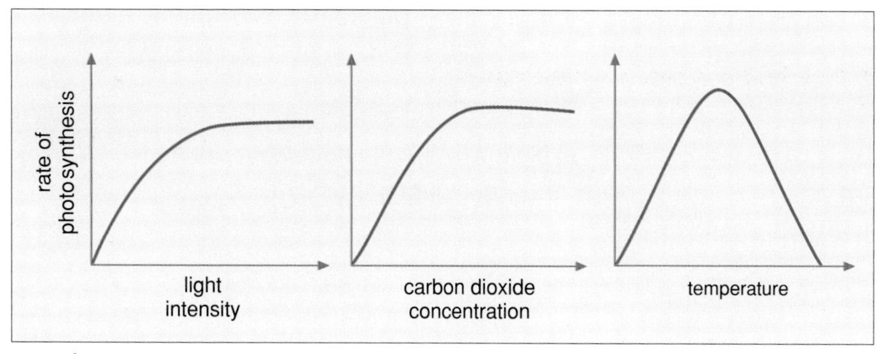

fig 6 | The effect of different conditions on the rate of photosynthesis

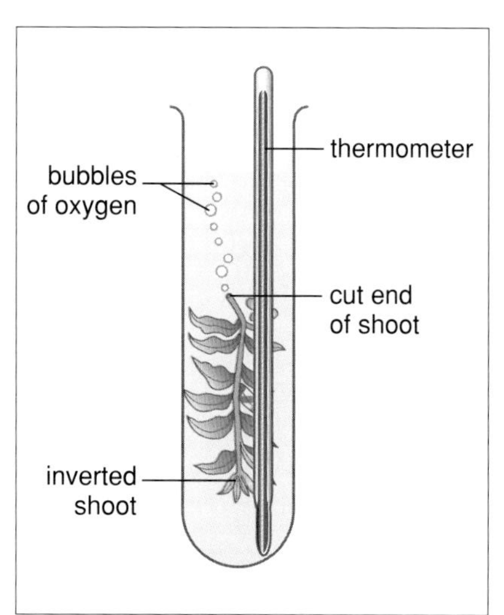

fig 7 | Measuring the rate of photosynthesis in pondweed – the number of bubbles of oxygen given off in a fixed time gives an indication of the rate of photosynthesis

One way to measure the rate of photosynthesis is to measure how much oxygen is given off by a plant.

c State another way you could use to measure the rate of photosynthesis.

Pondweed is a good plant to use because the oxygen forms bubbles in the water and these can be counted and measured (fig 7).

Reaching the speed limit

Light, temperature and carbon dioxide do not just *affect* the rate of photosynthesis, they also *limit* how fast it can go. For this reason they are called **limiting factors**. This difference is subtle and needs careful thought.

Look carefully at fig 8. It shows that carbon dioxide is a limiting factor. As the light intensity increases, so does the rate of photosynthesis, but then it reaches a maximum or optimum rate and the graph levels out. At this point, increasing the light further cannot increase the rate of photosynthesis. If, however, the level of carbon dioxide is then increased, the rate of photosynthesis does increase further. In other words, the level of carbon dioxide limits the rate of photosynthesis.

d State what happens when the carbon dioxide level is increased from 0.01% to 0.1%.

e Suggest what might happen to the 0.1% line if the temperature was increased from 20°C to 25°C.

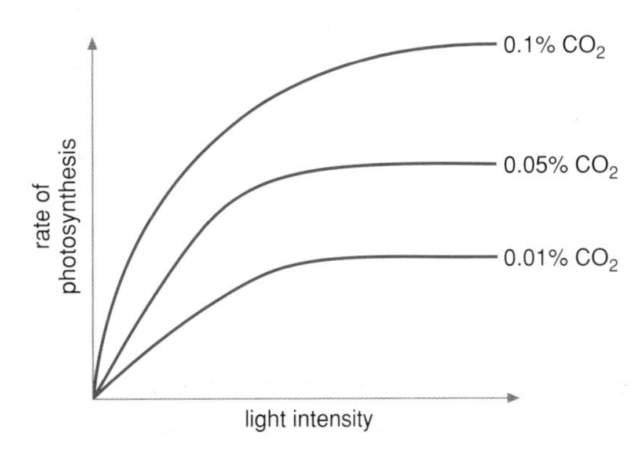

fig 8 | Carbon dioxide (CO_2) concentration as a limiting factor on the rate of photosynthesis

Thinking further

1 Ashraf grows tomatoes in his greenhouse. Suggest two things that he could do to increase the yield of his plants.

2 Michael cuts the grass in his garden. He knows that in the summer he has to cut it every week, but in the winter he hardly has to cut it at all. Explain why Michael only has to cut his grass in the summer.

◆ **3** Copy fig 8 showing limiting factors. On your graph draw an extra line to show what would happen to the rate of photosynthesis in 0.01% carbon dioxide if the temperature was reduced.

KEY WORDS

carbon dioxide • light intensity • limiting factor **• rate • temperature**

5.3 Photosynthesis and beyond

Key points

- Glucose is produced by photosynthesis.
- Glucose can be converted into many other substances.
- Mineral salts in the soil are required for all these processes.

First stop ... starch

You have probably done an experiment to test a plant leaf for **starch**. Most of the **glucose** that is produced by photosynthesis is rapidly turned into starch for storage. If we want to check that photosynthesis has taken place, it is usually easier to test for starch than it is to test for glucose.
If starch is present, photosynthesis has taken place. Fig 9 shows the steps involved in doing a starch test.

a Suggest why plants store food as starch rather than as glucose.

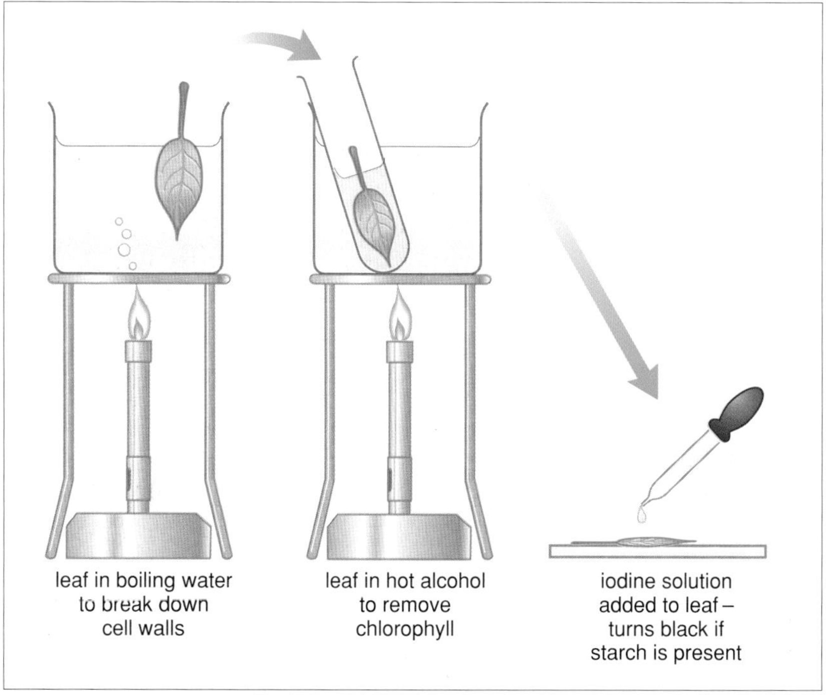

leaf in boiling water to break down cell walls

leaf in hot alcohol to remove chlorophyll

iodine solution added to leaf – turns black if starch is present

fig 9 | Performing a starch test on a leaf

Respiration

Some of the glucose produced by photosynthesis is used for **respiration**. Plants, just like all other living things, need energy, which they get from respiration. They cannot use the energy from sunlight directly. They have to trap the energy by making glucose and then release it by respiration.

Plants photosynthesise during daylight hours, but they respire all the time.

b Explain why some people think that vases of flowers should be removed from bedrooms at night.

Cellulose

Cellulose is a complex carbohydrate made from glucose molecules. It forms the plant cell wall (fig 10), and forms a large part of foods like apples. Unlike animals, plants do not have a skeleton.
The cellulose helps to support the plant. This is why many vegetables are crisp and crunchy.

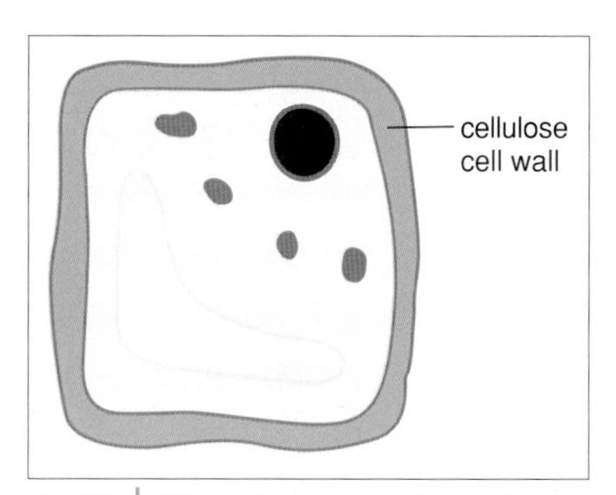

fig 10 | Plant cells have a cellulose cell wall

Protein

Protein is also made by the plant. Carbon, hydrogen and oxygen are obtained from the glucose made during photosynthesis and are combined with nitrogen to form amino acids. The amino acids are then assembled to make proteins. On spread 2.3 we learnt about a protein called gluten. It is found in wheat and gives bread its texture. Some people are unable to digest gluten.

Chlorophyll

Although **chlorophyll** is used in the process of photosynthesis, plants have to make it. The starting point for its manufacture is glucose.

What else do plants need?

Although plants make their own food for respiration – glucose – they also need small amounts of some elements. They obtain these from mineral salts in the soil.

Farmers put fertilisers on the soil. These provide the plant with:

- **Magnesium** – plants use this for making chlorophyll.
- **Nitrogen** – plants use this for making amino acids which they build into proteins.
- **Phosphorus** – plants use this for making DNA and cell membranes.

c Suggest what might happen to a plant if it was lacking in nitrogen, phosphorus and magnesium.

Fig 11 shows what happens to plants if they are lacking these elements.

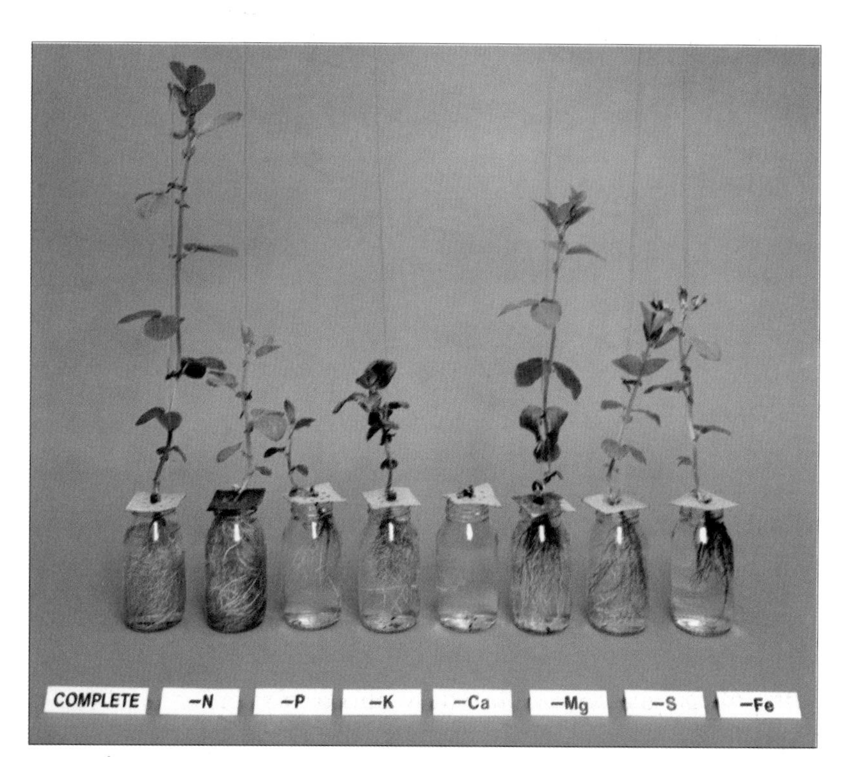

fig 11 The effects of magnesium, phosphorus and nitrogen deficiency on the growth of bean plants

Thinking further

■ **1** Suggest ways in which a plant might store food, other than as starch.

◆ **2** Nitrogen is a gas found in the air. Suggest why plants are unable to use it directly and have to get their nitrogen from mineral salts. Have a look at the nitrogen cycle (fig 20 on spread 7.5) to help you answer this question.

KEY WORDS

cellulose • chlorophyll • glucose • magnesium • nitrogen • phosphorus • protein • respiration • starch

 *Testing leaves for starch.*

Questions on photosynthesis

● 1 While walking along the beach, Neil found a strange object. He thought it might be alive, so he took a small sample back to school. Fig 12 shows what he saw under the microscope.

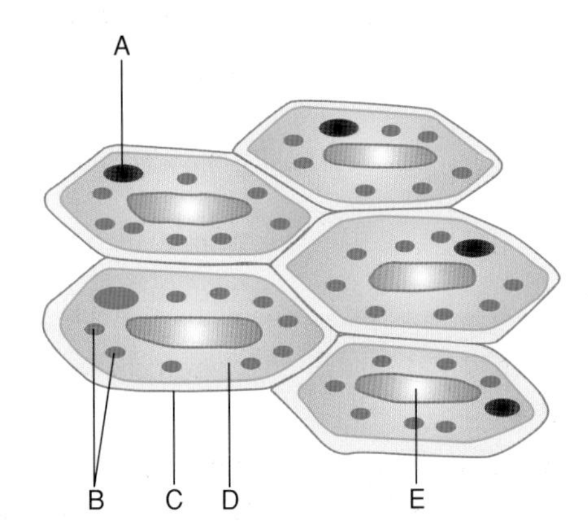

fig 12

a Copy fig 13 and complete it by matching each letter to the correct part of the cell. The first one has been done for you. *(3)*

part of a cell	letter
vacuole	*E*
chloroplasts	
cytoplasm	
cell wall	
nucleus	

fig 13

b Neil thought that the object was a plant. Suggest why he made this decision. *(2)*

2 The following list gives the steps performed when doing a starch test on a leaf but they are not in the correct order.

- Add iodine solution to the leaf.
- Put the leaf into boiling ethanol.
- Put the leaf into boiling water.

● a Write out the steps in the correct order. *(2)*

■ b Explain why each of the steps is performed. *(3)*

● c State the result you would expect if the leaf contained starch. *(1)*

■ 3 Fig 14 shows a section through a leaf.

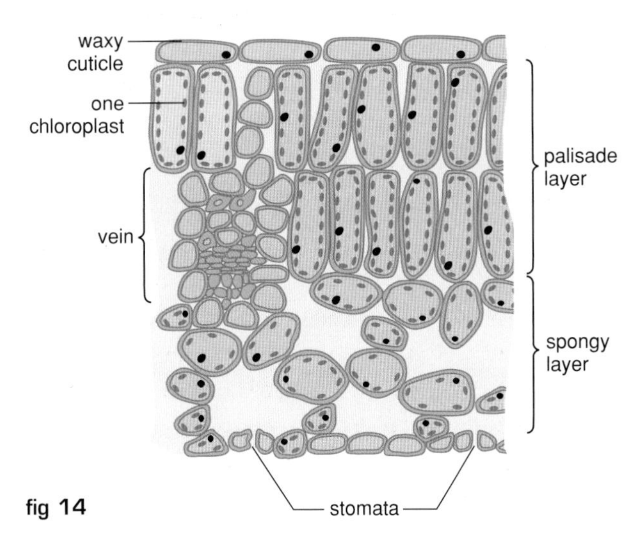

fig 14

a Copy fig 15 and complete it by matching the labelled parts of the leaf with their functions. The first one has been done for you. *(3)*

function	name of part
allows gases to diffuse through	*spongy layer*
transports water	
where carbon dioxide enters	
where most photosynthesis happens	

fig 15

b Suggest which *two* of the following features you would expect to find in a plant growing in dry conditions.

thick cuticle • thin cuticle • many stomata • few stomata • many chloroplasts • few chloroplasts

4 Bobby wanted to find out what effect fertiliser would have on his father's runner beans. He grew beans in four plant pots.

- The beans in the first pot had all the minerals that they required.
- The beans in the second pot were lacking magnesium.
- The beans in the third pot were lacking nitrogen.
- The beans in the fourth pot were lacking phosphorus.

■ **a** Why did Bobby have one plant pot in which the beans had all the nutrients that they required? *(1)*

■ **b** Draw a diagram of the four plant pots, showing how you would expect the plants in each pot to grow. *(4)*

■ **c** Explain why Bobby planted five bean seeds in each plant pot. *(2)*

● **d** Explain the process that is going on in the beans when they start to germinate. *(1)*

◆ **e** Explain what happens to the dry mass of the seeds when they start to germinate. *(1)*

● **f** When the seedlings start to photosynthesise, what substance do they produce? *(1)*

■ **g** State four other substances that are produced as a result of photosynthesis. *(4)*

5 Richard is a market gardener. He has a gas heater in his greenhouse.

■ **a** State two ways in which the gas heater could increase the rate of photosynthesis in his plants. *(2)*

● **b** Write a word equation for photosynthesis. *(2)*

◆ **c** Write a balanced symbol equation for photosynthesis. *(3)*

◆ **d** Richard tried increasing the light intensity in his greenhouse. He found, however, that the rate of photosynthesis would only increase up to a point and that no amount of extra light would increase it further. Explain why this happened. *(2)*

6 Anita grows tomatoes in her greenhouse. Fig 16 shows the effect of increasing light intensity on tomato production at different temperatures and carbon dioxide levels.

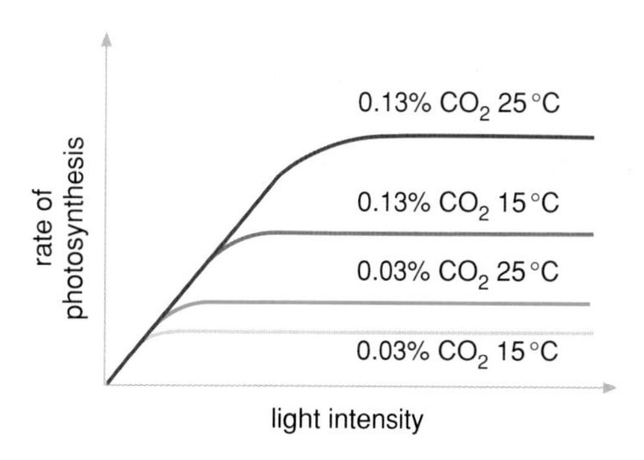

fig 16

■ **a** State three limiting factors shown by the graph. *(3)*

◆ **b** When the top curve levels out, which factor is definitely *not* acting as a limiting factor? *(1)*

◆ **c** Suggest what Anita could do to increase production of her tomatoes when the carbon dioxide concentration is 0.13% and the temperature is 25 °C. *(2)*

IDEAS AND EVIDENCE

◆ **7** The rain forests are sometimes called 'the lungs of the world' because they are responsible for extracting large amounts of carbon dioxide from the atmosphere and returning large amounts of oxygen to it. Local farmers are cutting down the rain forest and burning the remains so that grass will grow to feed their cattle. Suggest and explain who is right, the farmers, or the environmentalists who wish to protect the rain forests. *(5)*

◆ **8** Genetic engineering is beginning to produce types of crop that can photosynthesise more efficiently in a wide range of conditions. Do you think that a controversial science like genetic engineering should be used to produce more food for the developing world? *(5)*

Transport

Introduction

fig 1

Scientists think that life first appeared in the oceans on Earth about 3600 million years ago. This life probably consisted of organisms that were no larger than a single microscopic cell – far too small to be seen with the naked eye. When organisms are this small they can obtain all the nutrients they need by absorbing them through their cell membrane. They can also get rid of all their waste products in the same way.

After several millions of years, more complex organisms started to evolve. These were multicellular organisms – they consisted not of one cell but of several cells joined together. Being multicellular gave the organisms a big advantage because it allowed the different cells to become specialised in doing different jobs. This made the organisms more efficient.

Large complex organisms must be able to transport materials such as food, oxygen, water and waste material around their bodies. In single-celled organisms, this transport can happen by simple diffusion. However, as organisms get bigger and more complex, some kind of transport system is needed.

fig 2

A good way to understand this is to imagine someone shipwrecked on a desert island. As a single human being trying to survive, they would have to do everything themselves such as finding food, collecting water, building a shelter and making fire. No one would be there to help them, and simply surviving would be difficult. There would be no shops, electricity, or television to watch. However, when lots of people live together, they can all learn to do different jobs and specialise in what they do best. Life becomes better for everyone. However, it also becomes much more complicated, and transport systems are needed to ensure that everyone gets what they need.

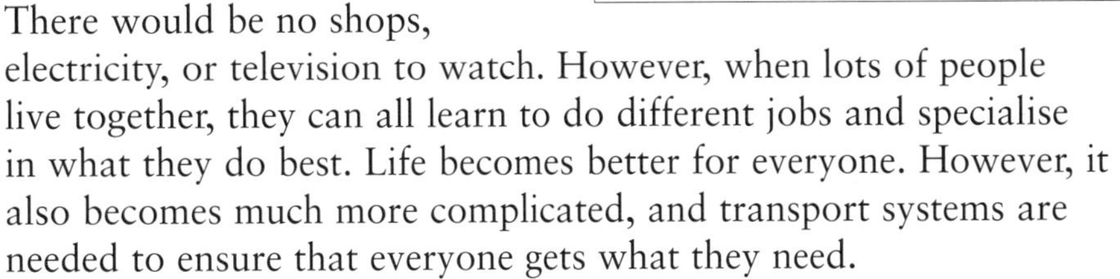

Large plants and animals are lots of cells living together and have evolved amazing mechanisms, such as the heart in animals and xylem and phloem vessels in plants, to be able to transport materials.

This Teaching block looks at how plants and animals manage to perform this important function of transporting materials.

Check-up

Have a go at the following questions. They will remind you of what you should know about transport in animals and plants.

a Copy the sentence below and choose a word from the following list to fill the gap.

digestion • movement • touch • transport • vision

When we eat food, it is digested in our gut, absorbed into our bloodstream, and we then __________ it throughout the body.

b Copy the sentence below and choose a word from the following list to fill the gap.

petals • leaves • root hairs • stem • seeds

Plants absorb water and mineral salts from the soil through their __________.

If you have difficulty, ask your teacher for a summary sheet.

Contents of the Teaching block

6.1 Blood circulation

This spread looks at how the blood circulates around the body in a 'closed' (rather than an 'open') system consisting of a series of large and small vessels.

6.2 The heart

The heart is a double pump that drives the blood all the way around the body and back again, and then to the lungs to pick up oxygen and release carbon dioxide.

6.3 Blood

Blood has many components which enable it to perform all the various jobs it has to do.

6.4 Water transport in plants

Plants have to transport water from their roots to their leaves. They do this to replace water that is lost while they are obtaining carbon dioxide for photosynthesis.

6.5 Transpiration

In plants, water moves up from the roots, not by being pushed up, but by being pulled from above by transpiration. The rate of transpiration is affected by environmental factors.

Links with other Teaching blocks

1.3 Transport and cells
2.3 Absorption
3.1 Aerobic respiration
4.2 Breathing rate and depth
5.1 The green machine
8.4 Hormones

6.1 Blood circulation

Key points

- The blood is carried around the body in blood vessels called arteries, veins and capillaries.
- The blood transports materials to and from the tissue fluid.

Arteries, veins and capillaries

Arteries carry blood away from the heart. Because the heart has to pump the blood all the way around the body, it has to pump at high **pressure**. The arteries have thick muscular walls to withstand this pressure (fig 3). If the blood vessels were made of rigid tubes, each time the heart pumped, blood would squirt quickly through the arteries and then come to a stop between the heart beats.

a Explain why this 'stop–go' method of pumping blood would not be a good idea for the body.

Instead, each time the heart beats, the arteries are able to expand slightly to absorb some of the pressure. This elasticity ensures that blood keeps flowing between heart beats.

Veins return blood to the heart at low pressure. (Think about when you use a long hose pipe. The water comes out of the tap at high pressure, but it is much more sluggish when it comes out of the other end of the hose.) This means that veins can have much thinner walls than arteries (fig 4).

b Suggest why blood pressure is a lot lower where the veins return blood to the heart.

Veins, however, have a problem. Have you ever noticed that when you stand still for a long time your feet and lower legs tend to swell? This is because the pressure of the blood in veins is so low that the blood tends to fall and collect at the bottom of our legs. To stop this happening, veins have **valves** that prevent blood from flowing backwards (fig 5).

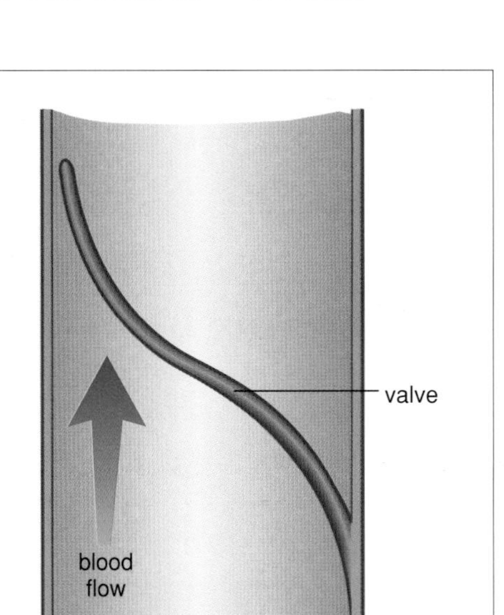

fig 5 A section through a vein to show the valves that prevent backflow

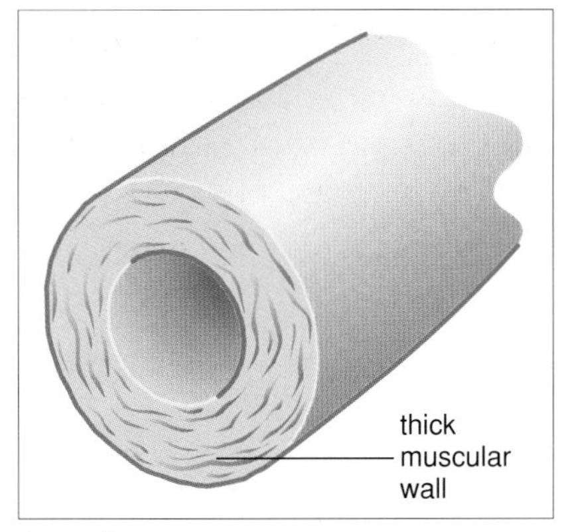

fig 3 A cross-section through an artery, showing the thick muscular wall

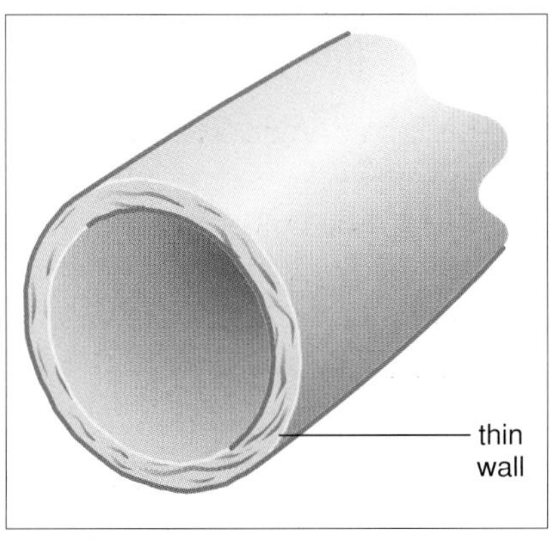

fig 4 A cross-section through a vein showing the thin wall

Capillaries are narrow, thin-walled blood vessels that link the arteries and the veins. There are thousands of miles of capillaries in the human body. In fact there are so many that every cell in the body is no more than a couple of cells away from a blood capillary (fig 6).

Tissue fluid leaks out from the capillaries and bathes all the cells. Nutrients and oxygen **diffuse** from the blood, through the capillary wall and tissue fluid to reach each and every cell. Carbon dioxide and waste materials return to the blood by diffusion.

c Suggest why capillaries need to have a wall that is just one cell thick.

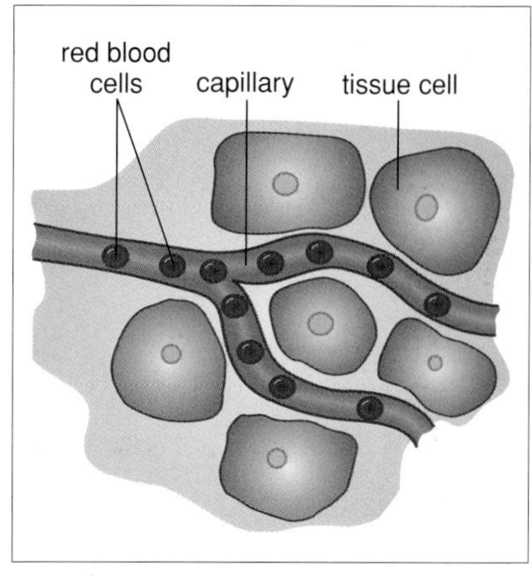

fig 6 | Every tissue cell is within one or two cells' distance of a capillary

IDEAS AND EVIDENCE

William Harvey and scientific method

William Harvey was a doctor who lived from 1578 to 1657. He observed how blood flowed round the body and noticed the existence of valves in veins. By careful observation and experimentation he correctly concluded that blood is pumped around the body by the heart through blood vessels.

This was a major medical breakthrough. Before this, people believed the ideas of Galen who lived over 1000 years before Harvey was born. Because Galen did not use the scientific method of observation and experimentation, he incorrectly thought that the blood just went straight from one side of the heart to the other, and did not realise that it transported materials all round the body, through tiny capillaries.

Even though capillaries were far too small for Harvey to see, he correctly predicted their existence, linking arteries to veins.

Thinking further

■ **1** List the differences between arteries and veins in the form of a table.

■ **2** Explain why arteries have thick muscular walls and veins have thin walls with valves.

◆ **3** Joy went to the doctor. He measured her blood pressure and told her that it was '120 over 80'. She asked the doctor what that meant. He told her that 120 was the pressure when her heart was contracting. Suggest what the number 80 referred to.

◆ **4** Suggest why Galen thought that blood went straight from one side of the heart to the other.

KEY WORDS

artery • capillary • diffuse • (blood) pressure • tissue fluid • valve • vein

6.2 The heart

Key points

- The heart is a double muscular pump that pumps blood around the body and the lungs.
- This means the body has a double circulatory system.

The double circulatory system

The heart does not just pump the blood around the body and back again. It also pumps the blood to the lungs and back in order to pick up oxygen and to get rid of carbon dioxide (fig 7).

a Explain why it is more efficient for the blood to return to the heart before being pumped to the lungs.

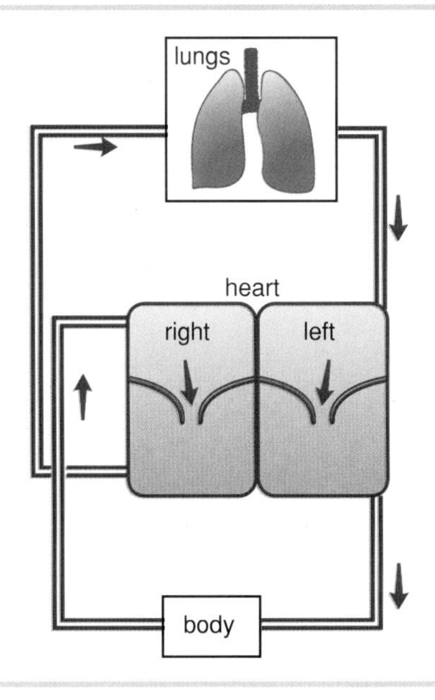

fig 7 | A diagrammatic representation of blood flow in the double circulatory system

The heart

The first thing to remember is that diagrams of the heart (see fig 8) are labelled as if it belongs to someone else. This means that the left side of the heart is always shown on the right side of the page. (You could imagine that you are lying face-up on the diagram if that helps!)

The blood is pumped from the left ventricle through the **aorta**, which is an **artery**. It then travels around the body, supplying cells with nutrients and removing waste, returning to the heart into the right **atrium** through a **vein** called the **vena cava**. The right atrium contracts and pumps the blood into a second more powerful chamber called the right **ventricle**. This then contracts, sending the blood through the **pulmonary** artery to the **lungs**. The blood then returns to the left atrium of the heart via the pulmonary vein. This in turn contracts and pumps the blood into the most powerful chamber of all, the left ventricle, ready to start the cycle all over again.

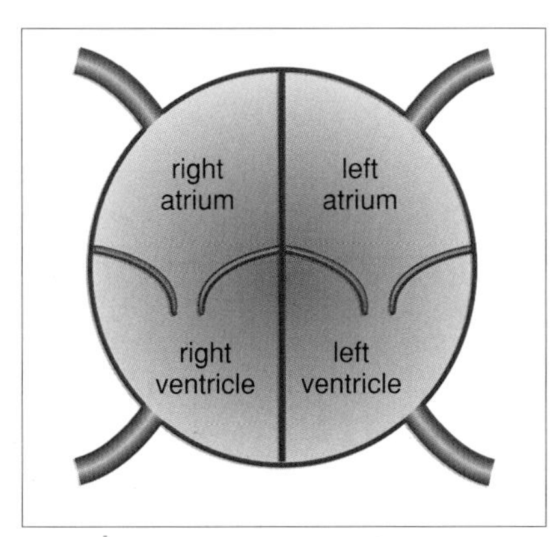

fig 8 | A diagrammatic representation of the four chambers of the heart

Valves between the atria and ventricles and in the openings to the blood vessels prevent the blood from flowing backwards when the heart contracts.

b Explain why it is important that the heart does not pump blood backwards.

There is an easy way to remember most of this: remember the two letters, A and V.

- A comes before V in the alphabet so we will start with A.
- Arteries leave the heart and Veins return blood to the heart.
- A stands for left Atrium, which pumps blood through the Aorta which is an Artery.
- V stands for Vena cava which is a Vein and returns blood to the heart.
- Atria are above ventricles: A is before V.
- All you have to remember now is that the right side of the heart is drawn on the left of the page and vice versa, and that the vessels to and from the lungs are called the pulmonary veins and arteries, respectively.

In reality a diagram of the heart does not look quite like the real thing. This is because the ventricles have more powerful muscles and are larger than the atria. The aorta leaves the back of the heart by looping up and round before returning in a downward direction. This can be quite confusing when looking at a real heart.

c Fig 9 is a diagram of the heart. Label it by writing down the letter and the name of the part.

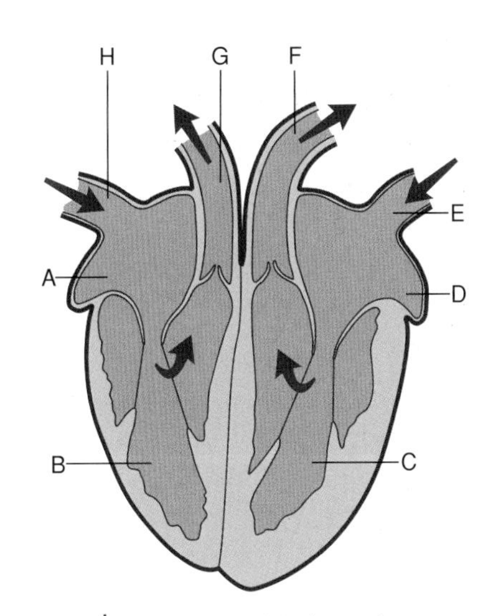

fig 9 | The structure of the human heart

Thinking further

■ **1** Look at the diagram of the heart (fig 9). Explain how the two valves prevent blood flowing from the ventricles into the atria.

■ **2** A red blood cell is pumped from Anita's left ventricle. Describe the path taken by the cell as it leaves her heart until it returns once again to her left ventricle.

◆ **3** Describe what is meant by a double circulatory system and why it is more efficient than a single circulatory system.

◆ **4** Suggest why some small animals have evolved with just a single circulatory system in which the blood passes through the heart once rather than twice for each circuit around the body.

KEY WORDS

aorta • artery • atrium • lungs • pulmonary • valve • vein • vena cava • ventricle

 *Pulse rates.* *Pulse rates.*

6.3 Blood

Key points

- Blood transports materials around the body.
- The blood and the skin act as a defence against infection.
- Blood can clot to seal wounds and prevent the entry of microbes.

The components of blood

Plasma

Plasma is the fluid part of the blood. It is a pale-yellow or straw-coloured liquid that is mainly water, but dissolved in it are substances. These include:

- digested food, like glucose and amino acids
- carbon dioxide from cellular respiration, which is being carried to the lungs to be breathed out
- urea, a waste material from the breakdown of protein
- hormones – chemical messengers that carry instructions to various parts of the body.

a Explain how diffusion helps digested food like amino acids get into the blood stream.

Floating in the plasma are other structures such as **red blood cells, platelets** and **white blood cells.**

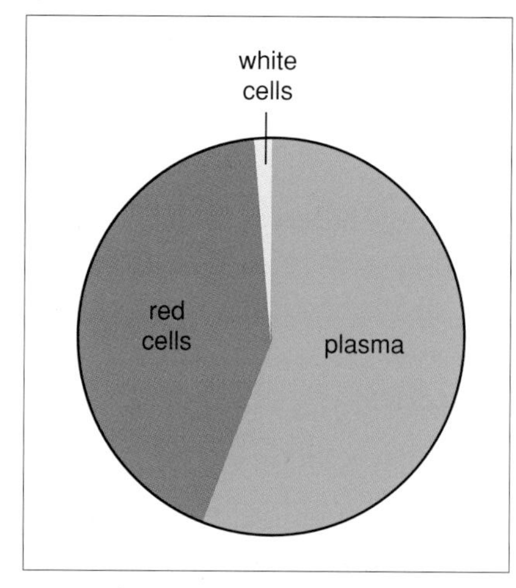

fig 10 | Composition of the blood

Red blood cells

Red blood cells contain the red pigment called haemoglobin. Haemoglobin is a remarkable substance. In the lungs, where there is a lot of oxygen, haemoglobin combines with oxygen to form oxyhaemoglobin:

oxygen + haemoglobin → oxyhaemoglobin

In the tissues, where the cells do not have enough oxygen, oxyhaemoglobin releases its oxygen and returns to haemoglobin.

oxyhaemoglobin → haemoglobin + oxygen

This ensures that the cells get a continuous supply of oxygen.

Red blood cells are biconcave discs (fig 11). They have this shape because they have lost their nucleus. This shape also ensures that the cells have a large surface area compared with their volume.

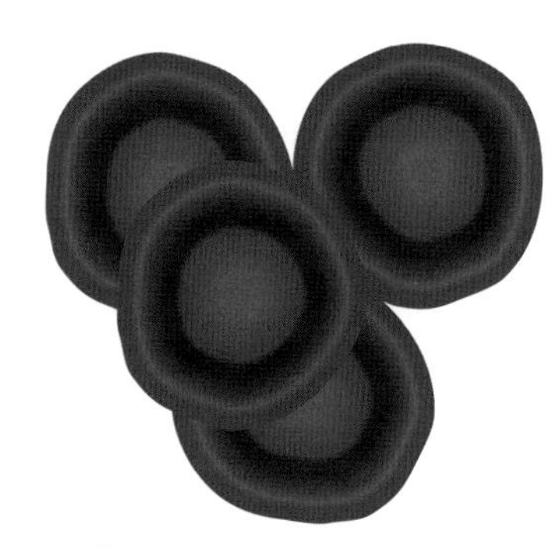

fig 11 | Red blood cells are biconcave discs

b Explain why it is important for a red blood cell to have a large surface area.

Platelets

Platelets are very delicate cell fragments that contain a clotting agent. They are easily damaged and burst open when they rub against a damaged blood vessel or are exposed to the air.
This releases the clotting agent, which causes the blood to clot and

seal the wound. This is important not only because it prevents loss of blood, but also because it seals the skin, which acts as a barrier to prevent the entry of microbes.

c Explain what would happen if a damaged platelet caused blood to clot inside the blood vessel.

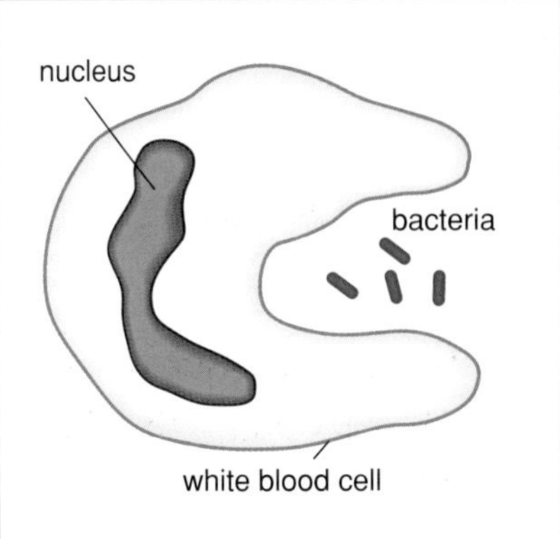

fig 12 | Some types of white blood cell engulf and destroy bacteria

White blood cells

There are several kinds of white blood cells. One type **engulfs** microbes and digests them (fig 12). Another type produces **antibodies**. These are chemicals that attack bacteria, or mark them so that they can be quickly engulfed by other white blood cells. It seems that our bodies had chemical warfare long before modern armies did!

Dirty hypodermics

Sometimes drug takers use dirty hypodermic needles. This is very dangerous because these needles puncture the protective barrier of the skin and can transfer microbes such as hepatitis and HIV from a previous user.

Thinking further

■ **1** John knows that his blood acts as a transport system. State three things carried by John's blood, and why it carries them.

◆ **2** Blood also acts as a defence system. State how the blood and the skin attempt to prevent microbes from giving us diseases.

◆ **3** Dirty hypodermic needles are just one way that microbes can get through the protective barrier of the skin. Suggest three other ways in which this can happen.

IDEAS AND EVIDENCE

Infection can be prevented by supplying drug addicts with clean needles. Suggest the advantages and disadvantages of this.

KEY WORDS

antibodies • engulf • plasma • platelets • red blood cells • white blood cells

6.4 Water transport in plants

Key points

- Water enters root hairs by osmosis.
- It travels up the stem through xylem vessels.
- Stomata close at night to minimise water loss.

Entering the plant

Water enters the plant through tiny **root hairs** by the process of **osmosis** (fig 13). This is because the root hairs contain a solution that is more concentrated than the water in the soil. As water enters, the root-hair contents becomes less concentrated as they are diluted with water. This causes water to pass from cell to cell by osmosis, moving inwards towards the centre of the root and the **xylem** vessels. This flow of water carries dissolved **mineral salts** from the soil into the plant.

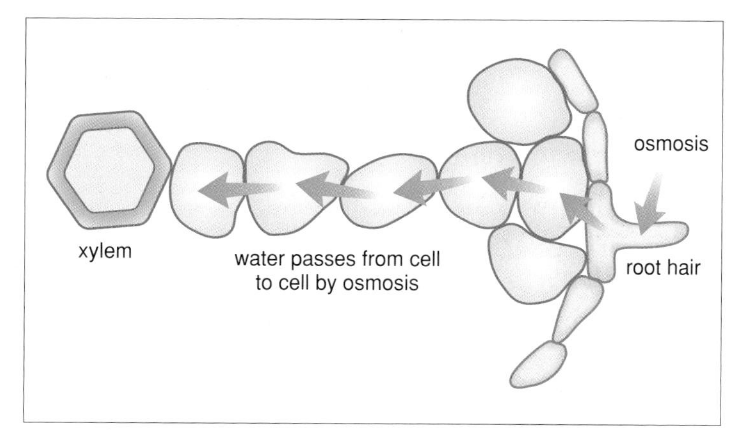

fig 13 | Water passes from the root hair to the xylem by osmosis

a Suggest another mechanism that could account for mineral salts entering a root hair.

Up the stem

From the roots water then enters the xylem vessels to bc carried up the stem. The cells in xylem tissue are unusual in that they are dead and empty of cytoplasm. The ends of the cell have been broken down to join with other cells, forming long hollow tubes. These tubes, called xylem vessels, go from the root all the way up to the leaves. It is in these vessels that water is carried up to the leaves.

To the leaf

Water enters the leaf through the xylem vessels. Have a look at a leaf and you will be able to see ridges or veins on the leaf. These veins are bundles of xylem and phloem vessels and are called **vascular bundles** (fig 14). Once inside the leaf, the water leaves the xylem and enters the cells of the leaf.

b Suggest a mechanism by which water enters the cells of the leaf.

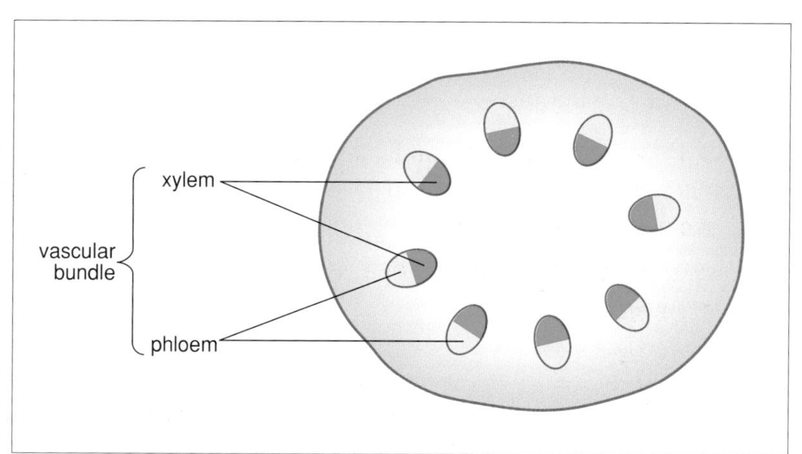

fig 14 | A cross-section of a stem to show the vascular bundles of xylem and phloem

Plants have a problem

Plants go to a lot of trouble to get water up to their leaves and they do not want to lose it. However, photosynthesis takes place in the leaves, and the leaves need to take in carbon dioxide and release oxygen. To do this, they open small holes or pores in the leaves called stomata (figs 15 and 16). Unfortunately this allows valuable water to evaporate.

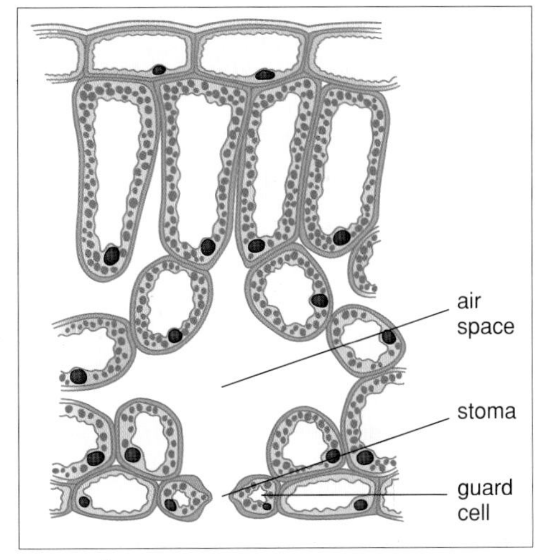

fig 15 | A cross-section through a leaf to show a stoma and an air space

How plants solve the problem

The stomata are on the underside of the leaf, away from the heat of the Sun and protected from the wind.

The opening of the stomata is controlled by **guard cells**. The guard cells close the stomata when the leaf cells are not photosynthesising (fig 17).

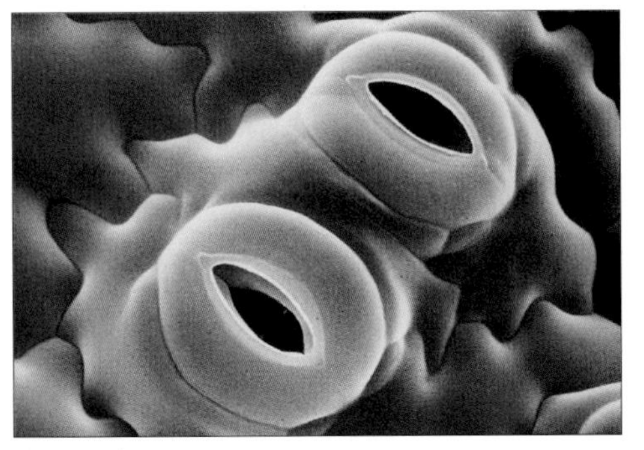

fig 16 | False-colour scanning electron micrograph of open stomata in a tobacco leaf (×460)

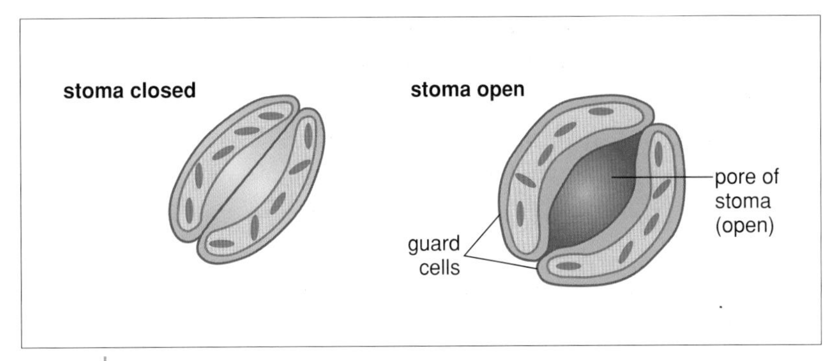

fig 17 | Guard cells inflate to open the stoma

Plants open their stomata by inflating the two guard cells with water. As the guard cells swell and expand, the inner walls of the cells curve, the space between the cells begins to get bigger, and the pore opens.

Most leaves have a **waxy cuticle** on their upper surface.

c Explain how these three points will prevent water evaporating from the leaf.

d Suggest under what conditions the plant will not be photosynthesising.

Thinking further

■ **1** Describe the path taken by a water molecule from the time it leaves the soil to the time it evaporates from the leaf.

◆ **2** Explain how a plant attempts to keep water loss to a minimum.

◆ **3** Explain how the plant uses the processes of diffusion and osmosis to transport water from the soil up to its leaves.

◆ **4** Explain how a plant manages to close its stomata at night when it is not photosynthesising.

KEY WORDS

guard cells • mineral salts • osmosis • root hairs • vascular bundle • waxy cuticle • xylem

 *Transport in plants.*

6.5 Transpiration

Key points

- Transpiration pulls water up the stem.
- Environmental factors influence the rate of transpiration.
- Sugars move up and down the stem through living phloem vessels.

Is it pushed or is it pulled?

Water moves upwards in a plant from the roots. Is this water pushed up or pulled up? If water was pushed up a tree, the maximum height it could reach would be about 10 metres. This is because even a vacuum will not support a column of water greater than this height. So how can water get to the top of a tree that might be as high as 100 metres? The answer is that water is pulled, not pushed, up a tree. This is known as **transpiration pull.**

Try to imagine a tree with all the wood and xylem vessels removed, leaving behind just the threads of water going from root to leaf. Surprisingly, these threads of water are extremely strong. They are difficult to stretch or snap.

You can demonstrate this peculiar property of water by placing a drop of water on a microscope slide and then laying another slide on top. You will find that even though the microscope slides move over each other, it is almost impossible to pull them apart .

This property of water means that as water molecules evaporate from the leaf through the stomata, the whole thread of water, all the way down to the roots, will not break or stretch but will be pulled upwards.

The rate at which water is pulled up the stem will depend upon the rate at which transpiration is taking place.

a Explain what will happen to the rate at which water is pulled up the stem as transpiration speeds up and slows down.

The rate of transpiration

Transpiration does not usually occur at all in the dark.

b Explain why transpiration does not usually occur in the dark.

If it is daylight and the stomata are open, the rate of transpiration will depend on how quickly water is evaporating through the stomata.

fig 18 | The rate of transpiration is affected by temperature, wind movement and humidity

An easy way to visualise this is to imagine clothes on a washing line (fig 18). The clothes represents the leaves on a tree. On some days the washing dries quickly whereas on other days it never seems to dry.

c Make a list of the factors that make a good drying day.

Temperature

Transpiration occurs more quickly on warm days than on cooler ones. The higher temperature gives greater kinetic energy to the water molecules, so they evaporate more quickly.

Air movement

Wind blows the molecules away as they evaporate from the leaf. On still days the molecules build up in the air close to the stomata and prevent other molecules diffusing out from the leaf.

Humidity

When the air is damp it is holding lots of water molecules which get in the way and prevent water molecules diffusing out from the leaf. On dry days the diffusion gradient between the leaf and the air is much greater, allowing faster diffusion.

What about phloem?

These are the other vessels in the vascular bundle and are responsible for transporting sugar produced by photosynthesis. The phloem vessels form a continuous system from the leaves to the roots and, unlike xylem, are living tissue filled with cytoplasm. They can transport the sugars both up and down the stem for storage or to wherever the sugar is required.

KEY WORDS

air movement • humidity • temperature • transpiration pull

Transpiration in plants.

Thinking further

■ **1** List the differences in structure and function between xylem and phloem.

◆ **2** Explain why transpiration is referred to as transpiration pull, rather than transpiration push.

Questions on transport

● **1** Bobby's teacher gave him a crossword (fig 19). Bobby could answer most of the questions, but was stuck on three of them. Copy the crossword and complete the questions Bobby was unable to do. *(3)*

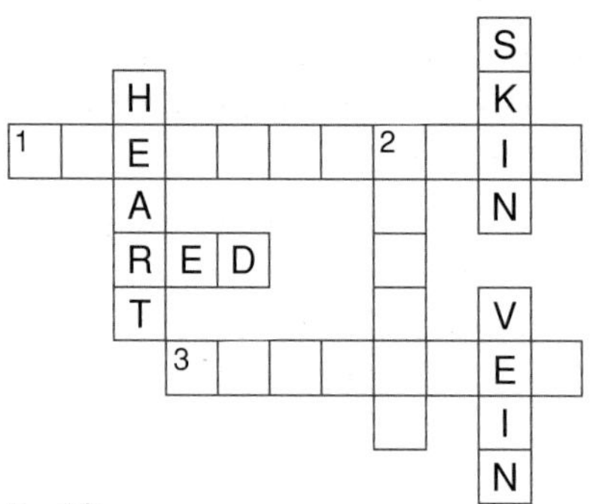

fig 19

1 across: red pigment in blood
2 down: gas carried by red blood cells
3 across: cell fragment that starts the clotting process

■ **2** Peter was involved in a car crash. The doctor gave him a blood transfusion by injecting blood into the vein in his arm. List the following words in the correct order to show where the blood went until it finally returned to the vein in his arm. *(6)*

aorta • left atria • left ventricle • lungs • pulmonary artery • pulmonary vein • right atrium • right ventricle • vena cava

3 Gaseous exchange takes place in the lungs of a human and in the gills of a fish. Fig 20 shows the circulation of the blood in the human and in the fish.

human (a double circulation)

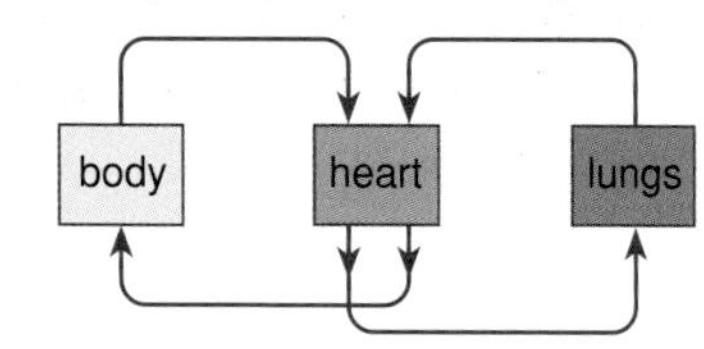

fish (a single circulation)

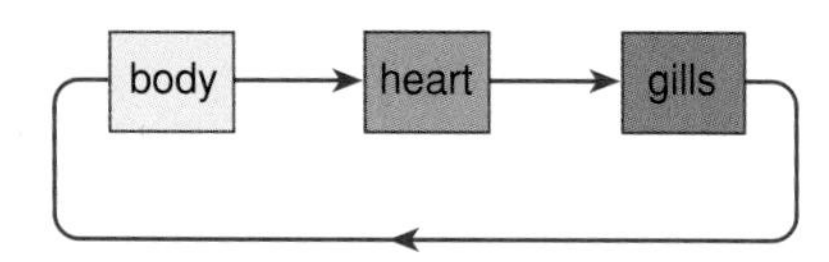

fig 20

■ **a** Explain why humans have a double circulatory system. *(2)*

◆ **b** Explain why the double circulatory system has a heart with four chambers, but the single circulatory system has a heart with only two chambers. *(2)*

◆ **c** Suggest and explain the advantages to humans of having a double circulatory system. *(2)*

4 Wendy stood some sticks of celery in a beaker of red ink and left them for 24 hours. When she removed the celery she noticed that the ink had travelled up the stalks and made red lines in the leaves at the top of the celery.

■ **a** Name the structure that is shown by the red lines that Wendy could see. *(1)*

◆ **b** Wendy didn't understand how the ink had reached the celery's leaves. She knew that nothing was pushing it up. Her teacher said the ink was pulled up by transpiration. Explain what her teacher meant. *(3)*

■ **c** Wendy cut across one of the celery stalks. She started to draw what she saw, but did not have sufficient time to finish her drawing. Copy and complete Wendy's drawing (fig 21) by adding and labelling all the things she would have been able to see. *(3)*

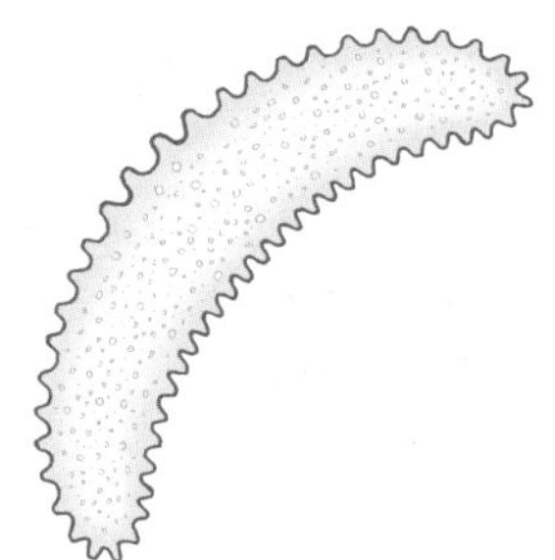

fig 21

5 Mary becomes pregnant. The developing fetus's heart pumps blood around its body and to the placenta and back again. As the blood flows round the fetus, it passes through valves.

■ **a** Explain what happens to the blood as it passes through the placenta. *(2)*

● **b** Explain why there are valves in the fetus's blood vessels. *(1)*

The fetus's heart has a hole that connects the right atrium to the left atrium. This prevents blood from going to the lungs.

◆ **c** Suggest and explain what must happen to this hole when the baby is born. *(2)*

6 David notices that on days when the washing on the line dries most quickly, the plants in his flower tubs need more water.

■ **a** State three factors that will increase the rate at which David's washing dries. *(3)*

◆ **b** Explain why these three factors also increase water loss from his plants. *(3)*

■ **c** Describe three ways by which the plants try to reduce the amount of water they lose. *(3)*

◆ **7** A surgeon is carrying out a heart transplant. Fig 22 shows the blood vessels that the surgeon has to connect. Copy the letters and next to each write the name of the blood vessel. *(3)*

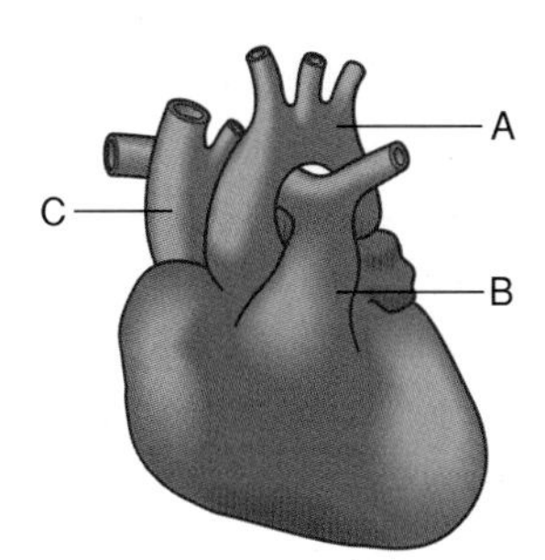

fig 22

8 Complex organisms such as humans, need an efficient transport system.

● **a** State three things that the blood system transports around the body and for each one state its starting and finishing points in the body. *(3)*

■ **b** The blood also has functions in addition to transport. Onc of these functions is to protect the body from disease. Explain the role of the following structures in this process:

  i white blood cells *(3)*
  ii platelets. *(3)*

9 Plants need to take carbon dioxide from the air into their leaves for photosynthesis. They do this through small holes called stomata. However, these holes also allow valuable water to escape from the plant.

◆ **a** Explain how the plant manages to reduce the loss of water through these small holes. *(3)*

■ **b** Suggest why stomata are usually found on the underside of the leaf. *(1)*

■ **c** Suggest why in floating plants like the water lily, the stomata are found on the upper side of the leaf. *(2)*

◆ **d** Plants such as cacti that live in dry desert conditions often have their stomata at the bottom of a deep sunken pit. Explain why this will reduce the water loss from the cactus. *(2)*

IDEAS AND EVIDENCE

◆ **10** The heart is such a hard working organ that sometimes it goes wrong. We now have the technology to undertake heart transplants, replacing a damaged heart with a healthy one from a donor who has died from other causes.

Do you think that everyone should have to carry a donor card, or should it be up to the conscience of the individual? *(3)*

◆ **11** William Harvey was the first person to accurately describe the workings of the circulatory system of the blood. Explain why, 1000 years earlier, Galen failed to come to the same conclusion as Harvey, even though he had the same materials to work with. *(3)*

◆ **12** Dirty hypodermic needles can introduce bacteria through the skin and into the body. Some people think that drug users should be supplied with clean hypodermic needles free of charge so that they do not use dirty needles. Other people think that this would encourage the habit of drug taking. Explain, with reasons, whether you think free needles should be supplied to drug users. *(3)*

Ecology

Introduction

We all know that millions of different species of organisms live on Earth. They do not live on their own but interact with each other. The study of the ways in which organisms interact with each other and with their environment is called ecology.

The most common way in which organisms interact is to eat one another! You should be able to draw a food chain to show how food passes from one organism to another. The first organism in any food chain is a green plant that gets its energy from the Sun. All the other organisms are dependent on this. Pyramids of numbers can be drawn to show the numbers at each feeding or trophic level.

In any habitat there is great competition for food. Animals and plants all have special features that enable them to survive in their environment. If an organism is not very well adapted, it will not be able to catch much food, or may be eaten itself. These organisms do not survive for long!

You should also be aware of some of the ways in which humans are damaging the environment. Hopefully you have heard of, or have taken part in, schemes to protect the environment.

fig 1

Check-up

Have a go at the following questions. They will remind you of what you should know about ecology.

a Draw a food chain to show the feeding relationships between the fox, the grass and the rabbit shown in fig 1.

b In this food chain, which organism is the producer and which is the primary consumer?

c Draw a diagram to show the shape of a pyramid of numbers for this food chain.

d Why are simple food chains unusual in nature?

e Add two more organisms to make this into a food web.

Fig 2 shows a food web that occurs in a garden.

f List the herbivores in this food web.

g Name the organism in the food web that is an omnivore.

h A person has a cat which keeps killing blue tits in the garden. Explain what effects this might have on the populations of aphids and shrews.

i The owner then sprayed a chemical on the garden to kill the aphids. Suggest two other effects that this might have on the animals in the garden.

If you have difficulty, ask your teacher for a Summary sheet.

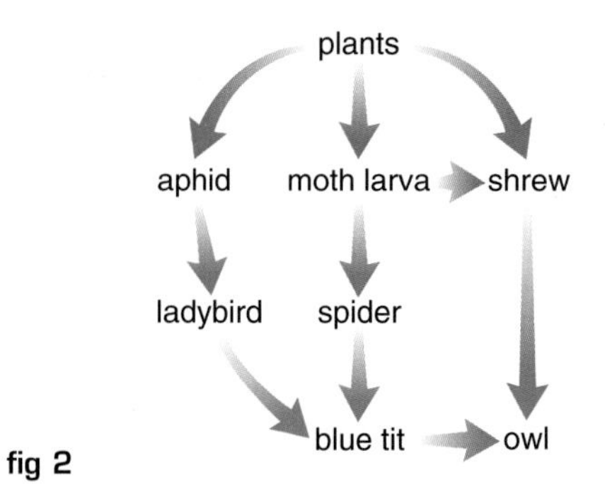

fig 2

Contents of the Teaching block

This Teaching block is divided into eight spreads. They show how organisms live together and depend on each other. Humans are endangering some of these relationships but we are now learning the need to control our activities.

7.1 Distribution of organisms

It is quite easy to map out where organisms live; when we do this we often find that they do not all live in the same habitats. Even in one habitat, they are not spread out at random.

7.2 Competition and adaptation

Organisms are constantly competing with each other for resources. Because of this competition, there is pressure on organisms to be adapted to their particular habitat.

7.3 Predation and co-operation

All animals eat other organisms for food and so the number of organisms that can survive in a habitat depends on how many predators or prey there are. Some organisms work together in order to increase their chances of survival.

7.4 Food chains and energy

As energy passes from one organism to another along a food chain much of it is lost. This means that the length of a food chain has a definite limit.

7.5 Decomposition and recycling

Bacteria and fungi perform an important job in habitats by decomposing waste products. This prevents the build-up of dead material and also recycles the minerals.

7.6 Food production

There is an ever-increasing demand for food. We are trying to meet this demand with new farming methods, some of which are not popular with everybody.

7.7 Energy and waste

More and more fossil fuels are being burned, causing more pollution. Methods to reduce this harmful pollution are now being developed.

7.8 Conservation

It is now clear that if we do not reduce pollution and protect organisms and their habitats, many will be lost forever.

Links to other Teaching blocks

5.1 **The green machine**
6.5 **Transpiration**
9.2 **Controlling temperature**
Chemistry 8.3 **Fertilisers**
Chemistry 8.4 **Fertiliser problems**

7.1 Distribution of organisms

Key points

- The terms habitat, population and community can be used to describe where and in what combinations organisms live.
- Organisms are not spread out at random where they live but prefer certain areas.
- Various methods can be used to map the distribution of organisms in their environment.

A place to live

The place where an organism lives is called its **habitat.** Each habitat has specific conditions such as certain weather patterns and type of soil. These conditions vary from one habitat to another. Examples of different habitats are shown in fig 3.

a Write down the particular conditions that make each of the habitats in fig 3 different.

A group of organisms of the same species that live in the same habitat is called a **population.**

b Write down the names of two types of organisms that may have populations in each of the habitats shown in fig 3.

All the populations of plants and animals that live in a habitat form a **community.** Different habitats contain different communities of organisms because of the different environmental conditions.

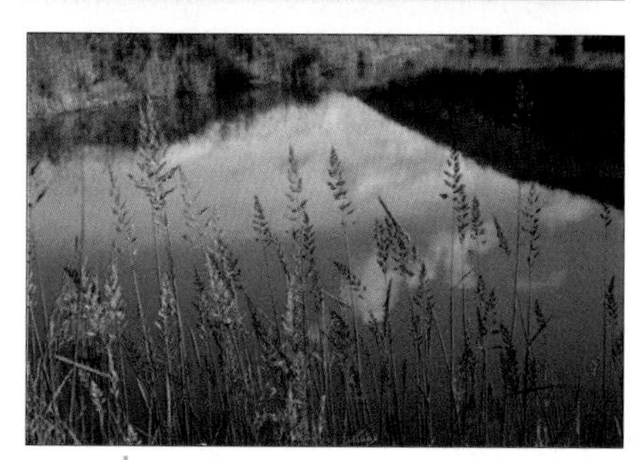

fig 3 | Different habitats have different environmental conditions

Counting organisms

If we want to study and compare different habitats, we need to know which organisms live in each area. If the area is small, or if the organisms are large, we can count all the organisms. However, if the numbers are too large we have to use a sampling technique. For example, this might be used to find out the number of daisy plants on a football pitch. The technique involves counting the organisms in a small patch and then using this to estimate the number in the whole area. To sample a patch of a certain size, scientists usually use a metal or plastic square called a **quadrat** (fig 4). This can be placed on the ground and the number of organisms inside it is counted.

c What are the advantages and disadvantages of using sampling to identify the organisms that live in a habitat?

fig 4 | A quadrat can be used to count organisms underwater, as well as on land

Finding patterns

Using a quadrat at random in a habitat can tell you which organisms are found but not where they are found. Organisms are not usually spread evenly around a habitat because conditions differ slightly from one area to another. To investigate this, quadrats can be placed in a regular pattern.

For example, some students wanted to investigate the plants that lived on a field containing a large sycamore tree. They stretched a tape measure in a straight line away from the tree. They then placed a quadrat next to the tree and made a note of the area of the quadrat that was covered by four main species of plant. They repeated this every two metres along the tape measure, as shown in fig 5. The results are shown in fig 6.

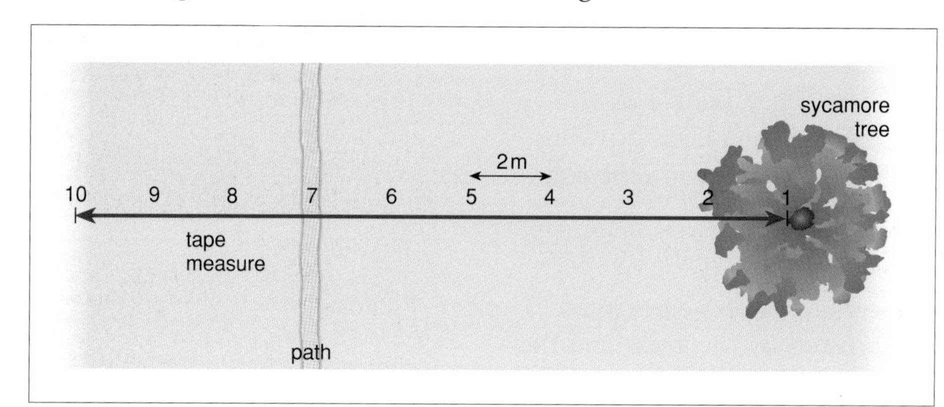

fig 5 | Map of the area studied by the students

	quadrat									
plant type	**1**	**2**	**3**	**4**	**5**	**6**	**7**	**8**	**9**	**10**
grass	10	15	35	75	80	90	65	90	90	90
chickweed	15	10	5	2	0	0	5	0	0	0
daisy	0	0	0	5	5	5	0	5	10	10
sycamore seedling	0	0	5	5	10	5	2	0	0	0

fig 6 | Percentage coverage of plants in each quadrat

Thinking further

- **1** Plot four bar charts to show how the percentage coverage of each plant varied at different distances from the tree.
- **2** Describe where in this habitat each plant seems to prefer to live.
- **3** Why are the results in quadrat 7 different from the rest?
- **4** Why is it difficult to use quadrats to sample animal populations?
- ◆ **5** Suggest ways of estimating animal populations.
- ◆ **6** Students wanted to sample a football pitch in order to work out the number of daisies present. How could the students make sure that they sampled at random with their quadrat?

KEY WORDS
community • habitat • population • quadrat

7.2 Competition and adaptation

Key points

- The number of organisms in a habitat is often affected by competition from other organisms.
- Organisms tend to be adapted to live in a particular habitat.

Competing for resources

From the results of the student mapping experiment shown on spread 7.1 you can clearly see that the plants did not grow very well close to the tree. The tree is taking resources away from the plants and therefore limiting their growth. This 'fight' for resources is called **competition.** The tree and the plants growing below it are probably competing for water, minerals in the soil and light.

a Which plant seems to compete most effectively with the tree?

Further away from the tree there appears to be less chickweed growing. It has probably been out-competed by the grass and the daisies. Plants such as chickweed grow very quickly and can often grow in areas where other plants find it difficult to grow. However, when the full resources are available, they are easily out-competed.

b Plants like chickweed are often called weeds. What does this mean?

Animals also compete for resources. The most common competition is for food. This may even lead to fights between animals. Competition may be between animals from two different species but often it is between individuals of the same species.

c Why are members of the same species likely to compete with each other?

Some animals such as chickens set up a pecking order. The chickens have an order of dominance so that a chicken higher in the order can feed before one lower in the order.

d What are the advantages and disadvantages of such a pecking order?

Adaptation

In order to survive in the particular weather and soil conditions found in their habitat, animals have become well suited or **adapted** to their habitat. They are said to show certain **adaptations.** These features also enable them to compete with the other organisms that live in the habitat.

Good examples of animals that are well adapted to completely different climates are the polar bear and the camel.

Camels live in a desert habitat where daytime temperatures may be as high as 40 °C but at night the temperature can be very low. The high daytime temperatures cause water to evaporate very quickly so camels need to be adapted to hot, dry conditions. Some of their adaptations are shown in fig 7.

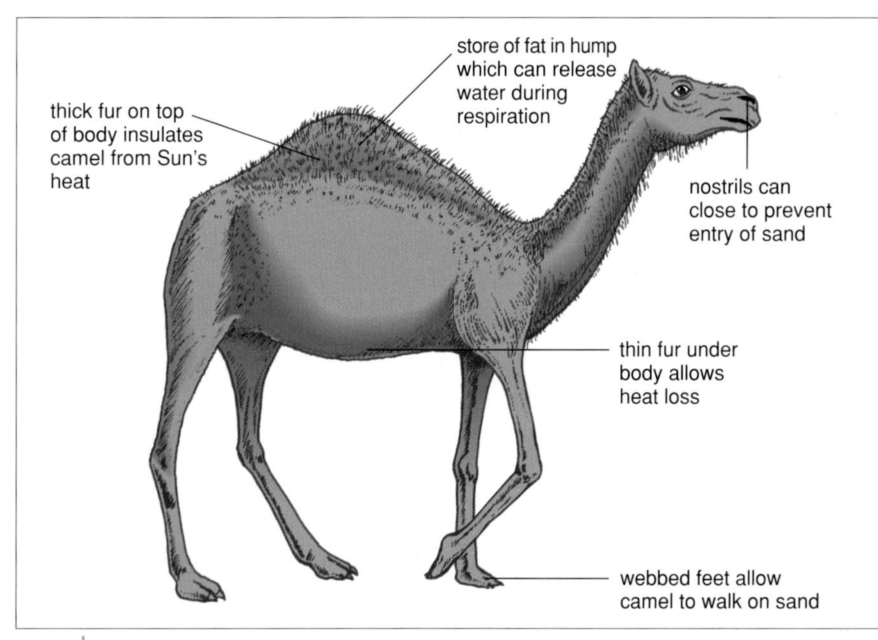

fig 7 | Adaptation of the camel to living in the desert

Polar bears live mainly in Alaska, spending most of their time on the ice floes or hunting in the water. Fig 8 shows how they are adapted to this habitat.

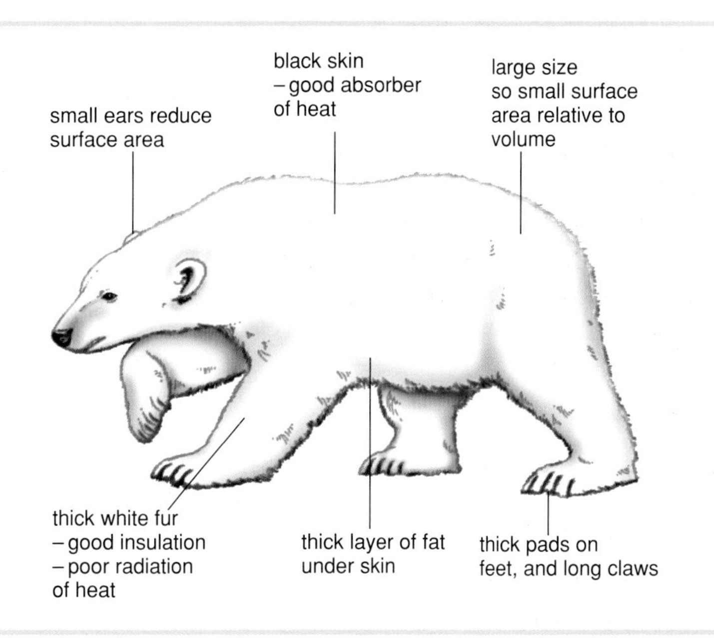

fig 8 | Adaptations of the polar bear to living in the Arctic

Thinking further

■ **1** Why do flowers such as bluebells that live in woods grow and flower early in the spring?

◆ **2** During the day a camel can allow its body temperature to go up by 7 °C without having to sweat much or suffering any damage.
What advantage is this to the camel in the warm days and cold nights of the desert?

◆ **3** A polar bear has thick fur with plenty of trapped air. Explain how this helps keep it warm whilst standing on the ice. Why is it less effective when it is swimming?

KEY WORDS
adaptation • competition

 *Changes in bird populations.*  *Killer algae.*

7.3 Predation and co-operation

Key points

- Predators are animals that catch and eat other animals, called prey.
- If large numbers of these predators survive in a habitat, the number of prey will go down.
- Instead of eating each other, other types of organisms may work together and some may rely completely on each other.

Predators and prey

Animals feed in a number of different ways. Some animals are **parasites.** They feed on a live organism, which is called the **host.** Their aim is not to kill the host straight away but to keep it alive, gradually taking food from it.

a Write down the name of a parasite and the host that it lives on.

b Why is it an advantage for a parasite not to kill the host straight away?

Other animals catch and kill other animals for food. They are called **predators** and the animals they catch are called **prey**. The predators have many adaptations that help them to catch prey, for example the long claws and sharp teeth of the polar bear shown in fig 8 on spread 7.2. Prey animals are also adapted to avoid capture. Many can react and move very fast and others may blend in with the background (they are camouflaged – see fig 9).

fig 9

An experiment to see how the numbers of predators and prey changed was set up in a tray containing oranges. A number of small mites were put into the tray. These mites fed on the oranges. Some spiders that fed on the mites were also put in the tray. The numbers of mites and spiders in the tray were counted at intervals. The results are shown in fig 10.

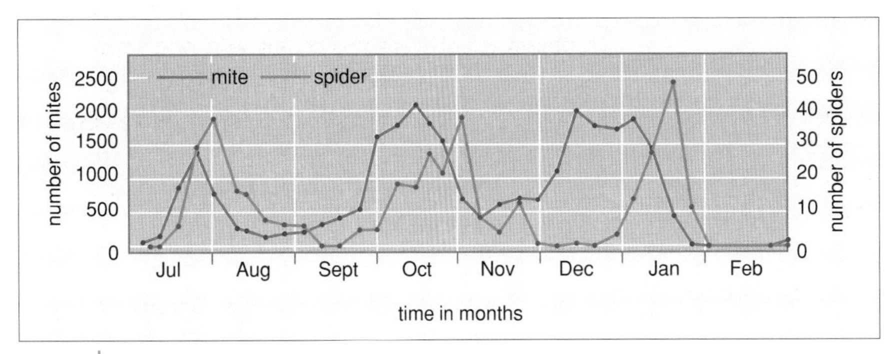

fig 10 | Predator–prey graph

c Why is the type of graph shown in fig 10 called a predator–prey graph?

The number of mites increased at first because there was plenty of food. This meant that there was more food for the spiders, so they started to increase in number. There were more spiders so they ate more mites, therefore reducing the number of mites. The spiders then began to starve. The numbers of the two populations therefore went up and down, with the peaks in the number of spiders coming just after the peaks in the number of mites.

Co-operation

Instead of competing with each other or trying to eat each other, some organisms of different species co-operate with each other. This is called **mutualism** because both organisms gain from the relationship. There are many examples of mutualism. Oxpecker birds move from giraffe to giraffe eating small parasites that live in the fur of the giraffes (fig 11).

d Explain how each of these organisms gains from this relationship.

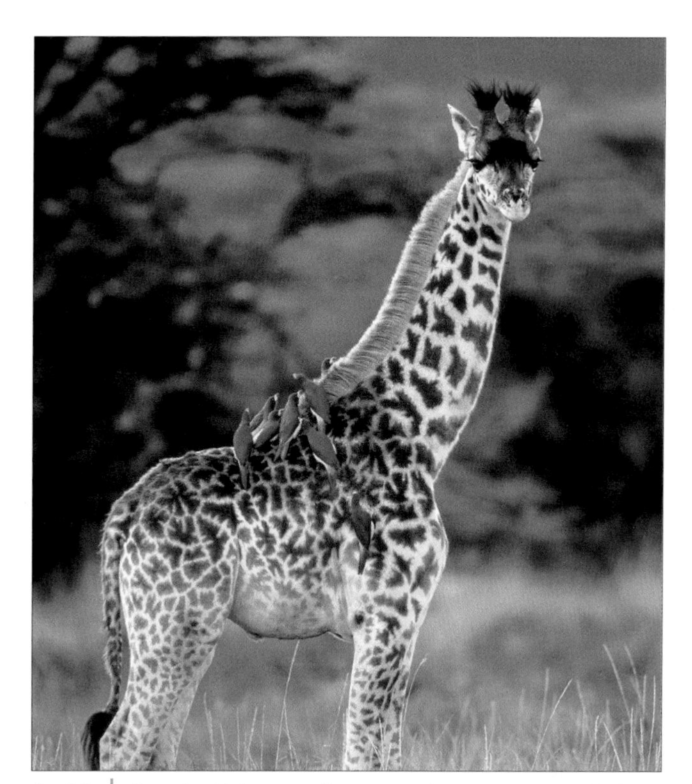

fig 11 | Oxpecker birds eat small parasites that live in the giraffe's fur

Lichens (fig 12) are another example of mutualism. These are relationships between fungi and algae, the algae living inside the fungus. Many of these algae and fungi cannot live on their own. The fungi absorb water and minerals much more efficiently than can the algae and so lichens can live in very dry places.

e Suggest what the algae give to this relationship.

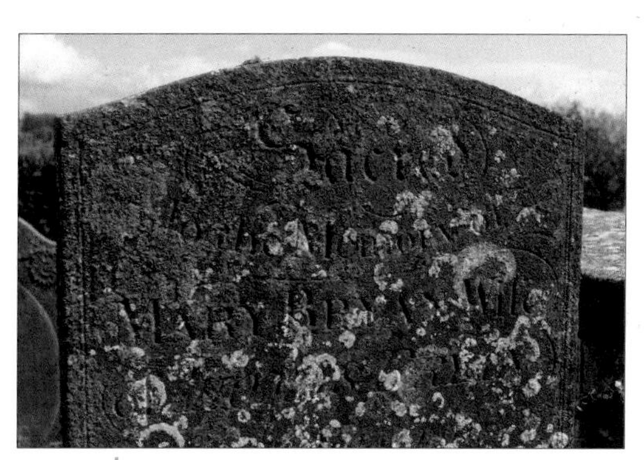

fig 12 | Lichens are mutualistic partnerships between algae and fungi

Thinking further

■ 1 For each of these relationships, write down whether each organism is a predator, prey, parasite, host or mutualistic partner. Explain your answers.

a A lion kills a deer and eats it.

b A sea anemone with protective stinging tentacles lives on the back of a crab, feeding on food that the crab drops.

c A tapeworm lives in the human small intestine, absorbing food.

◆ 2 The predator–prey graph showing the numbers of spiders and mites (fig 10) was obtained in a laboratory situation. It is difficult to obtain graphs like this in the wild because many other factors can change the size of a population. Suggest what some of these factors might be.

KEY WORDS

host • mutualism • parasite • predator • prey

7.4 Food chains and energy

Key points

- Pyramids of biomass are a useful way to describe food chains.
- Food chains can also be thought of as showing the flow of energy through a community.
- This flow of energy can be used to explain various properties of food chains such as the shapes of pyramids of biomass.

Pyramids of biomass

You have seen how a simple food chain can be used to construct a pyramid of numbers. This is an example of a simple food chain:

oak tree → greenfly → ladybird → blue tit

The probable pyramid of numbers for this food chain is shown in fig 13.

a This food chain does not form a perfect pyramid. Why is this?

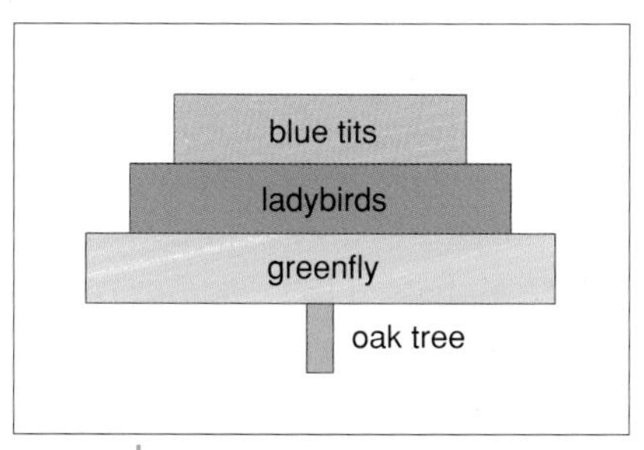

fig 13 A simple pyramid of numbers

Another way of representing this food chain is to draw a **pyramid of biomass.** Biomass is the mass of living material. The mass of all the organisms at a particular trophic level is measured and added together. For example, all the greenfly are weighed and their total mass worked out. The size of the box for each trophic level is drawn to scale in order to represent the total mass of the organisms. The pyramid of biomass for the food chain above might look like the one in fig 14.

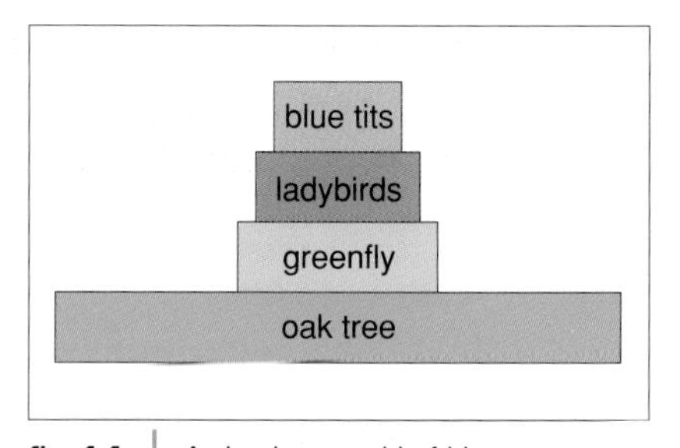

fig 14 A simple pyramid of biomass

b The box representing the oak tree now appears larger than the greenfly box. Why is this?

Scientists use pyramids of biomass to show how much food is available for each trophic level.

Energy flow

Another way of looking at food chains is to study **energy flow** through them. An example is shown in fig 15. Energy enters the food chain as sunlight. Most of this energy is reflected. A small amount is trapped by photosynthesis and is converted into chemical energy in organic molecules.

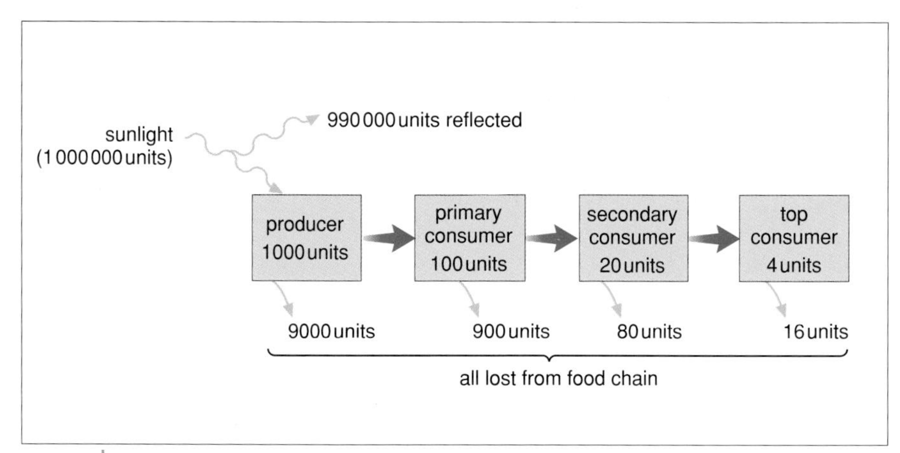

fig 15 Energy flow through a food chain

c Name the pigment in the producer that traps this energy.

The producer uses most of this energy for respiration but a small amount is used to make new cells and so is available to the primary consumers.

The energy passes through the chain from organism to organism as organic molecules. Large amounts of energy escape the food chain at each step. This energy is released as heat, in the waste products of respiration and in urine and faeces. Some of these waste products may be fed on by decomposers, which then pass the energy on to other food chains.

d Name one organic chemical that passes along the food chain.

Using energy flow

The idea of energy flow can be used to explain a number of observations about food chains. Firstly, we can use energy flow to explain the shape of pyramids of biomass. These diagrams are usually a pyramid because of the energy lost at each level of the food chain. This means that a larger mass of organisms in a lower level is needed to support the level above.

The loss of energy also explains why food chains rarely contain more than five or six trophic levels. By the time the food has passed through this many organisms, there is very little energy left to support another trophic level.

Thinking further

■ **1** Are pyramids of numbers or pyramids of biomass easier to collect data for? Explain your answer.

■ **2** To construct a proper pyramid of biomass, the mass should be the dry mass of the organism – the mass after all the water has been removed.

a Why is this the most accurate way of measuring biomass?

b Why is this difficult to obtain?

◆ **3** **a** Use the information in fig 15 to work out the percentage of the biomass in the producers that is turned into biomass in the primary consumers.

b How does this compare with the transfer from primary to secondary consumer?

KEY WORDS

energy flow • pyramid of biomass

7.5 Decomposition and recycling

Key points

- Decomposers feed on dead organisms and organic material that is given out from food chains.
- To work properly, these organisms need the correct conditions.
- This is the first step in recycling all the elements back into the environment.

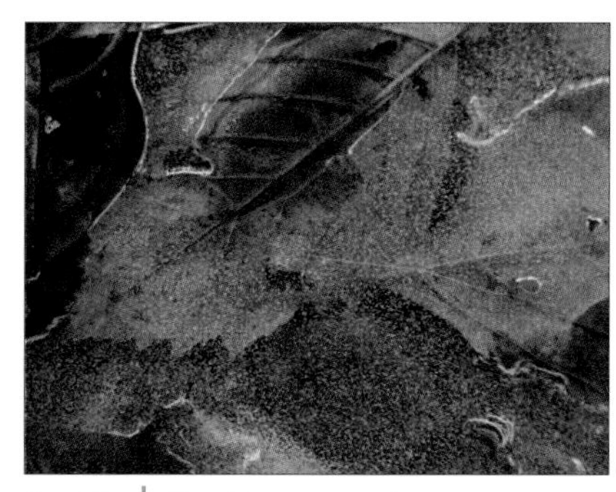

fig 16 | Dead leaves decaying

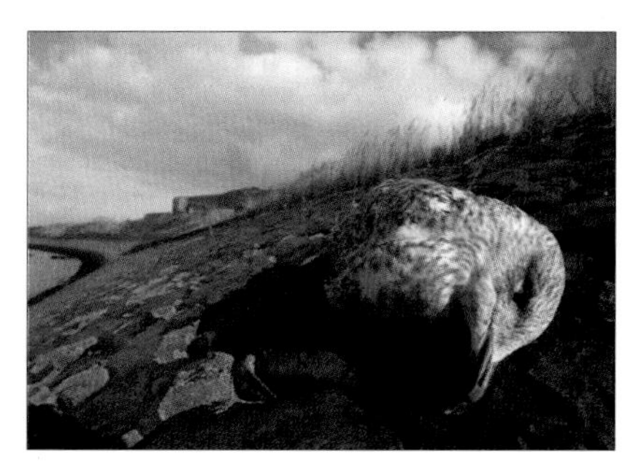

fig 17

Decomposers

After animals or plants die, their dead bodies eventually disappear. Animals such as vultures, maggots and woodlice may feed on some of the material. Even without these animals, the dead material will rot away. Bacteria and fungi release enzymes. These digest the material, and the bacteria and fungi then take up the soluble chemicals. This is called **decomposition** and the organisms that carry it out are called **decomposers**.

The decomposers use the soluble chemicals as food for respiration and growth but also release some of the elements back into the soil.

Rotting well

Decomposers need suitable conditions to be able to rot dead material and to reproduce. They need a suitable temperature and pH, together with sufficient oxygen and water. If one of these conditions is missing then the rotting stops.

Fig 18 shows an ideal compost heap. Gardeners make compost heaps to rot down the dead plant material from the garden. The rotted material can then be returned to the soil.

a Why is the wall of the compost heap made of chicken wire?

b Why should the compost heap be watered in dry weather?

fig 18 | A compost heap constructed from chicken wire

Cycles in nature

If decomposers did not exist then dead organisms and their waste products would build up in the environment. This would be unpleasant but the main problem would be that all the elements that are needed for living organisms would become trapped inside the dead material. The decomposers make these minerals available again. The way in which each element is made available can be drawn in a cycle.

The carbon cycle

Fig 19 shows how carbon is recycled in nature.

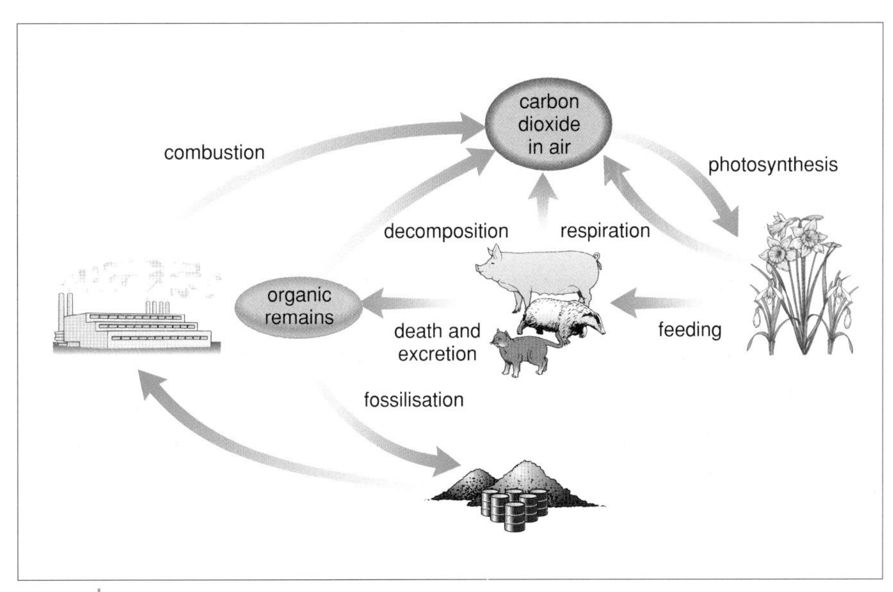

fig 19 | The carbon cycle

The nitrogen cycle

The nitrogen cycle (fig 20) is more complex than the **carbon cycle** because it involves four types of bacteria: the decomposing bacteria and three others. Three of these types of bacteria live in the soil. **Nitrogen-fixing** bacteria can live in the soil or in dwellings called **root nodules** which are found on plants of the pea family.

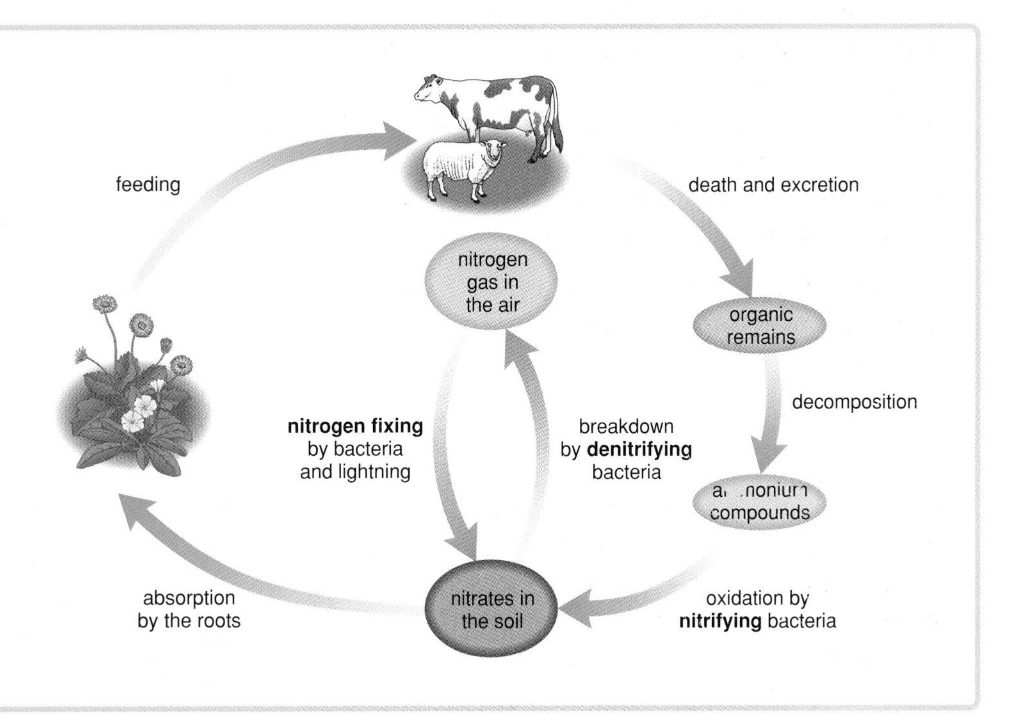

fig 20 | The nitrogen cycle

Thinking further

1. Explain why compost is formed faster in the summer than in the winter.
2. Write down the processes that release carbon dioxide into the air and those that take it up.
3. If we cut down and burn large areas of rainforest, what might happen to the carbon dioxide levels in the air?
4. Some farmers cannot afford to add nitrate fertilisers to their soil. Explain how adding
   a ammonium fertilisers **b** manure
   can increase the nitrate content of the soil.

KEY WORDS
carbon cycle • **decomposers** • **decomposition** • denitrifying • nitrifying • nitrogen fixing • root nodules

7.6 Food production

Key points

- The human population is increasing, which means that more food is needed.
- Knowledge of energy flow in food chains can be used to make food production more efficient.
- Various pests try to eat our food and various methods are used to try to stop them.

Populations and food

The world's population has doubled nearly four times in the last 500 years (fig 21). Some people think that by the year 2050 the population may be over 9000 million.

a How can scientists estimate the population of the world in AD 400?

This increase in population means an increased demand for food. Some scientists think that improved methods of food production will be able to produce enough food. The aim is to produce as much food as possible from an area. This is called **intensive** farming and the amount of food produced is the **productivity**. Unfortunately, the main growth in population is occurring in the developing world whereas new methods of food production are being used mainly in the developed world.

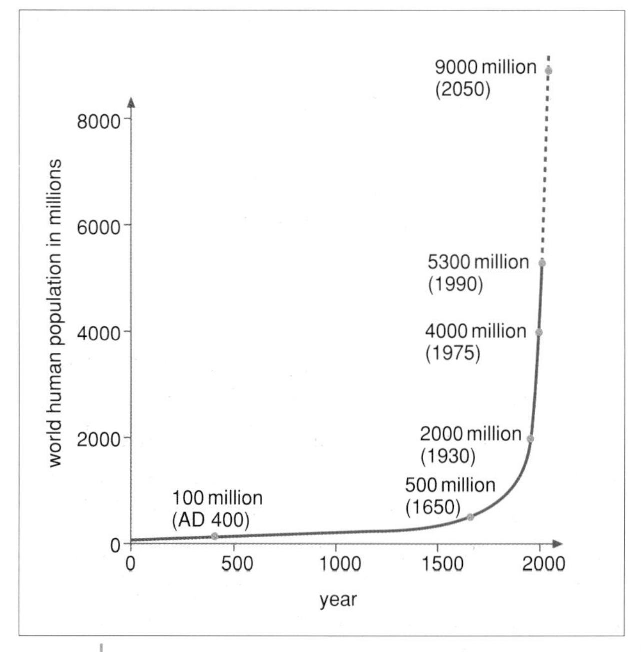

fig 21 | World population growth curve

Other scientists believe that the increased demand for food will be too much for the planet and that the Earth's resources will run out. If this is the case, then the increase in the population must be limited. Attempts have been made to do this by setting up schemes to advise about contraception and to make sterilisation operations available in areas where the population is increasing.

Food productivity

We saw in spread 7.4 that all the energy trapped in our food comes from the Sun and that much energy is lost as it passes along food chains. This loss of energy limits the rate at which we can produce food. Some of the losses in the production of chicken meat are shown in fig 22.

By reducing some of the energy losses, food productivity can be improved. In intensive farming methods, animals like pigs and chickens are often kept indoors in temperature-controlled

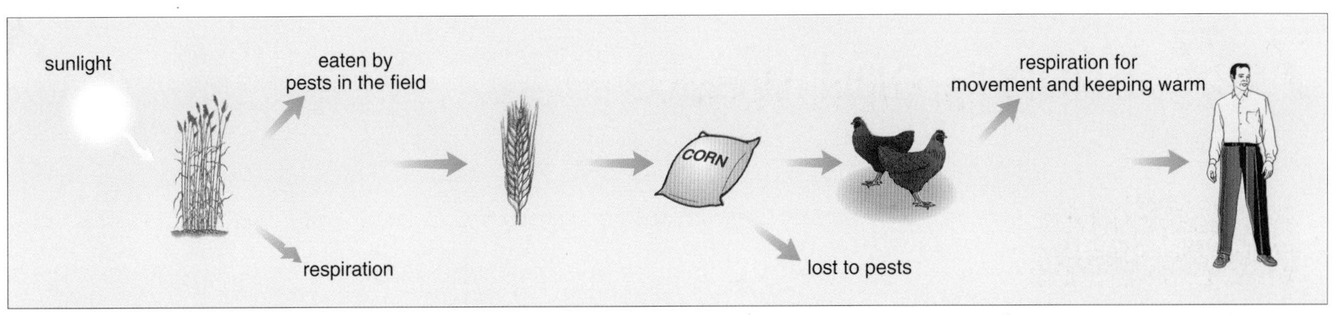

fig 22 | Energy losses in the production of chicken meat for human consumption

conditions. They do not have to look for food because it is provided by the farmer.

b How do these conditions help to prevent energy loss and increase productivity?

Other people argue that if we were all **vegetarian,** eating plant produce but no meat, we would need to grow fewer crops. In the example given in fig 22 we should eat the corn, rather than eating the chickens.

c Why would being vegetarian mean that we would need to grow fewer crops?

d Are there areas where growing crops would not be possible but where animals could graze?

Pest control

Another way of improving productivity is to reduce the amount of a crop that is eaten by pests. It has been estimated that one-third of the world's food is eaten by pests, most of which are insects. In 1939, a chemical called DDT that killed insects was discovered. Such chemicals are called **insecticides**. DDT was used to kill insects on crops and was very effective, resulting in greater productivity.

Soon, however, problems started to appear. Insects developed resistance to chemical insecticides such as DDT, and the insecticides killed useful insects such as pollinators and natural predators of the insect pests.

Scientists also realised that DDT and similar insecticides are very stable; they break down very slowly in the environment and in living organisms. They are described as **persistent**. The advantage of this was that an area only had to be sprayed once. The disadvantage, however, was that the insecticide was passed along food chains. Because animals further along the food chain need to eat many smaller animals, the concentration of insecticide increased along the food chain, and top consumers started to die.

Recently, scientists have started to use other methods to control pests. They have introduced living organisms that eat the pest or cause disease in it. This is called **biological control**. It can take some time to work but kills without pollution. However, scientists must also make sure that the control organism does not start to eat other organisms and become a pest itself.

Thinking further

■ 1 Why do many people object to intensive animal farming?

◆ 2 Make a table to show the advantages and disadvantages of chemical insecticides compared with biological control.

KEY WORDS

biological control • insecticides • **intensive** • persistent • **productivity** • **vegetarian**

7.7 Energy and waste

Key points

- With the increasing world population, there is a great demand for energy.
- Producing this extra energy produces a number of waste products that have caused serious pollution.

Energy demands

The rapidly increasing world population has produced an increasing demand for energy. Originally this energy would have come from the burning of wood or peat but now tends to be produced from burning fossil fuels such as coal, oil and gas.

The demand for energy depends on the size of the population and on the lifestyle that the people lead. Fig 23 shows the populations of different regions and the amount of carbon dioxide given off in each region by the burning of fossil fuels.

a Which region burns the most fossil fuel per person and which burns the least?

b Why is the use of fossil fuel in these two regions so different?

region	population in millions	carbon dioxide given off each year in billions of tonnes
Africa	732	0.4
China	1257	2.3
Eastern Europe	418	4.7
India	1537	1.2
United States	265	4.9

fig 23

The greenhouse effect

Energy from the Sun hits the Earth's surface and causes warming. This heat is radiated back into space as longer wavelength infrared radiation. The Earth's atmosphere absorbs some of this infrared and stops it leaving. This helps to keep the Earth warm. The glass in a greenhouse acts in the same way and so this process is called the **greenhouse effect.** The part of the Earth's atmosphere that absorbs much of this heat contains carbon dioxide and so this is called a greenhouse gas. The greenhouse effect is illustrated in fig 24.

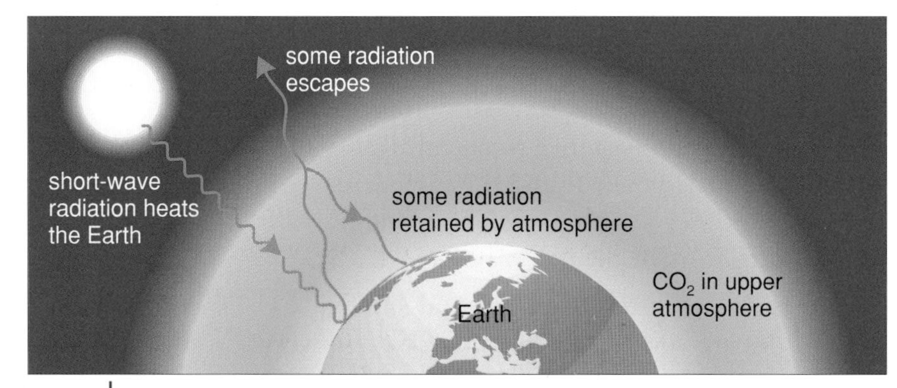

fig 24 | The greenhouse effect

There is great concern that the increased burning of fossil fuels is increasing the level of carbon dioxide in the atmosphere. This gradual increase has been measured in detection stations on remote islands.

c Why are these detection stations on remote islands?

Acid rain

Many fossil fuels contain small amounts of sulphur as an impurity. When they are burned, sulphur dioxide is formed in addition to carbon dioxide. Worldwide about 150 million tonnes of sulphur dioxide are produced every year, half of which comes from the burning of coal.

The sulphur dioxide rises into the atmosphere and dissolves in rain water to form sulphuric acid. This falls as **acid rain.** It acidifies lakes and washes minerals from the soil. Fish in the lakes die and large areas of forests have been damaged. Acid rain can also dissolve the limestone in buildings.

fig 25

Limiting the damage

It is possible to limit the effects of the pollution that is being caused by the increasing demand for energy.

Fuels can be treated to reduce sulphur impurities and the chimneys of the power stations can be modified. This involves adding limestone filters in order to neutralise the acid. Lime is also added to acidic lakes.

Carbon dioxide production can be decreased by switching to types of energy production that do not release carbon dioxide. Fig 26 shows how the sources of energy used in the USA have changed.

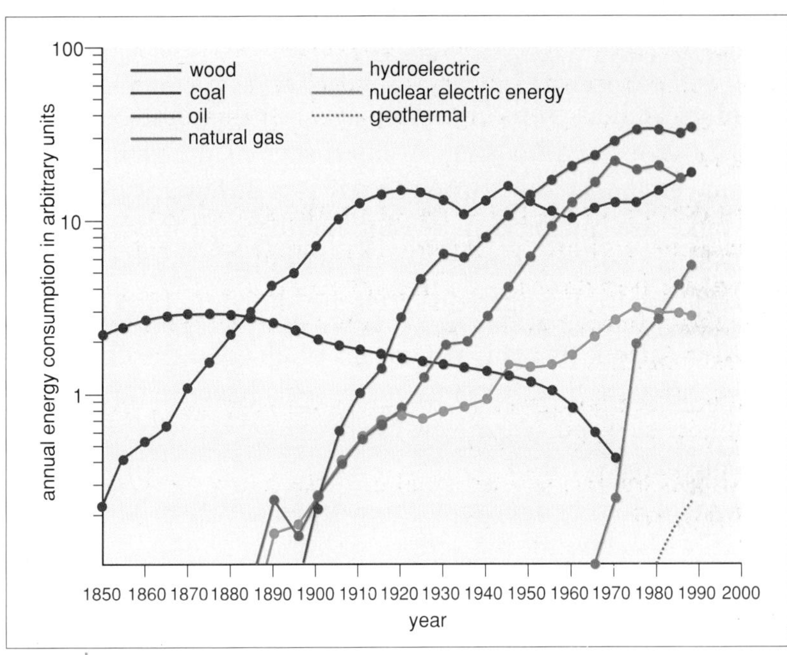

fig 26 | Energy consumption from different sources in the USA from 1850

The only real solution, however, is to reduce the demand for energy so that it reaches a **sustainable** level. This is a level that will not use up the Earth's resources or pollute the planet. This can be achieved by limiting the growth in the population and preventing energy waste.

Thinking further

1 Which of the methods of energy supply shown in fig 26 do not produce carbon dioxide?

2 How has the use of the three different fossil fuels changed in the USA since 1850?

◆ 3 What are the possible problems and limitations of using the alternative methods of energy supply?

KEY WORDS
acid rain • greenhouse effect • sustainable

 *Action of acid rain on seedlings.*

7.8 Conservation

Key points

- The increasing population of the world and their demand for resources is causing the destruction of habitats and organisms.
- There are many reasons why we should try to stop this. Many conservation projects are underway throughout the world.

The pressure on wildlife

We have seen how the growing world population has led to increased demand for fuel and food, as well as producing more polluting waste products.

Habitats such as tropical rainforests are being destroyed to make way for crops and housing. Animals such as the giant panda have become endangered because of their loss of habitat. Animals such as whales are caught in increasing numbers for food; other organisms such as elephants are being killed for luxury items such as ivory. Some endangered species are shown in fig 27.

Pollution also kills many organisms or changes the climate so that they cannot survive. Recently many seals have become the victims of pollution. Some organisms can no longer survive and have become **extinct**.

a Write down the names of three organisms that have become extinct because of the actions of humans.

Why conserve?

Many people believe that we should prevent habitats and organisms from disappearing and so keep alive the wide variety of life that exists today. This is called **conservation.** This is thought to be a good idea for a number of reasons. People enjoy spending time in the countryside and experiencing different habitats and learning about different organisms. Some of the large variety of organisms alive today may prove useful to us in the future. Plants that have not yet been investigated may be a source of useful drugs. Now that genetic engineering is possible, organisms may also be useful for the genes that they contain.

Removing organisms may have unseen effects on the environment. For example, the cutting down of rainforests may make the greenhouse effect worse. Woods and hedges act as windbreaks and so removing them can lead to soil being blown away. Many people also think that it is morally wrong to destroy other organisms.

b Why should farmers want to remove hedges?

c Why might this lead to more pests in their fields?

fig 27 Examples of endangered species: panda (top), rhino (middle) and Bengal tiger (bottom)

How is it done?

The world's resources can be conserved by adopting a policy of 'the three Rs' – *Reduce, Re-use and Recycle.* Everybody can reduce energy consumption by insulating their homes and by turning off lights when not needed. Glass bottles can be re-used by being returned to the factory for refilling. Recycling of many waste products is possible and collection points for glass, paper and plastic recycling are now appearing in many towns. All this helps prevent pollution and so helps conservation of habitats.

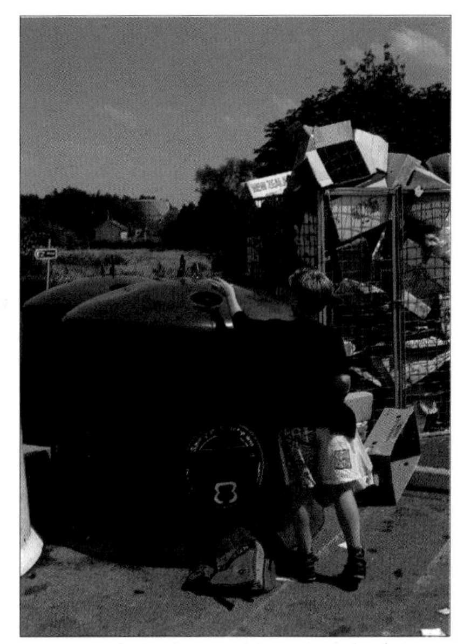

fig 28

Habitats and living organisms can also be protected by more direct action. This can be in a number of ways:

- Laws can be passed to limit the number of animals that can be hunted, or hunting could be banned altogether. This must be coupled with education and financial help because in some developing countries hunting is one of only a few ways that people have for obtaining food or earning money.
- Gene banks of frozen eggs, sperm or embryos of endangered species can be set up. These can be used if numbers of the organism fall to very low levels.
- Many zoos have captive breeding programmes to breed rare animals and release them into their natural habitats.
- Conservation areas have been set up to try to preserve rare habitats. This often involves managing the area and employing people to look after the site. Examples of these areas are National Parks and Sites of Special Scientific Interest.

IDEAS AND EVIDENCE

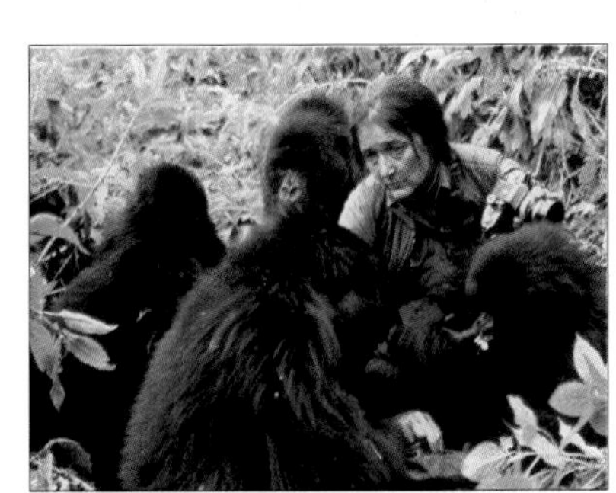

fig 29

Dian Fossey devoted much of her life to conservation. In 1967, she began observing mountain gorillas in Zaire. These gorillas only live in Rwanda, Congo and Zaire and their numbers were very low, dropping at one stage to 250. They suffered because their habitat was destroyed and because poachers killed them for souvenirs. Dian Fossey lived near the gorillas for almost 18 years, gaining their trust and protecting them from poachers.

During this time she wrote the book *Gorillas in the Mist* which was later made into a feature film starring Sigourney Weaver.

Dian Fossey was murdered in her camp on December 26th 1985.

Her work is still being continued and mountain gorilla numbers are now about 650.

Thinking further

1 Write down the names of three species that have been protected by banning or restricting hunting.

2 Why is it difficult to:

a breed animals in zoos

b release these animals back into the wild?

3 Why do zoos need to exchange animals rather than just continue breeding with their own small group?

KEY WORDS

conservation • extinct

 *Species under threat.*

Questions on ecology

● **1** Complete the paragraph below using words from the following list. *(4)*

community • habitat • population • species

The place where organisms live is called a __________ . A collection of organisms of the same __________ that live there is called a __________ . Many other types of organism will probably live there and all together they are called a __________ .

■ **2** Explain the following observations.

a The dead body of a man was found in a glacier after about 2000 years and very little decomposition had happened. *(2)*

b Another 2000-year-old body was found well preserved in a peat bog. *(2)*

c Onions are pickled to stop them going rotten. *(2)*

3 A student wanted to find out how many daisy plants were growing on the school football pitch. He placed a quadrat on the pitch and counted the number of daisy plants inside it. He repeated this three more times but he stayed out of the penalty areas because they were muddy. His results are shown in fig 30.

quadrat number	1	2	3	4
number of plants	2	3	4	1

fig 30

● **a** What was the average number of plants per quadrat? *(2)*

■ **b** The quadrat was a square, with sides of 0.5 m. What was the average number of daisies per square metre? *(2)*

■ **c** The football pitch was 50 m wide and 100 m long. Estimate the number of daisy plants on the whole pitch. *(2)*

■ **d** Explain why the method that he used is likely to give an inaccurate answer. *(2)*

◆ **4** Fig 31 shows the percentage of trees that have been damaged by acid rain in different European countries. It also shows how much of the acid rain falling in a country is self-produced.

a How is acid rain produced? *(3)*

b Which two countries have the highest percentage of trees that have been damaged by acid rain? *(2)*

c Most of the acid rain in Norway, Sweden and Finland comes from elsewhere. Where do you think it is produced? *(1)*

d How does this acid rain reach these countries? *(2)*

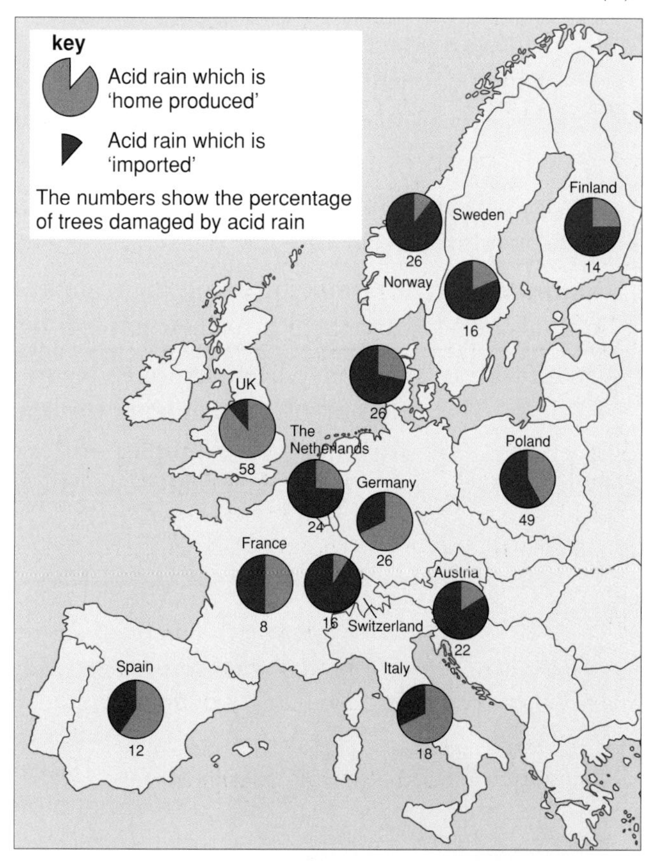

fig 31

◆ **5** Explain the following observations, which involve the nitrogen cycle.

a A groundsperson noticed that the grass on his cricket pitch always looked greener a few days after a thunderstorm. *(3)*

b A farmer was growing broad beans on his farm. He cut the plants off just above the soil after harvesting the beans and ploughed the roots into the soil. *(2)*

c A farmer notices a strong smell of ammonia in his cattle shed. *(2)*

d In the winter a large pile of horse manure was seen to be giving off steam, even though it had passed out of the horse several days earlier. *(2)*

e Compost can be made quickly in a special type of compost bin that can be spun round every few days to mix the contents. *(2)*

◆ **6** A farmer who grows sunflowers wanted to find out the optimum number of plants to grow in a certain area. He grew different numbers of sunflowers in certain areas of soil and counted the number of seeds that each sunflower produced. He also weighed all the seeds produced. His results are shown in fig 32.

number of plants per m^2	50	100	200	500	2000
number of seeds produced per flower	900	500	200	100	10
seed yield in kg/m^2	2.9	2.8	4.0	3.0	1.6

fig 32

a Plot the results in fig 32 on one graph. Plot the number of plants grown on the *x* axis and use two different scales for the *y* axes, one for the yield and the other for the number of seeds per flower. *(4)*

b Draw the best curve for each set of data. *(2)*

c Describe how the number of seeds produced per flower changes as the density of sowing changes. *(2)*

d Suggest two reasons for this change. *(2)*

e How many seeds should the farmer sow per square metre if he wants to get the highest yield from his plants? *(1)*

f Explain why this number of seeds may give the highest yield but not the highest number of seeds. *(2)*

IDEAS AND EVIDENCE

7 Read the following passage and answer the questions that follow:

The rabbit was introduced into Australia by Thomas Austin in 1759. He imported 24 rabbits from England and released them on his property for hunting. The rabbits spread rapidly, the population advancing over 110 kilometres each year. The rabbit had no real competition and few predators.

In 1919 Dr Aragao suggested introducing the myxoma virus into Australia in order to kill the rabbits. After many years of testing and arguments, the virus was introduced in 1950. It killed over 90% of the rabbits. Today, however, myxomatosis kills only about 40% of infected rabbits. Another virus is now being tested.

● a Why did the rabbits introduced by Austin increase in numbers faster in Australia than in England? *(2)*

● b What is the name given to the type of pest control suggested by Aragao? *(1)*

◆ c Why was the virus tested for many years before being introduced? *(2)*

◆ d The fact that nearly all the rabbits in Australia were descended from the original 24 made the virus a very effective killer. Explain why. *(2)*

◆ e Suggest why myxomatosis now kills only 40% of the rabbits. *(2)*

Response to stimuli

Introduction

The ability to respond to changes in the environment is one of the seven main characteristics shared by plants and animals. It is sometimes called sensitivity or irritability.

In animals the main structures for responding are muscles. Muscles are arranged in pairs because a muscle can either contract or relax but it cannot actively expand and push. The muscles of the skeleton are arranged across the bones so that they act as levers.

fig 1

You should also know about some of the details of human reproduction. A number of changes take place in the bodies of young people before they become adults. These changes are called puberty. Teenagers often worry that they are reaching puberty later than their friends but it is perfectly normal for teenagers to reach puberty at different ages.

You should also be aware of some of the effects that alcohol and illegal drugs have on the body. People drink alcoholic drinks and take drugs because they have some pleasurable effects on the body. Unfortunately there are also many harmful and dangerous side-effects.

Check-up

Have a go at the following questions. They will remind you of what you should know about responses to stimuli in animals and plants.

a Which of the following is not a characteristic of living organisms?

feeding • **growth** • **reproduction** • **sensitivity** • **sound production**

b Why are muscles arranged in pairs?

c What are these pairs called?

d Give the names of two muscles that act against each other.

e Make a list of the physical changes that occur during puberty in:

i boys ii girls.

f Why are these changes called the secondary sex characteristics?

g What emotional changes may occur during puberty?

h What is ovulation? When does it occur?

i Which organs of the body can be damaged by drinking too much alcohol?

j Write down the names of four illegal drugs.

If you have any difficulty, ask your teacher for a Summary sheet.

Contents of the Teaching block

This Teaching block is divided into seven spreads. The spreads concentrate on the different processes involved in detecting and responding to a stimulus. These processes occur in this order:

stimulus → detection → co-ordination → response

8.1 Detecting stimuli

Our bodies contain receptors that detect slight changes around us, such as a change in temperature. The receptors convert this information into a nerve impulse which goes to the central nervous system (CNS). The eye is an example of a sense organ. It is a collection of many receptors.

8.2 Nerves

Information is carried around the body by special cells called neurones. These neurones are specially designed for the job they have to do. Between the neurones are small gaps called synapses. Various drugs can affect these synapses.

8.3 Co-ordination and response

The CNS consists of the brain and the spinal cord. Its job is to co-ordinate all the information received from the receptors and to bring about the correct response.

8.4 Hormones

Hormones are messengers that are sent around the body in the bloodstream.

8.5 The role and use of hormones

Hormones control many important body processes, including reproduction.
Although hormones can be used medically to bring about benefit, they can also be misused.

8.6 Response to stimuli in plants

The actions of hormones are also important in plants. Plants also respond to changes in the environment around them.

8.7 Uses of plant hormones

Farmers and gardeners can use plant hormones to control the growth of their plants.

Links with other Teaching blocks

9.1 Controlling glucose levels
9.3 Kidneys and lungs

8.1 Detecting stimuli

Key points

- Receptors detect different stimuli and convert the information into nerve impulses.
- The retina of the eye contains many light receptors. The eye also has a number of other structures that help to focus the light so that a clear image can be formed.

The role of receptors

Receptors are cells that are specialised to respond to stimuli. The stimulus could be light, sound, pressure, temperature or chemicals. A receptor may detect more than one type of stimulus but usually they are much more sensitive to one particular type. The role of the receptors is to send information about the stimulus to the central nervous system in the form of nerve impulses.

There are also receptors that detect changes occurring inside the body, such as changes in the blood.

a Make a list of the features of the blood that you think the body needs to measure.

Sense organs – the eye

Many receptors are gathered together into sense organs such as the eye. This allows them to have other structures that can help the receptors to gather as much information as possible. The external features of the eye are shown in fig 2 and the internal features in fig 3.

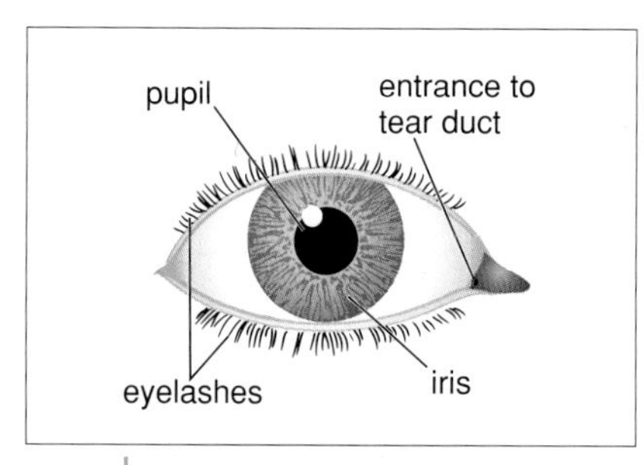

fig 2 External view of the eye

Light enters the eye through the **pupil**. The **iris** is a coloured disc of tissue that surrounds the pupil. It contains muscle that can change the size of the iris and so make the pupil larger or smaller.

b Why might the body want to change the size of the pupil?

The receptors in the eye are the cells of the **retina**. They detect the light that enters the eye and send nerve impulses to the brain via the

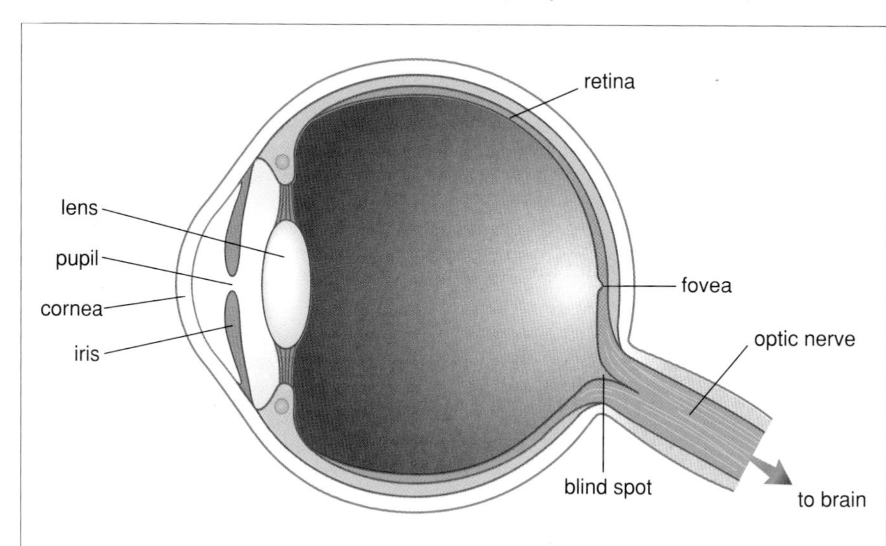

fig 3 Internal structure of the eye

optic nerve. The brain then constructs a picture of the objects that the person is looking at. The **fovea** is a small area on the retina that contains the highest concentration of receptors.

c What is the **blind spot**?

Forming a focused image

The light that enters the eye has to be focused onto the back of the retina. This enables the brain to produce an accurate image of a nearby or a distant object. The **cornea, lens** and **ciliary muscles** bring about this focusing. This process is shown in fig 4.

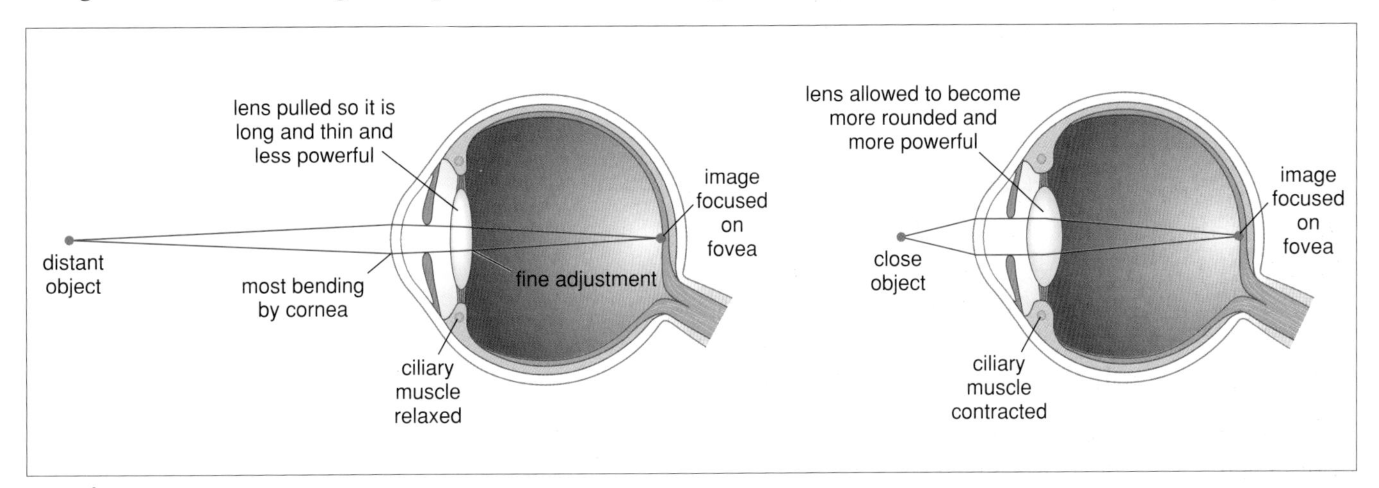

fig 4 | The process of accommodation – light is focused onto the fovea by the cornea and the lens

Rods and cones

The retina contains two types of receptor cells. They are called **rods** and **cones** because of their shapes. Both transduce the energy from light into nerve impulses but they respond in slightly different ways.

Rods can detect dim light but cannot detect colour or detail. Cones need bright light to work but can detect fine detail and colour. Cones are found mainly in the fovea whereas rods are found outside the fovea.

Thinking further

■ 1 Write down the stimuli detected by:

a taste buds b skin c the ear.

◆ 2 Why do the eyes often become tired when looking at a close object such as a book, but not when looking into the distance?

◆ 3 Why does the body make sure that when looking directly at an object, the light falls on the fovea?

KEY WORDS

blind spot • ciliary muscles • cones • cornea • fovea • iris • lens • optic nerve • pupil • retina • rods

8.2 Nerves

Key points

- Information is sent around the body as nerve impulses in special cells called neurones.
- These neurones are specialised so that they can carry out this job efficiently.
- Synapses allow impulses to be passed between neurones and can be affected by various drugs.

The structure of neurones

Neurones are cells that transmit **nerve impulses** around the body. Neurones are gathered together into bundles called **nerves.** The body has different types of neurones but they are all specialised for the role of transmitting impulses. The structure of a motor neurone is shown in fig 5.

a Which structures present in neurones tell you that they are cells?

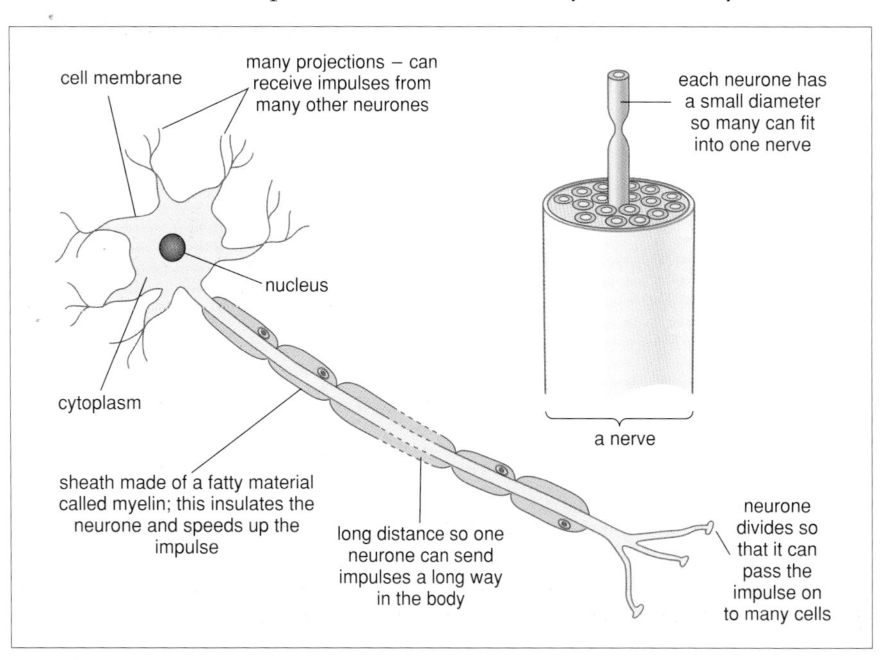

fig 5 | The structure of nerves and a motor neurone

Synapses

Neurones are not connected directly to each other. Between the projections from two neurones are minute gaps. These are called **synapses.**

b What would happen if each neurone in the body were connected directly to another?

When an impulse, or a sufficient number of impulses, reaches a synapse, the neurone releases a chemical called a **neurotransmitter.**

Taking it further

A nerve impulse is caused by the movement of electrically charged ions across the cell membrane of the neurone. This occurs in order along the neurone, causing the impulse to move along. This process was discovered using giant neurones from squid (fig 6).

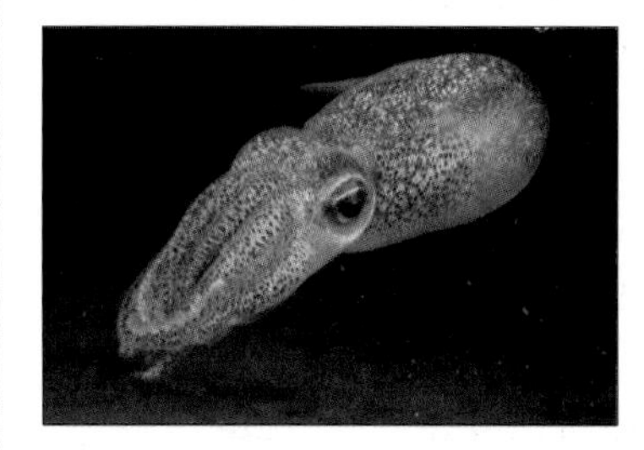

fig 6

Some neurones have a myelin sheath that encloses the axon. This stops the ions from passing across the axon membrane and so they can only pass at the gaps in the sheath. The impulse therefore 'jumps' from gap to gap, making it travel much faster. A nerve impulse may travel at 100 metres per second along such a neurone.

This chemical diffuses across the small gap and joins with receptor sites on the next neurone. This causes an impulse to be sent along this neurone. This process is shown in fig 7.

After the impulse has been sent along the second neurone, enzymes are released to destroy the neurotransmitter.

c What would happen if the transmitter substance was not broken down?

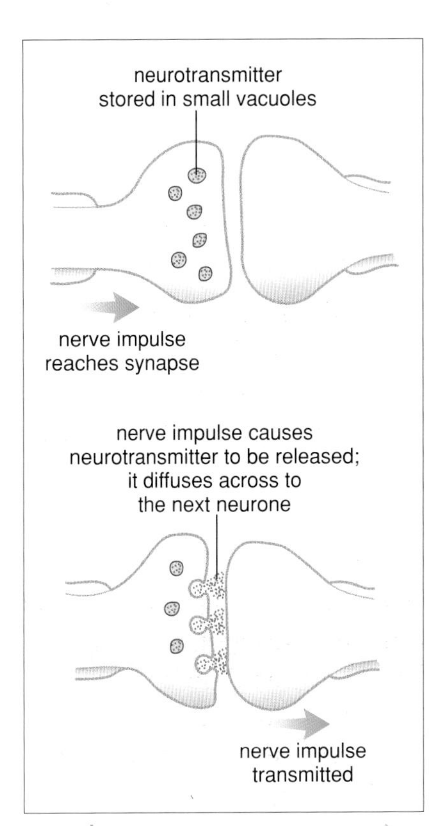

fig 7 | The working of a synapse

Synapses and drugs

The body contains millions of synapses, which use a number of different neurotransmitters. Drugs can affect these synapses in different ways.

- A drug might stimulate synapses by acting like the neurotransmitter. LSD and nicotine work in this way.
- Other drugs may block the action of the enzyme that normally breaks down the neurotransmitter.
- Alcohol acts on particular synapses in the brain. These synapses reduce the activity of certain areas of the brain and so alcohol acts as a **depressant**. In small doses it depresses the areas responsible for worry and anxiety but in larger amounts it affects the areas involved in balance and conscious thought.

Solvents that are found in products such as glues, aerosols, lighter fuels and stain removers can also act on synapses, depressing the action of the brain. Some people inhale these solvents in an attempt to achieve pleasurable feelings. Unfortunately this can lead to headaches, sickness and damage to the liver and kidneys. Death may also occur immediately because of heart failure or accidents (fig 8).

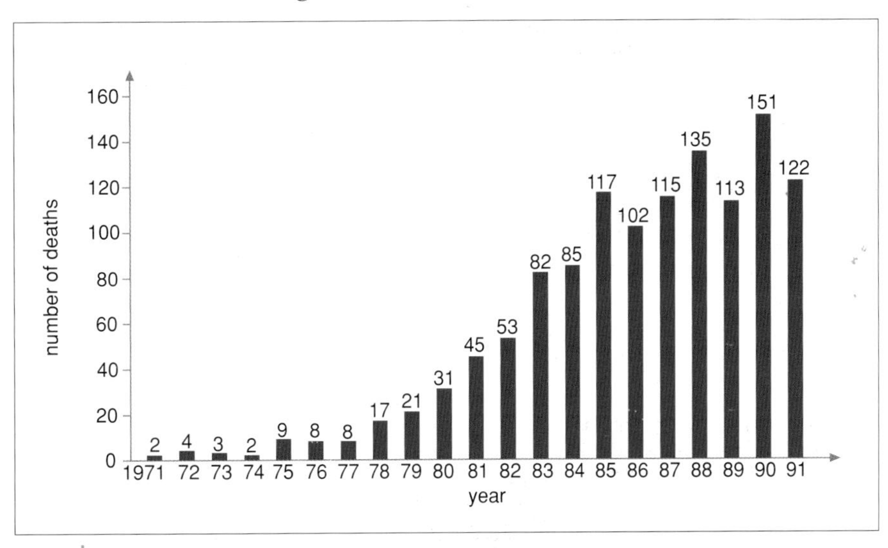

fig 8 | Number of sudden deaths between 1971 and 1991 caused by solvent abuse

Thinking further

■ **1** Make a list of the ways in which a neurone is specialised for the role of carrying nerve impulses around the body.

■ **2** Many of the drugs that affect synapses are addictive. What does this mean?

◆ **3** People are likely to have accidents whilst experiencing the effects of alcohol or solvents. Why is this?

KEY WORDS

depressant • nerve • nerve impulse • neurone • neurotransmitter • synapse

8.3 Co-ordination and response

Key points

- Nerve impulses are sent from receptors to the central nervous system (CNS) along sensory neurones.
- The CNS co-ordinates all the information from the receptors and brings about a response. This may be a reflex or a voluntary action.
- Nerve impulses are then sent to the effectors along motor neurones.

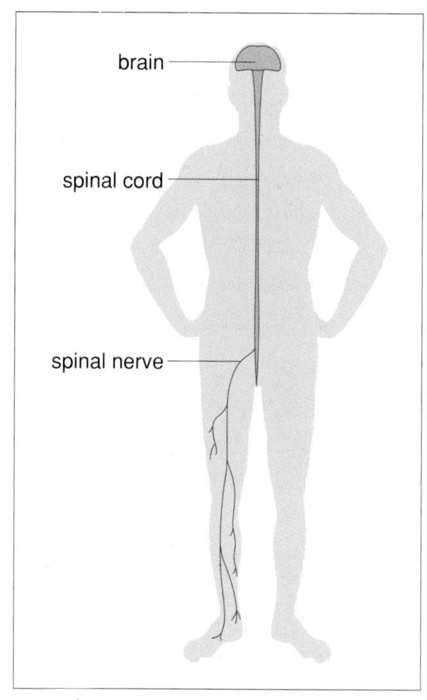

fig 9 | The human nervous system (only one spinal nerve is shown)

Into the CNS

The **CNS** is made up of the **brain** and the **spinal cord.** The spinal cord is a collection of millions of neurones that pass down from the brain. It passes through the centre of the backbone or vertebral column. At regular intervals, spinal nerves enter and leave the spinal cord (fig 9).

a What is the advantage of the spinal cord being surrounded by the vertebral column?

All the receptors in the body send nerve impulses to the CNS along **sensory neurones.** These may enter the brain or the spinal cord through a spinal nerve. Sensory neurones have many structures in common with the motor neurone shown in fig 5 on spread 8.2.

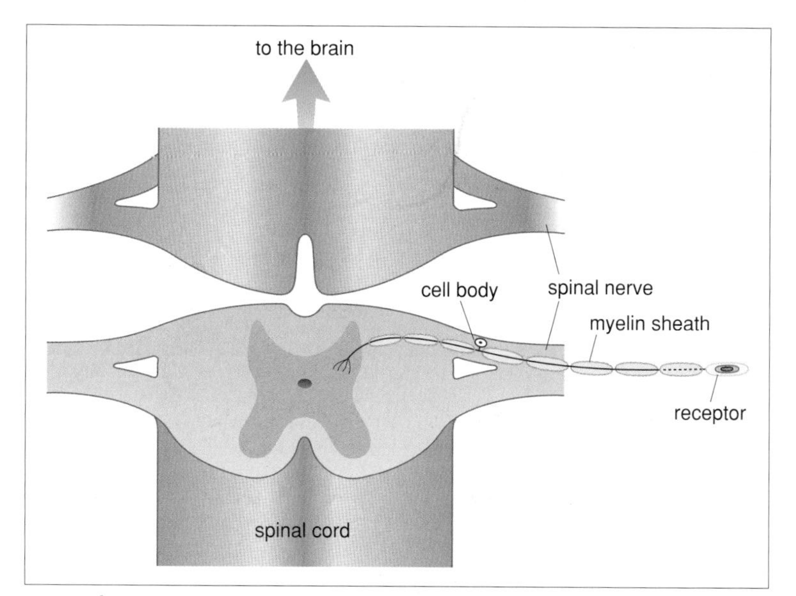

fig 10 | Section through the spinal cord to show the entry of a sensory neurone

Co-ordination by the CNS

The CNS has to decide how the body should respond, using the information received from all of the receptors. This decision-making process is called **co-ordination.** The responses are usually of two main types: reflexes and voluntary actions.

- **Reflexes** – this type of response is very rapid and does not involve conscious thought. It is often used to protect the body from damage.
- **Voluntary actions** – these responses always involve the brain and require conscious thought. The brain will consult memories of past events before deciding on a response.

b A voluntary action involves a larger number of neurones than a reflex. Why does this make the voluntary response a lot slower?

Responses

When the CNS has decided upon a response, nerve impulses are sent to the effectors along **motor neurones.** A motor neurone is shown in fig 5 on spread 8.2. The motor neurone leaves the spinal cord through a different branch of the spinal nerve than the one through which the sensory nerve entered.

In the case of some reflexes, the nerve impulse may enter the spinal cord along the sensory neurone and pass directly to the motor neurone. An example of this is the knee-jerk reflex, which is often tested by doctors (fig 11).

c The knee jerk is often called a monosynaptic reflex. Why is this?

In other reflexes a **relay neurone** may separate the sensory and motor neurones (fig 12). An example of this is the withdrawal reflex. It occurs when the pain receptors in part of the body are stimulated and the muscles respond to remove that part of the body from danger. The pathway that the nerve impulses take in a reflex is called a **reflex arc.**

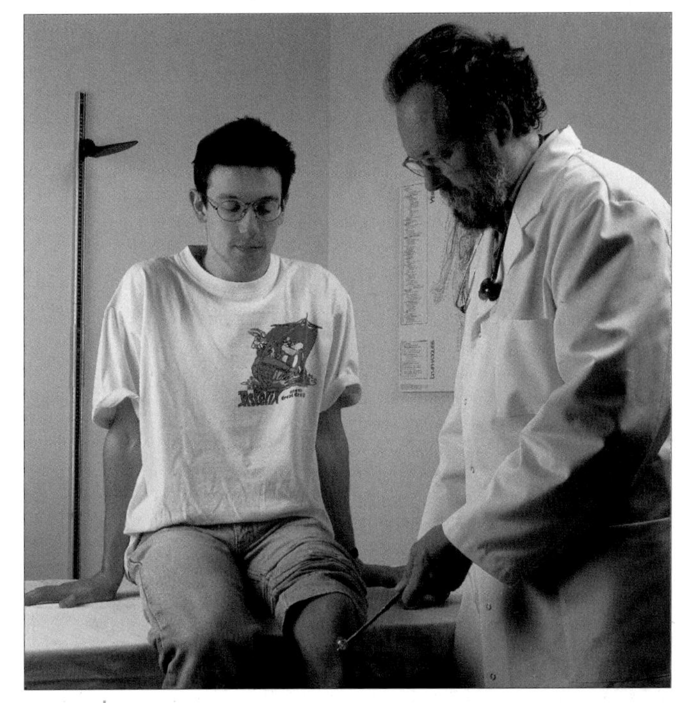

fig 11 | The knee-jerk reflex is used to test the connections between the sensory nerve, spinal cord and motor nerve. The doctor taps the tendon below the kneecap, which makes the thigh muscle contract and the leg jerks up. The patient cannot prevent this reflex.

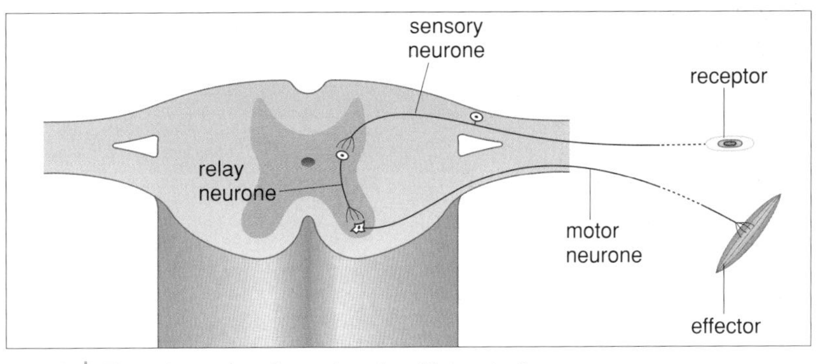

fig 12 | The pathway of a reflex such as the withdrawal reflex

Thinking further

1 Explain the difference between the following structures:

a a sensory neurone and a motor neurone

b a reflex and a voluntary action

c the spinal cord and the CNS.

2 Sneezing and blinking are both reflexes.

a Suggest what the stimulus, receptors and effectors might be in each of these reflexes.

b How does each of these reflexes protect the body?

◆ **3** A monosynaptic response such as the knee-jerk reflex cannot be prevented from happening, no matter how hard the subject tries. The withdrawal reflex can be stopped by conscious thought. Explain why.

KEY WORDS

brain • CNS • co-ordination • motor neurone • reflex • reflex arc • relay neurone • sensory neurone • spinal cord • voluntary action

8.4 Hormones

Key points

- Hormones are chemical messengers carried around the body in the blood.
- They are produced by various ductless glands in the body and are an alternative to communication by nerves.

What is a hormone?

Hormones are chemicals (usually proteins or lipids) that are used as messengers in the body. They are produced and released from various glands (fig 13) and are secreted directly into the blood as it passes through the gland. The hormones are not released via ducts, as enzymes are, but directly into the blood. The glands are therefore often called **ductless** glands.

a The pancreas produces and releases both hormones and enzymes. Write down the names of the enzymes that it produces.

b Name the duct that these enzymes are released into.

Once released, hormones are carried in the blood plasma to every part of the body. They will be detected by certain target cells or organs and will cause these organs to change their action. For example, **insulin**, which is produced by the pancreas, affects most cells in the body but not the brain. It makes the cells more permeable to glucose. Once hormones have been released, they are gradually destroyed by the liver.

c Why is it necessary to destroy hormones after they have been released?

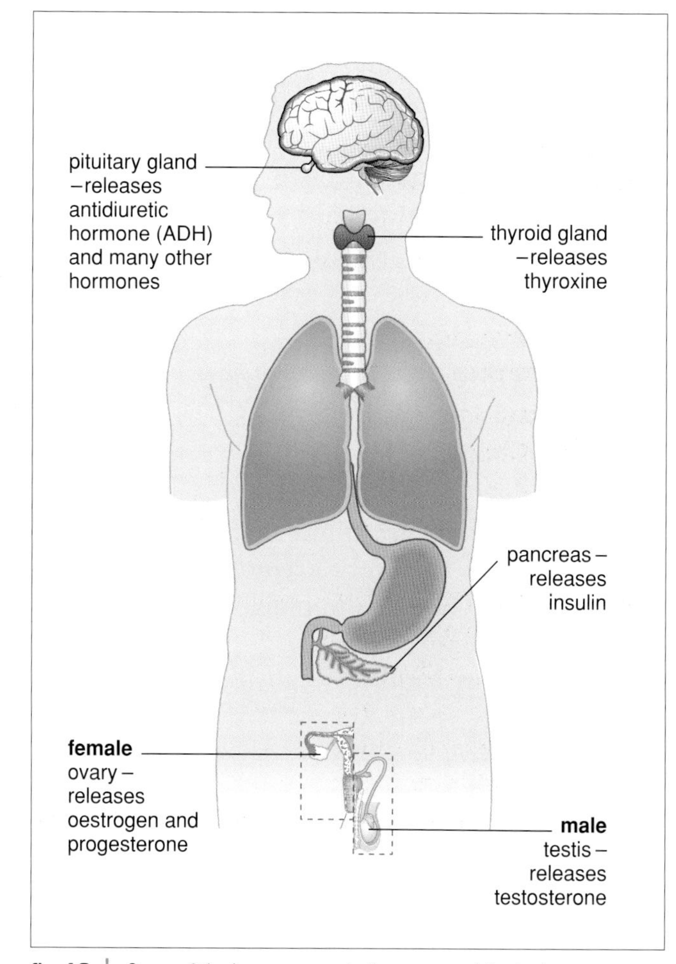

fig 13 | Some of the hormone-producing organs of the body

Studying the action of hormones

Some people develop an over- or under-secretion of a particular hormone. By studying the symptoms shown by these people, scientists have been able to work out the actions of the hormone. If symptoms arise because of lack of the hormone, then the symptoms should be reversed by injecting the hormone.

d What could scientists do to treat the over-production of a hormone?

Comparing nerves and hormones

The body uses both nerves and hormones to carry messages around the body. These two systems work in different ways. They are compared in fig 14.

nervous communication	hormonal communication
• by means of electrochemical impulses • brings about a fast response • the response is usually short lived • usually targets one specific effector	• by means of chemicals in the blood • response is slower • response may last for hours or longer • may produce effects on many targets

fig 14

Taking it further

Many hormone-producing glands are controlled by the pituitary gland in the brain. The pituitary gland produces hormones that stimulate the release of other hormones from other glands. This control is usually by a process called negative feedback (fig 15). When the level of the hormone in the blood drops, the pituitary gland produces more of the stimulating hormone and so the gland will release more hormone. This continues until the correct level is reached; secretion is then reduced.

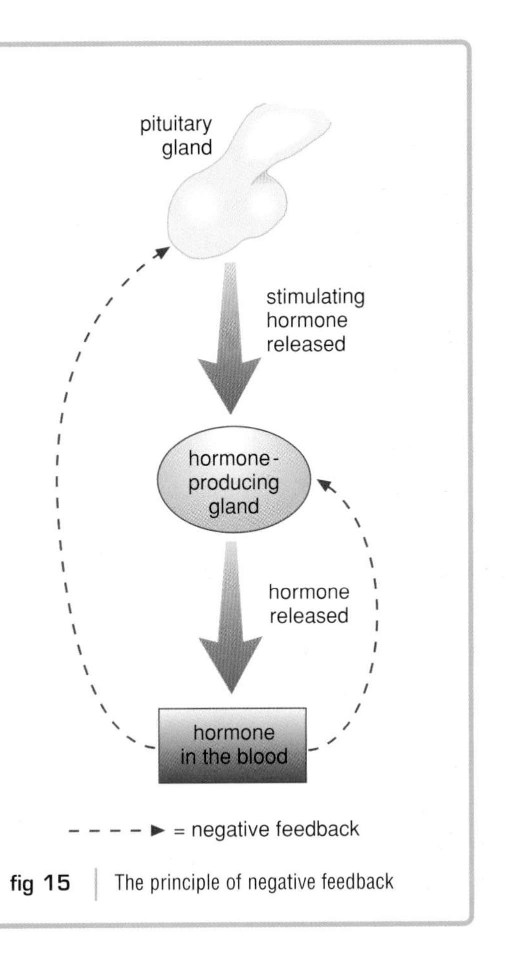

fig 15 | The principle of negative feedback

Thinking further

1 Name the male and female sex organs and write down the hormones that they produce.

2 A blockage in the pancreatic duct does not affect the action of insulin. Why?

3 Why is it difficult to correct over-secretion of the pituitary gland surgically?

KEY WORDS
ductless • hormone • insulin

8.5 The role and use of hormones

Key points

- Physical changes during adolescence are controlled by sex hormones. These hormones are produced by the sex organs.
- In females, the menstrual cycle is controlled by oestrogen, progesterone, and hormones from the pituitary gland.
- We now use hormones medically to control fertility. Hormones may be used illegally by some sporting competitors.

Puberty

The secondary sex characteristics that develop during adolescence are due to the increased production of sex hormones. One of these characteristics is the production of the sex cells or gametes.

In males at puberty, the testes produce large amounts of **testosterone** in response to hormones from the pituitary gland. This causes the testes to produce sperm. Sperm production is then continuous for most of the male's life.

Controlling the menstrual cycle

In females, gamete production is not a continuous process. Eggs start to be released at puberty as part of a repeating series of events called the **menstrual cycle**. The sex hormone **oestrogen** controls the cyclical changes that occur in the ovaries, uterus and vagina (fig 16). **Progesterone**, and hormones from the pituitary gland are also involved.

If the egg is fertilised it sends a message to the ovary so that progesterone continues to be produced. Another hormone is used

fig 16 | Hormonal control of the menstrual cycle

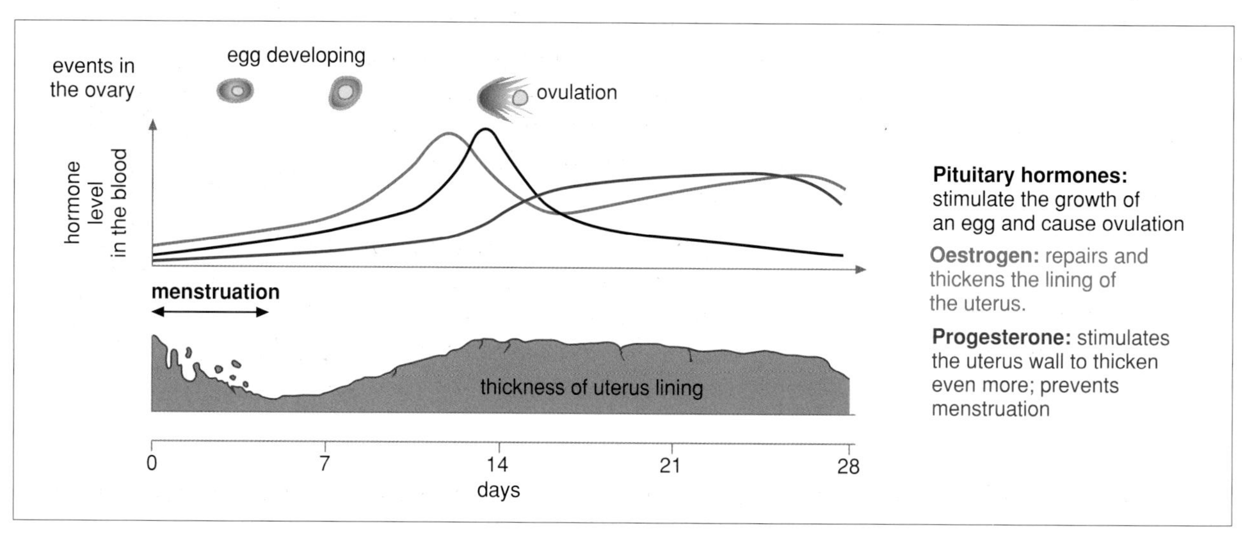

to send this message – it is this hormone that is tested for in many pregnancy tests.

a What would happen to the fertilised egg if the production of progesterone stopped?

Controlling fertility

Doctors can use the hormones that control the menstrual cycle to either decrease or increase a woman's fertility. The contraceptive pill has been used by large numbers of women to prevent pregnancy occurring. The combined pill contains a combination of oestrogen and progesterone and prevents the release of the pituitary hormones.

b How does taking the combined pill stop a woman from becoming pregnant?

The 'mini-pill' contains progesterone only. It allows ovulation but the vagina and uterus are not receptive to sperm or a fertilised egg.

About one in six of all couples suffers from some type of **infertility** and has difficulty conceiving a child. Some causes of infertility can be treated with hormones. Women who release eggs infrequently can be given injections of pituitary hormones to stimulate the ovary. It is very difficult to judge the dose correctly and many women may 'super-ovulate', releasing many eggs at once.

Hormones and sporting performance

Evidence shows that significant numbers of sporting competitors have used hormones in an attempt to improve their performance.

Anabolic steroids are similar to testosterone. Athletes may take these to increase muscle growth and so that they can train more aggressively. The hormones may, however, reduce the release of the hormones from the pituitary gland that normally stimulate the testes to make testosterone.

Thinking further

- 1 If a woman's menstrual cycle lasts a month, work out how many eggs she would release between the ages of 15 and 50 years.
- 2 Explain why the actual number may be higher or lower than this.
- 3 What might happen if a woman super-ovulates?
- ◆ 4 What are the arguments for and against storing eggs or embryos for future use in treating an infertile woman?
- ◆ 5 Explain why the use of anabolic steroids by male athletes may reduce their fertility.

fig 17

IDEAS AND EVIDENCE

Louise Brown was the first 'test tube baby'. She was born on July 25th 1978. An egg had been removed from her mother's ovary and fertilised outside the body. This was necessary because the Fallopian tubes were blocked. The embryo was returned to the uterus.

The two doctors involved, Robert Edwards and Patrick Steptoe, measured the level of pituitary hormones in the mother's blood. When the level increased dramatically, they knew that the egg was ripe and about to be released. They could then quickly remove it from the ovary before ovulation.

Pituitary hormones are now given to women so that they produce many eggs. This increases the chance of success and allows some embryos to be frozen and stored.

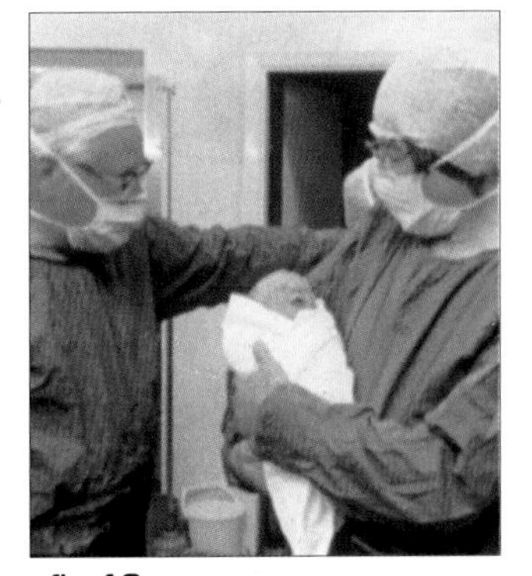

fig 18

KEY WORDS

anabolic steroids • infertility • menstrual cycle • menstruation • oestrogen • progesterone • testosterone

8.6 Response to stimuli in plants

Key points

- Plants usually respond to stimuli by growing in a particular direction.
- These growth responses are usually controlled by plant growth substances or hormones.

Responses by plants

Plants are living organisms and so can respond to changes in their environment. Occasionally, these changes are rapid, as shown when the Venus flytrap plant catches flies (fig 19). Usually, however, they are much slower growth responses.

a Why do animals usually have to respond faster than plants?

Plants can respond to a number of stimuli such as light, temperature, gravity, touch, water or chemicals. Sometimes the stimulus is a general change, such as a warming of the air or increased light in the morning. Plants can respond to these changes with **nastic** responses, such as the opening of flowers in the morning.

Tropic responses occur when a plant grows in a particular direction, either towards or away from a stimulus. This can be seen when a plant is left by a window for some time and the shoot grows towards the light (fig 20).

b What advantage does this tropism give to the plant?

This tropism involves light and so is called **phototropism.** Because the shoot grows towards the light it is called positive phototropism.

Plants can also respond to gravity. This is called **geotropism.** Roots show positive geotropism from a young age, growing downwards, whereas shoots show negative geotropism.

c Explain why both these responses are necessary in a young plant that has just started to grow from a seed.

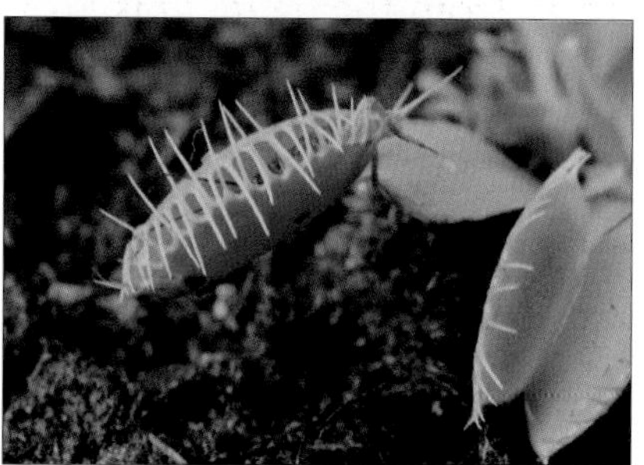

fig 19 The Venus flytrap plant: touch-sensitive hairs on the inner surace of the leaf are triggered by the movement of the insect and cause the leaf to close. The insect is then digested by enzymes.

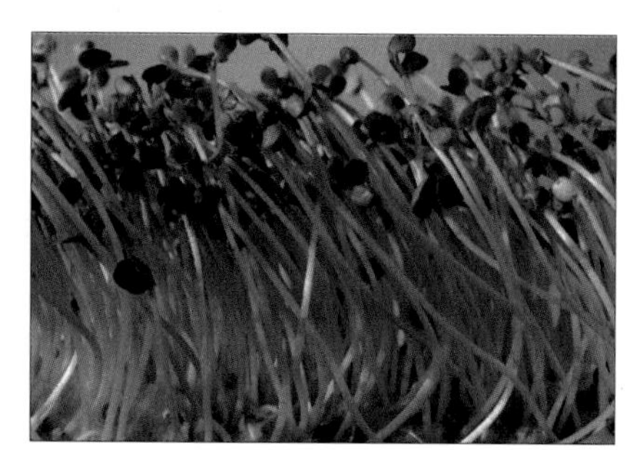

fig 20 Mustard seedlings growing towards the light

How do tropisms work?

As in animals, a response in plants needs a receptor, an effector and some means of communication between the two.

A number of scientists have studied tropisms to try to find out how they work. The diagrams in figs 21, 22 and 23 show some of this work.

d What conclusion could Darwin make about the site of the light receptor?

e Does Boysen-Jensen's experiment indicate that the message is sent by nerves or chemicals?

f Is the effector in the tip of the shoot or a little distance behind it?

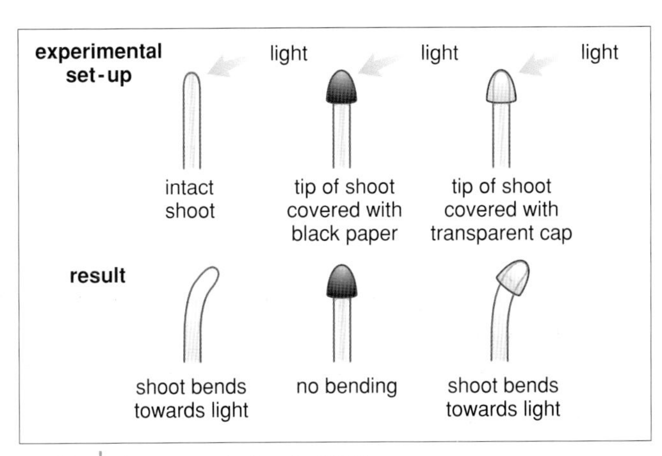

fig 21 | Experiments by Darwin (1880)

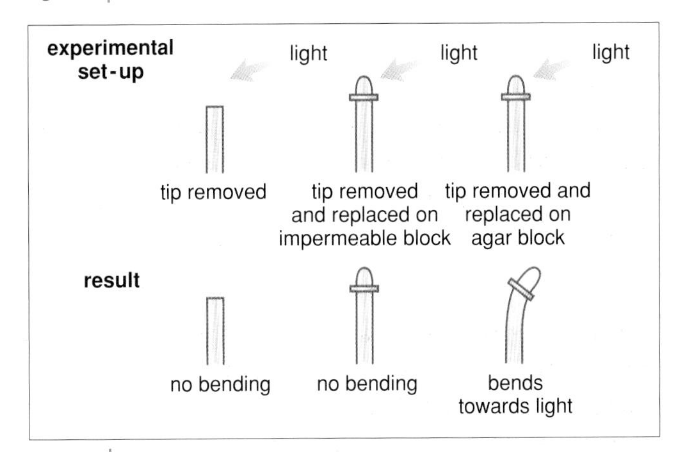

fig 22 | Experiments by Boysen-Jensen (1913)

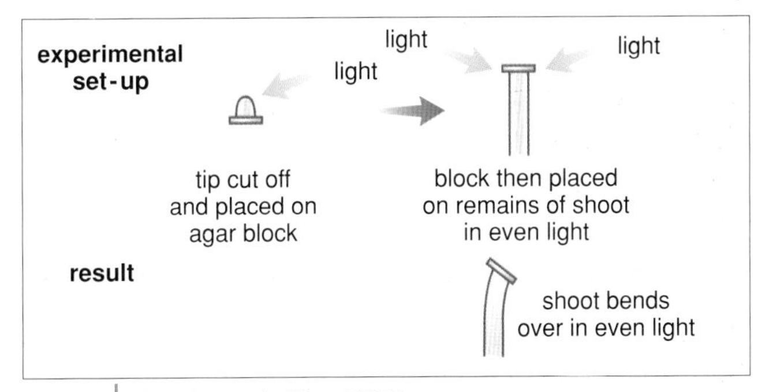

fig 23 | Experiments by Went (1928)

Auxins

Following Went's experiment (fig 23), the chemical messenger was found in the agar blocks. It is called **auxin** and this is one of a collection of plant hormones or plant growth substances. Auxins are produced in the tip of a shoot and pass back to an area behind the tip where they cause cells to grow.

It is thought that light shining on one side of the shoot causes more auxin to be sent to the side away from the light. This grows faster than the lit side and so the shoot bends towards the light. This is shown in fig 24.

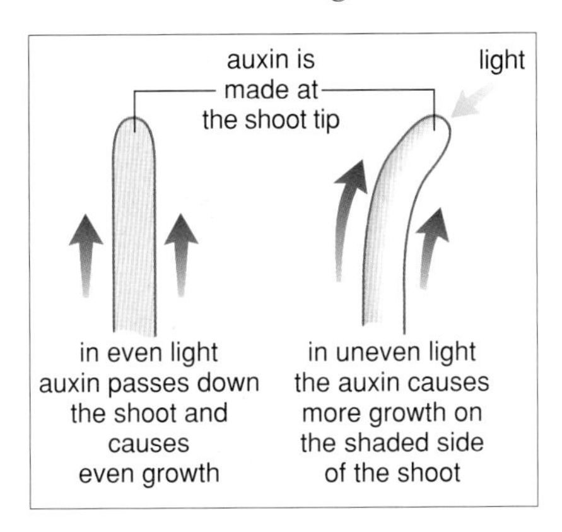

fig 24

Thinking further

1 State whether the following responses are tropic or nastic responses.

a Pea shoots growing up around a twig

b Bean shoots growing taller when kept in the dark for a day

2 What would you expect to happen in each of the cases shown in fig 25?

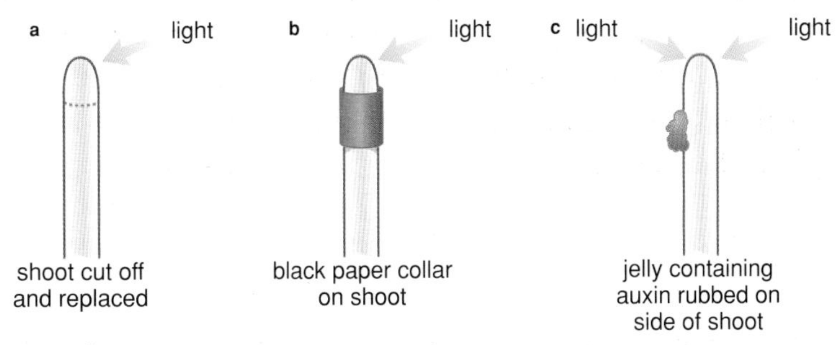

fig 25 | The action of auxin in a shoot

KEY WORDS

auxin • geotropism • nastic • phototropism • tropic

 *How much auxin?*

8.7 Uses of plant hormones

Key points

- Plants produce a number of growth substances that control all aspects of their growth and development.
- We can use many of these substances to try to change the way in which plants grow.

Processes controlled by hormones

All aspects of plant growth are controlled by plant hormones. Some are controlled by auxins, some by other hormones and many by combinations of different hormones.

Examples of the processes controlled by auxins are illustrated in figs 26, 27 and 28.

a What effect do auxins have on the growth of the segments of the stem (fig 26)?

b What effect does the auxin have on the cut base of the stem (fig 27)?

c What action does auxin have on the shoot that has had the tip removed (fig 27)?

d What effect does removing the 'pips' have on the growth of the strawberry (fig 28)?

e What evidence is there that the growth of the fruit is caused by auxins (fig 28)?

These experiments show that auxins control many aspects of growth in plants:

- They stimulate shoots to grow rapidly.
- The normal production of auxin from the shoot tip stops side shoots from growing.
- Auxins stimulate the growth of roots from the base of stems or leaves.
- Auxins produced from seeds cause the surrounding fruits to swell.

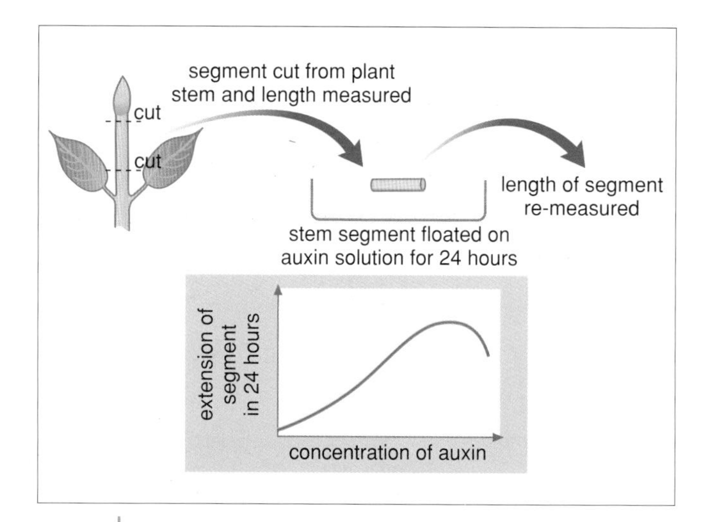

fig 26 | The growth of shoots in auxin solution

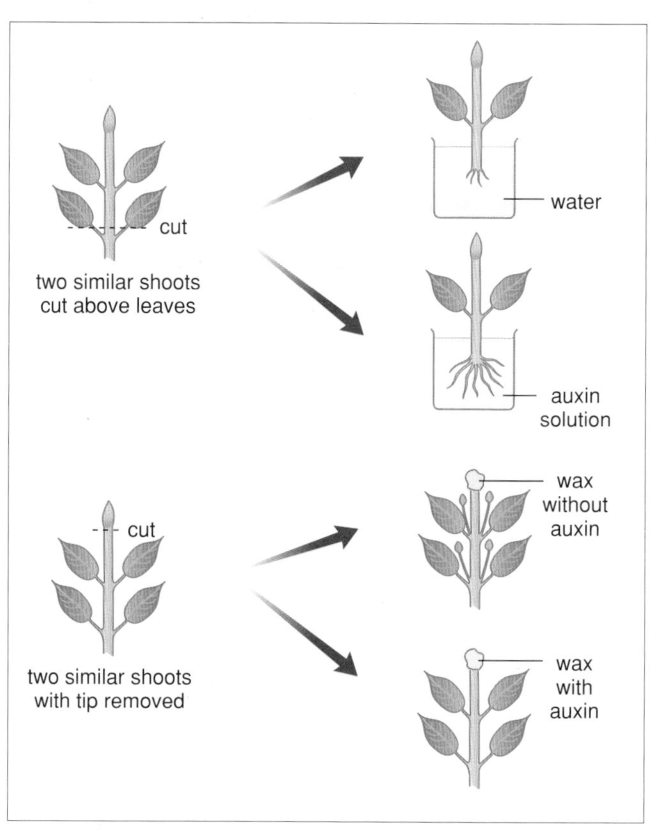

fig 27 | The action of auxin on the cut ends of shoots

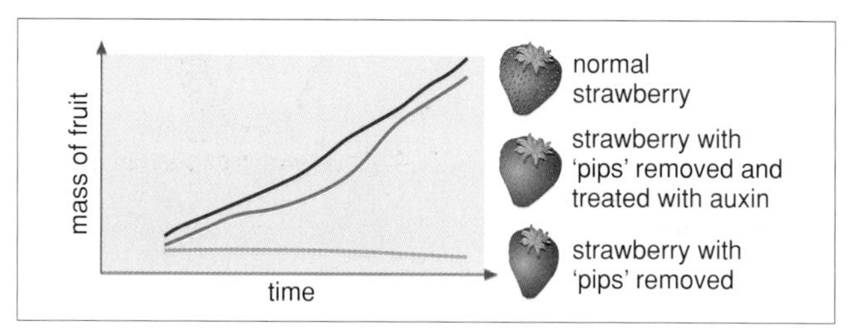

fig 28 | Function of auxins in promoting fruit growth – the growth of strawberries under different conditions

Using auxins

Gardeners and farmers use auxins to alter the growth of their plants in a number of ways.

Taking cuttings

Hormone rooting powder used by gardeners contains auxins. A gardener can take a **cutting** from a stem and dip the end of the stem in the hormone rooting powder. The shoot is then planted in soil and the auxin stimulates the growth of roots from the cut end of the stem.

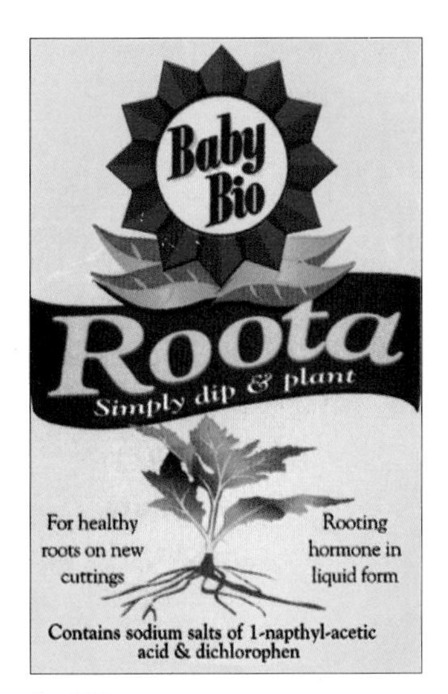

fig 29

Producing seedless fruits

Some fruits are more popular if they do not contain seeds. Examples of popular **seedless fruits** are grapes, bananas, pineapples and cucumbers. Treating these plants with auxins may encourage the ovary to develop into a fruit without the seed developing.

f How would the farmer prevent the seed from developing?

Selective weedkillers

Scientists have developed chemicals that are similar to auxins. An example of this is 2,4-D. In low concentrations it works like auxins and stimulates shoots to grow. When sprayed on to plants in high concentrations, it causes the plants to grow too fast and in an uncontrolled way. This results in their death. Narrow-leaved plants such as grass do not take up 2,4-D very easily and so it can be used on lawns to kill weeds without killing the grass. It is therefore a **selective weedkiller**.

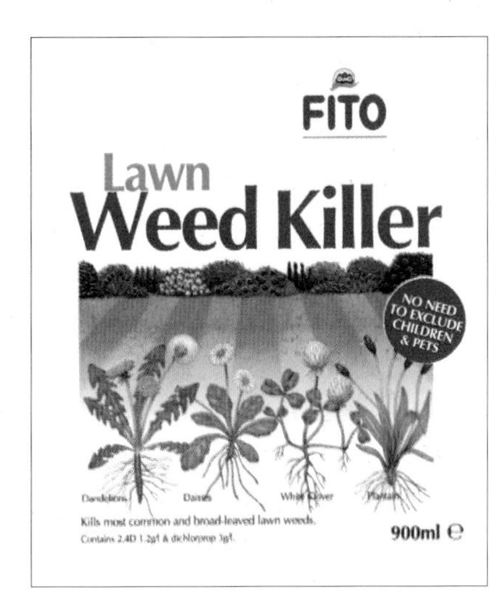

fig 30

Thinking further

Look at the instructions in fig 31 for taking cuttings and answer the following questions.

1 Why must the cuttings be planted as soon as possible?

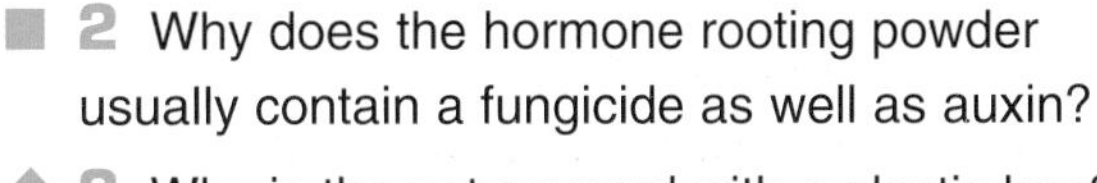

2 Why does the hormone rooting powder usually contain a fungicide as well as auxin?

3 Why is the pot covered with a plastic bag?

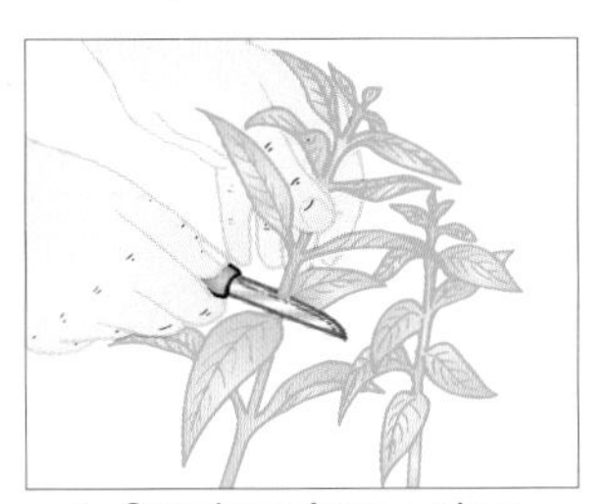

1 Cut shoot from a plant.

2 Dip cut end into hormone rooting powder.

3 Plant in pot of soil as soon as possible after cutting.

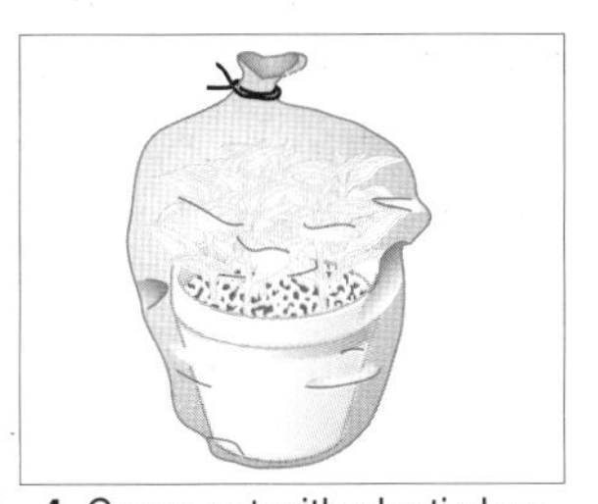

4 Cover pot with plastic bag.

fig 31

KEY WORDS

cutting • seedless fruit • selective weedkiller

Questions on response to stimuli

1 ● **a** Write these processes in the order that they occur in a response. *(3)*

co-ordination • stimulus • response • detection

● **b** Match the following structures in the eye to their correct functions. *(4)*

Structure	**Function**
• iris	• detects light
• cornea	• carries nerve impulses to the brain
• optic nerve	• fine focusing of incoming light
• lens	• adjusts the size of the pupil
• retina	• responsible for the main bending of light

■ **c** Describe the changes that occur in a person's eye as they change from looking at a close object to a distant one. *(3)*

2 Fig 32 shows the number of deaths caused by solvent abuse in the age range 11 to 19 years. The data are for the years 1971 to 1991 in the UK.

age in years	11	12	13	14	15	16	17	18	19
number of deaths	5	19	49	136	193	192	140	100	67

fig 32

■ **a** Plot the data in fig 32 in a suitable way. *(4)*

● **b** Describe the pattern shown by this graph. *(3)*

c ● **i** What was the total number of deaths in the age range 11–19 years? *(1)*

◆ **ii** Fig 8 on spread 8.2 shows that 1225 people died of solvent abuse between 1971 and 1991. What percentage were aged 11–19 years? *(2)*

3 Read the passage and answer the questions that follow.

Plant hormones control most aspects of growth in plants and so have been used by man to manipulate crops. Most of the hormones used are synthetic hormones similar to the natural ones. They may be used to encourage parthenocarpy – the development of fruits without seeds. They are also used to stop fruit from falling from trees. Another use is as selective weedkillers, particularly on cereal crops such as wheat. Another plant hormone is the gas ethene. It causes fruit to ripen and inhibits growth in stems.

■ **a** Explain what is meant by the following terms: *(3)*

i synthetic hormone
ii parthenocarpy
iii selective weedkiller.

◆ **b** Why can selective weedkillers be used on wheat fields? *(1)*

■ **c** Why are hormones used to stop fruit from falling from trees? *(1)*

■ **d** The gas that was burned in houses in Victorian times produced ethene gas. Explain why people found it difficult to grow houseplants. *(1)*

■ **e** Bananas are picked green, transported and then treated with ethene. Why is this? *(2)*

◆ **4** Fig 33 shows some information about animal hormones. Copy the table and fill in the missing statements. *(8)*

hormone	**site of production**	**action on the body**
	pancreas	controls blood glucose level
testosterone		
		prevents menstruation
	pituitary gland	controls water levels of body
oestrogen		

fig 33

5 A new chemical is discovered in the body. It is thought that it is produced in the pancreas and is a hormone.

■ **a** How would a scientist show that it is produced in the pancreas? *(2)*

◆ **b** How would a scientist try to work out the actions of the hormone in the body? *(2)*

◆ **6** Fig 34 shows a number of experiments on the shoots of young plants. Look at the diagrams and answer the questions that follow.

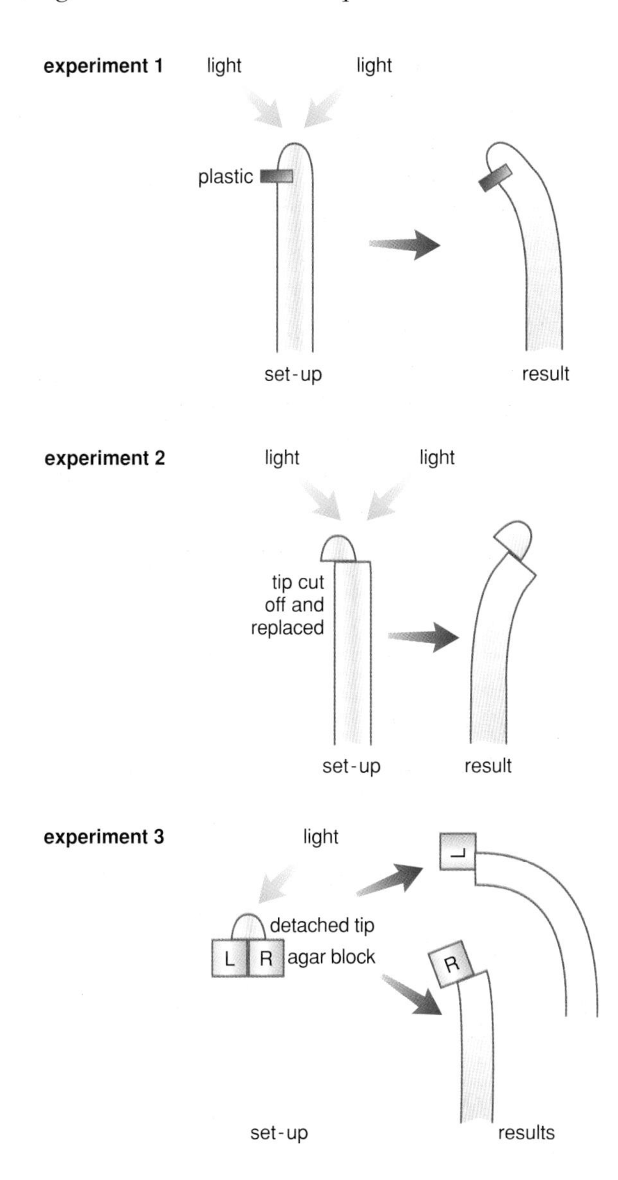

fig 34

a Explain why the shoot in experiment 1 bends to the left. *(2)*

b Explain why the shoot in experiment 2 bends to the right. *(2)*

c Account for the different amount of bending in the two shoots in experiment 3. *(2)*

◆ **7** Fig 35 shows the number of rods and cones found at different positions across the retina.

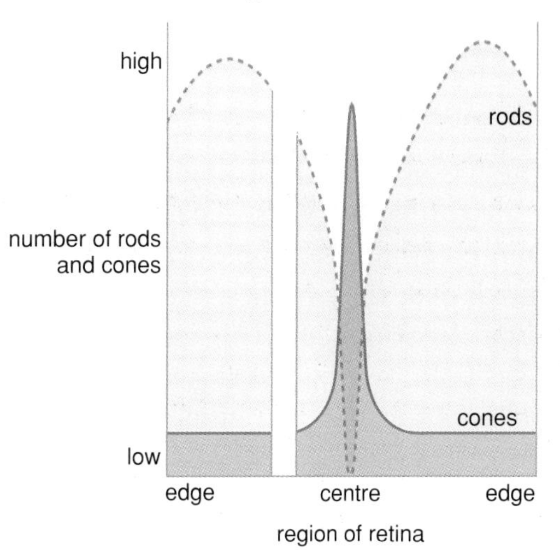

fig 35

a Copy the graph and mark with an A the position of the fovea. *(1)*

b Mark with a B the position of the blind spot. *(1)*

c A person is looking at a very distant star. Mark with a C the best place for the image to fall if the person wishes to see the star. *(1)*

d Would the person be looking straight at the star? Explain your answer. *(2)*

e Explain why the person would find it difficult to see the colour of the star. *(2)*

IDEAS AND EVIDENCE

8 In the 1800s, two scientists, Magendie and Bell, carried out a series of experiments in an attempt to work out how spinal nerves entered the spinal cord. In one animal they cut the sensory neurones coming from the leg, just before they entered the spinal cord. On another animal, they cut the motor neurones going to the leg.

◆ **a** Why is it possible to cut only the sensory neurones or only the motor neurones from a spinal nerve? *(2)*

◆ **b** What were the effects on the animal of cutting:

i the sensory neurones from the leg

ii the motor neurones to the leg? *(2)*

■ **c** How would Magendie and Bell have informed other scientists about their discoveries? How would this be different if they had made their discoveries today? *(4)*

Homeostasis

Introduction

Animal life has evolved from single-celled organisms to the complex life forms that we see around us today. As animals have become more and more complex, they have needed to have much more control over their bodies. We need to be able to regulate our own internal environment. This means that when it gets hot, or when it gets cold, our bodies stay at the same temperature. This enables us to survive even in adverse surroundings. It explains why we have been so successful as a species and colonised many different kinds of environment.

Some animals like snakes and lizards cannot control their own body temperature. When it gets too cold they have no choice but to slow down and sleep.

Other things that we need to be able to regulate include blood glucose level, water content, and metabolic wastes such as carbon dioxide and urea. In this Teaching block we will look at how the body manages to carry out these functions.

Check-up

Try the following questions. They will remind you of what you should know about homeostasis.

a The food we eat is broken down, or digested. The substances produced by digestion are absorbed into the bloodstream. From the list pick out the substances that are absorbed.

carbohydrates • glucose • protein • water • starch • fat • fibre

b Enzymes are special proteins in the body. What jobs do they do?

c The lungs absorb oxygen and excrete carbon dioxide. How does their structure help them to do this?

d Use a word equation to explain what happens to oxygen and glucose to release energy by aerobic respiration. How are substances transported around the body?

If you have difficulty, ask your teacher for a Summary sheet.

Contents of the Teaching block

9.1 Controlling glucose levels

Glucose is a product of digestion and is used for aerobic respiration. We will see that it is important for the body to keep the level of glucose constant. The hormone insulin has a vital role to play in ensuring this. We will see that people with diabetes do not produce enough insulin to control their blood glucose levels.

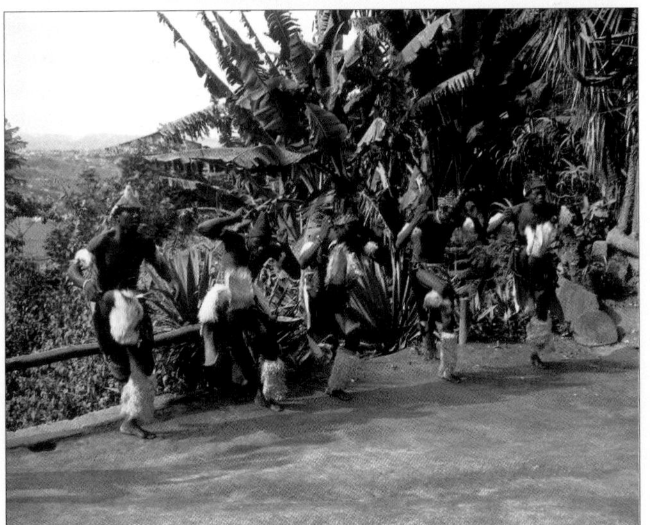

fig 1 | Some people live in cold places and others live in hot places

9.2 Controlling temperature

It is important for mammals and birds that their body temperature changes as little as possible. This enables them to live in hot places as well as cold ones. We will look at why we need to keep a constant body temperature and how our blood and skin achieve this.

9.3 Kidneys and lungs

These organs ensure that the levels of water and carbon dioxide in the body change as little as possible. We will look at how the kidneys regulate the water content of the body and how they rid the blood of waste. It is the job of the lungs to get rid of carbon dioxide and to absorb oxygen from the air.

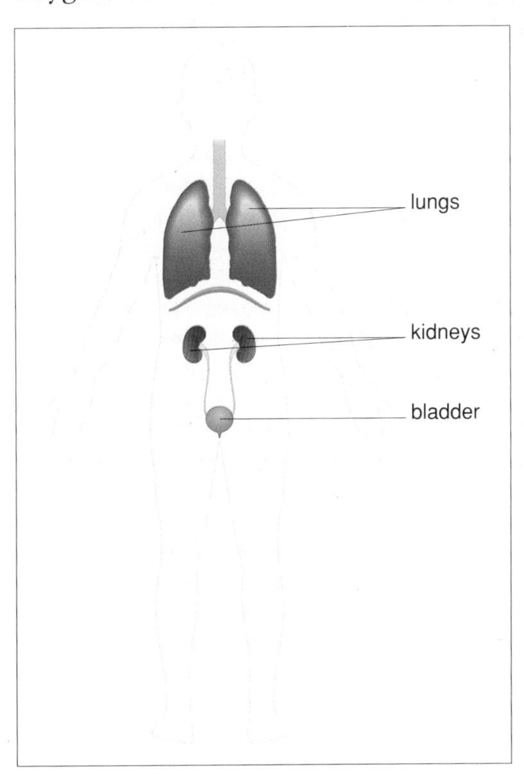

fig 2 | The organs of excretion

Links with other Teaching blocks

2.1 Enzymes
3.1 Aerobic respiration
4.2 Breathing rate and depth
8.1 Detecting stimuli

9.1 Controlling glucose levels

Key points

- Homeostasis means maintaining a constant internal environment in the body.
- It involves keeping the body's levels of glucose, water and metabolic waste unchanged.
- The hormone insulin is involved in homeostasis, keeping the level of glucose constant.

Maintaining a constant glucose level

Glucose is a product of the digestion of carbohydrates. It is a vital source of energy for the body. Glucose enters the bloodstream from the gut. It is used in respiration to release energy.

a Why does the body need a constant supply of energy?

b How would you expect the level of glucose in the blood to change after a meal?

c Why is the level of glucose in the blood normally low first thing in the morning?

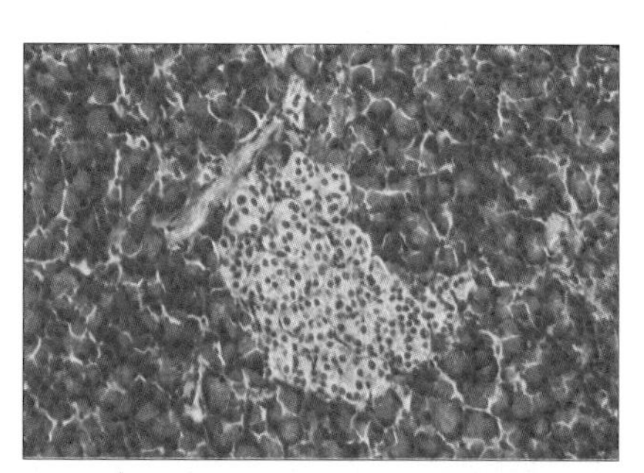

fig 3 | Insulin is released by islets of Langerhans in the pancreas, shown as the pale-pink central area (×100)

Insulin is a **hormone** that is produced in the **pancreas** (fig 3). It helps to control the level of glucose in the **blood.**

Insulin does this by promoting the conversion of any excess glucose that arrives in the blood after a meal into a substance called **glycogen**. Glycogen is not found in the blood, but is stored in the **liver** until it is required. It can then be turned back into glucose when needed (fig 4).

d If the level of glucose in the blood remains constant, how does the level of glycogen change after a meal?

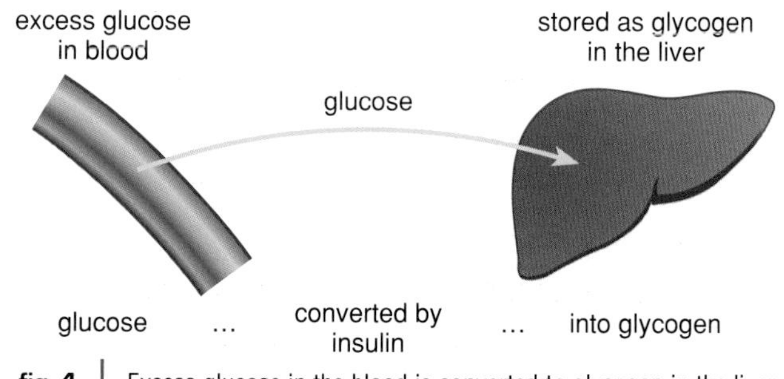

fig 4 | Excess glucose in the blood is converted to glycogen in the liver for storage

Some people have a condition called **diabetes.** Diabetics do not make enough insulin. This means that after digesting a large meal, the glucose level in their blood starts to rise. This can be very dangerous and may result in unconsciousness and even death.

e Why is it better for diabetics to eat small meals often rather than eating a large meal once a day?

Some diabetics produce no insulin at all and must have regular injections of insulin.

f Insulin is a protein. Why do diabetics have to inject insulin rather than swallowing tablets?

▷▷ Taking it further ▷▷

Insulin and genetic engineering

In the past insulin was extracted from the blood of animals. This process was both time-consuming and expensive. The insulin produced in this way inevitably contained some impurities, and some diabetics had adverse reactions to the insulin.

Scientists have now identified the human gene that codes for insulin and have been able to transfer the gene into microbes such as yeast and bacteria by using genetic engineering. These micro-organisms reproduce quickly, so they can rapidly produce large quantities of human insulin. This can be extracted easily, and provides a high quality product at a much cheaper price. Initially, however, some diabetics were not keen to use the new insulin because they got fewer warning signs that their blood sugar level was either too high or too low.

fig 5 | Insulin pen

Thinking further

- 1 Explain what is meant by the term homeostasis.
- 2 Explain why the pancreas produces the hormone insulin.
- 3 Peter eats a sandwich for his lunch. Explain what might happen to the carbohydrate in the sandwich after he has digested it.
- 4 Diabetics used to use insulin that was extracted from other animals such as pigs. Genetic engineering has now enabled scientists to produce human insulin. Suggest why using human insulin is better than using insulin extracted from an animal.
- 5 Suggest how scientists use genetic engineering to make human insulin.
- 6 Suggest how diabetics might be able to tell when they need to inject themselves with insulin.
- 7 Explain what would happen to the glucose in the blood of a diabetic if they injected too much insulin.

KEY WORDS

blood • **diabetes** • **glucose** • glycogen • **hormone** • **insulin** • liver • **pancreas**

9.2 Controlling temperature

Key points

- The skin is an important organ in temperature control.
- Changes in body temperature can prevent enzymes from working.
- The skin controls temperature by sweating and by regulating the flow of blood near the surface.
- Cells in the brain detect the core temperature of the body and regulate the skin's temperature-control mechanisms.

The need for a constant body temperature

A healthy person needs to maintain a constant body **temperature** of about 37 °C.

a Suggest what happens to a person whose body temperature:
  i drops too low
  ii gets too high.

The body needs to maintain a constant body temperature because most **enzymes** work at their best (**optimum**) efficiency at 37 °C (fig 6).

b What other factors can affect how well enzymes work?

Enzymes are responsible for controlling all the chemical reactions that take place in the body. If the temperature of the body drops, the rate of reaction slows down because the substrate molecules have less kinetic energy. If the temperature of the body increases, the enzymes change shape and become denatured. This change is permanent and means the enzymes are useless.

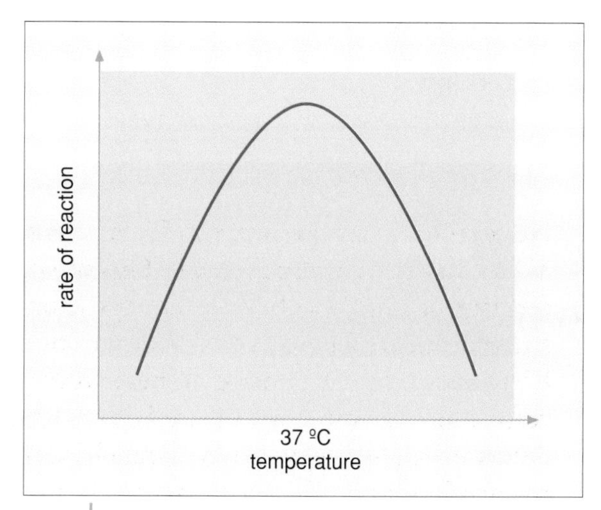

fig 6 The body's enzymes are most efficient at 37 °C

Maintaining a constant temperature

Fig 7 shows a cross-section of the **skin**. Fig 8 summarises the changes that occur if the body becomes too hot or too cold.

c Look at fig 7. What is the outer layer of skin called?

d Suggest the purpose of the muscle that is attached to the hair.

e What else can the skin do to conserve or to lose heat?

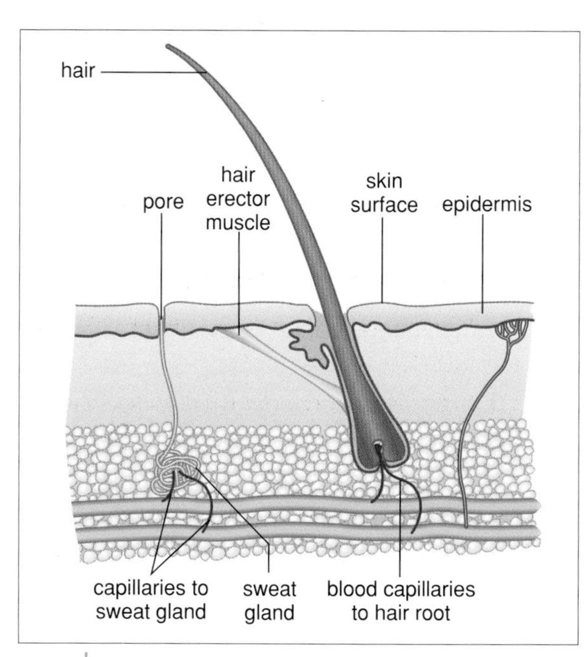

fig 7 A cross-section through the skin to show the parts involved in temperature regulation

when the body is too hot ...	when the body is too cold ...
blood vessels near the surface of the skin open and the skin becomes flushed with warm blood – this blood can then cool	blood vessels near the surface of the skin close down and the skin becomes whiter – the blood retains its warmth deep in the body
sweating increases and cools the skin as it evaporates	sweating is minimal
people relax and avoid activity that will generate heat	**shivering** starts – this releases energy in the form of heat

fig 8 | Changes that occur when the body gets too hot or too cold

Cells in the brain detect changes in the temperature of the blood and control how the skin responds in order to maintain a constant body temperature.

▷▷ Taking it further ▷▷

Temperature control is a balance

Normal body temperature is 37 °C. This is usually much hotter than our surroundings. This means that whether we feel hot or cold, the body is always losing heat to the surroundings. We do not cool down, however, because the body is constantly producing heat from the process of respiration. Body temperature is therefore maintained by a delicate balance between how much heat is produced by respiration, and how much heat is lost to the surroundings. If we lose heat too quickly we feel cold; if we do not lose enough heat we feel hot.

Thinking further

■ **1** Anita goes out in the snow to build a snowman. Her hands feel cold but her body temperature does not change.

a Why does Anita's body need to maintain a constant temperature?

b What would happen to Anita's enzymes if her body temperature were to change?

■ **2** Anita's skin starts to go white as it feels colder. How does Anita's skin prevent her body temperature from changing?

◆ **3** Suggest why, even on a warm day, we feel cold when we get out of a swimming pool.

KEY WORDS

blood vessels • enzymes • optimum • shivering • skin • sweating • temperature

Effect of size on heat loss.

9.3 Kidneys and lungs (1)

Key points

- The kidneys ensure that urea, excess water and excess salt are removed from the body.
- The lungs ensure that carbon dioxide is removed from the body.

What do the kidneys do?

One role of the **kidneys** is to remove **urea** from the blood. Urea is produced when we eat protein. Protein is digested into amino acids that are absorbed into the blood. The amino acids are used to build new materials in the body. However, we can use only some of these amino acids. The rest are broken down into urea, which is removed from the blood by the kidneys.

a Suggest why the body does not use all the amino acids that it gets from the digestion of protein.

b Explain what happens to the excess glucose that the body gets from digesting carbohydrate.

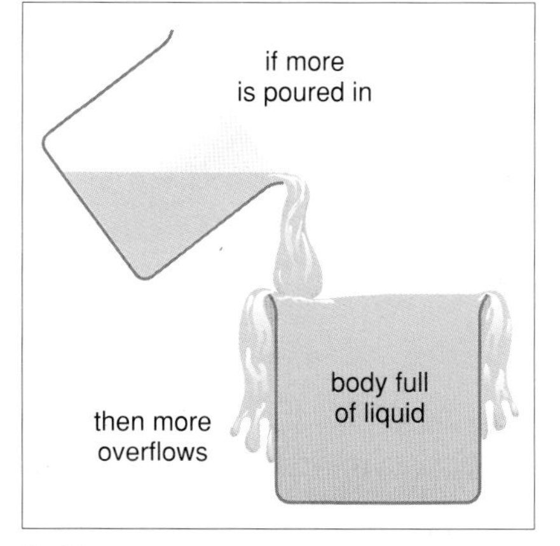

fig 9

Another role of the kidneys is to remove any excess **water** from the blood. This is called **osmoregulation**. You can think of the body as a container that is full. If more water enters, the container will overflow. We obviously take in water when we drink liquids.

c Suggest other ways in which we take water into our bodies.

We also produce water by aerobic respiration:

glucose + oxygen → carbon dioxide + *water*

All of the water taken in has to be lost as urine, sweat, or water vapour from the lungs.

d Draw a table to summarise the ways in which water enters the body and the ways in which it leaves the body.

Remember: the amount of water that enters the body must be balanced by the amount of water that leaves the body.

The amount of **salt** that enters the body must also balance the amount of salt that leaves it. This is another role performed by the kidneys.

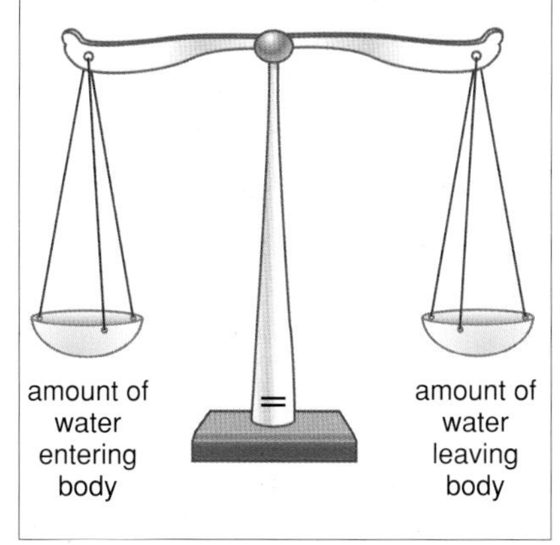

fig 10 | The amount of water entering the body must equal the amount of water leaving it

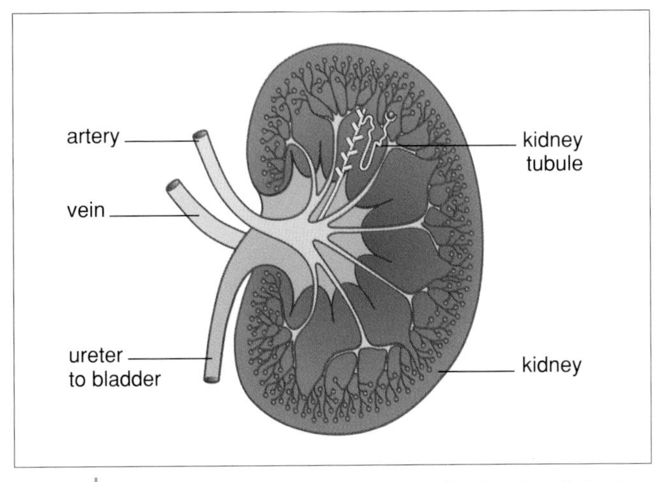

fig 11 | A cross-section through the kidney showing the internal structure

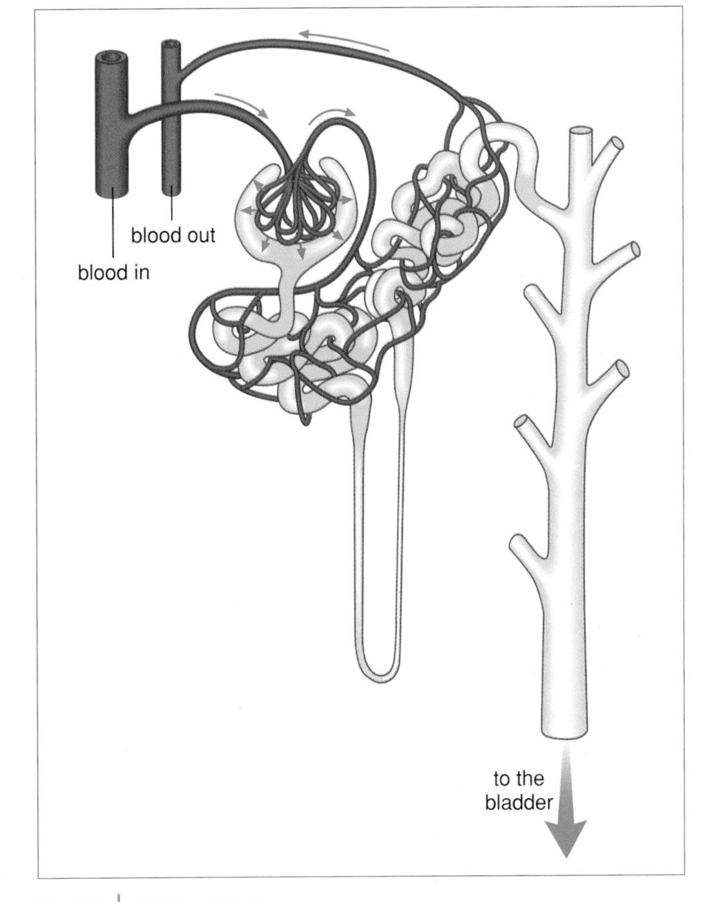

fig 12 | A kidney tubule

How the kidneys work

The kidneys (fig 11) are made up of thousands of small **kidney tubules** (fig 12). Blood enters the kidneys via small blood vessels that carry the blood at high pressure. This pressure causes small molecules such as water, salt, **glucose** and urea to be **filtered** out of the blood vessel. The liquid is then collected in the kidney tubules.

e Suggest why large molecules such as proteins are not filtered out of the blood.

However, the body now has a problem. If all this liquid were allowed to go through the tubules, it would end up in the bladder and be eliminated as **urine** (fig 13). This would mean that as well as getting rid of urea from the blood (a good idea!), the kidney would also get rid of useful molecules such as glucose and water (a bad idea!). To prevent this from happening, the tubules reabsorb most of the water and all of the glucose back into the blood (fig 14).

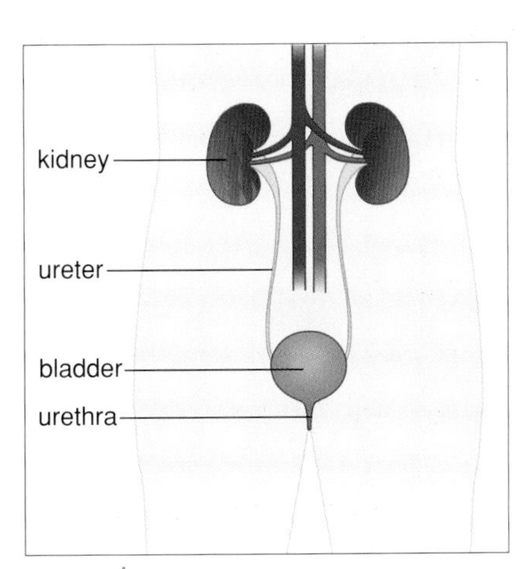

fig 13 | The urine leaves the kidney via the ureter and is stored in the bladder

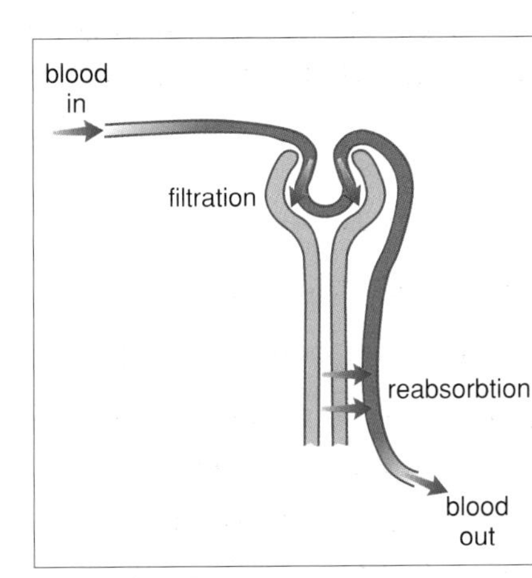

fig 14 | Filtration and reabsorption in the kidney tubule

f Explain why it would be a bad idea to get rid of all the water and glucose from the blood.

continued overleaf

9.3 Kidneys and lungs (2)

Sometimes, however, the body does not take in enough water to replace that lost by urine, sweat and evaporation from the lungs.

In this situation we feel thirsty and the kidney has to reabsorb as much water as possible back into the blood. The brain monitors how concentrated the blood is. The more concentrated the blood, the thirstier we get. As the blood gets more concentrated, the pituitary gland in the brain releases a hormone called antidiuretic hormone – **ADH** for short (fig 15). ADH makes the kidney tubules reabsorb more water into the blood by osmosis. It does this by making the tubules more permeable, allowing more water through.

g Explain why making the tubules more permeable will let more water be reabsorbed back into the blood.

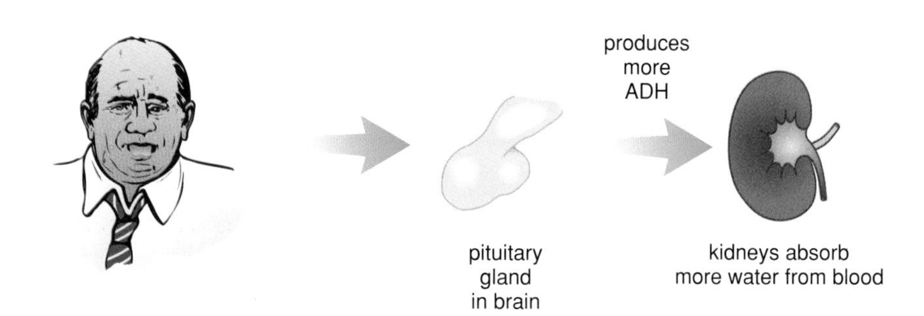

fig 15 | When we are thirsty, the pituitary gland releases ADH which makes the kidneys absorb more water from the blood

When the kidneys fail to work properly, people either need a transplant or have to use a kidney machine, which is called **dialysis**.

What do the lungs do?

Just as the kidneys get rid of unwanted urea, the lungs get rid of unwanted carbon dioxide. The carbon dioxide is produced by aerobic respiration:

Glucose + oxygen → *carbon dioxide* + water

The lungs absorb oxygen and excrete carbon dioxide

To understand how the lungs work there are four things to remember (fig 16):

- The lungs have a large surface area.
- The respiratory surface is very thin – one cell thick.
- The respiratory surface is moist.
- The lungs have a good blood supply.

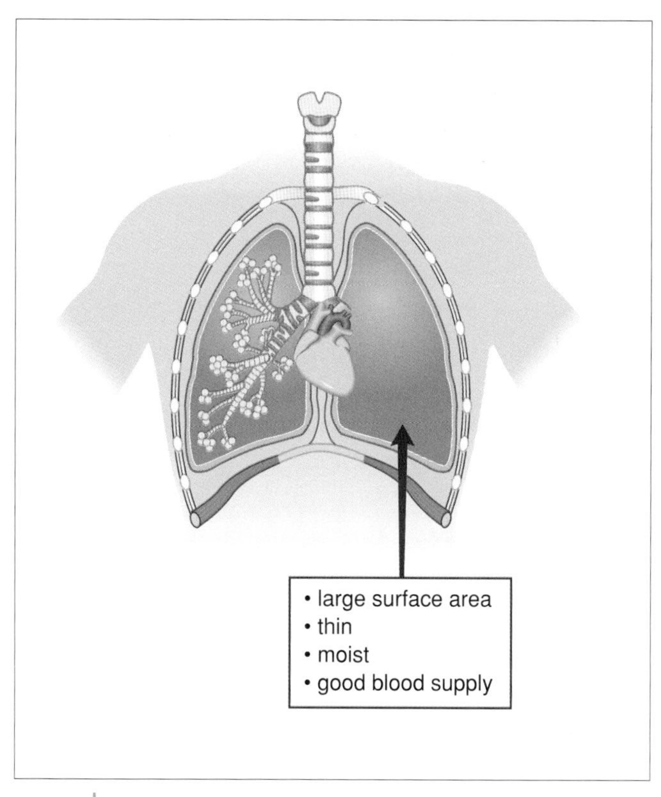

fig 16 | The lungs

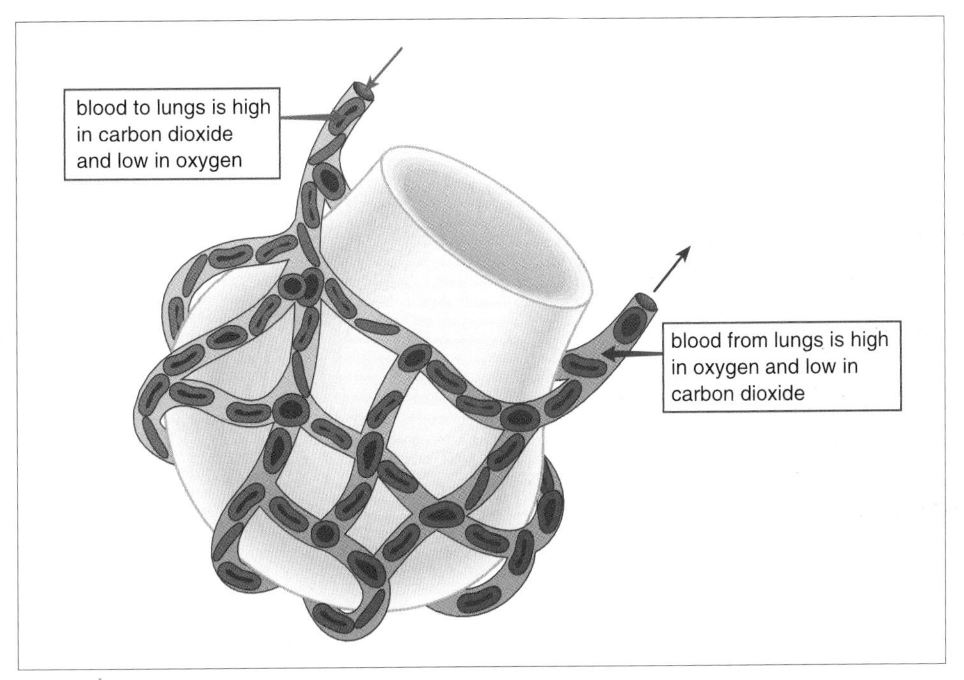

fig 17 | An air sac (alveolus) in the lungs

Carbon dioxide diffuses from the blood, where its concentration is high, through the thin moist cell membranes of the blood capillaries, and into the alveoli (the air spaces in the lungs) where the carbon dioxide concentration is low (fig 17).

Thinking further

■ **1** Name four substances that are filtered from the blood by the kidneys.

■ **2** Neil drinks lots of lemonade at a party. Explain what happens to this extra water that he drinks.

◆ **3** The next day Neil drinks very little. What does his body do to ensure that the retains enough water?

◆ **4** The body produces carbon dioxide before and after exercise. Explain how this carbon dioxide gets from the body into the lungs to be breathed out.

KEY WORDS

ADH • dialysis • filtered • glucose • kidneys • kidney tubules • osmoregulation • salt • urea • urine • water

Movement of ions through a membrane.

Questions on homeostasis

1 Copy the passage below and fill in the gaps using words from the following list. You may use each word once, more than once, or not at all.

breakdown • homeostasis • temperature • urea • water

It is most important that the body maintains a constant internal environment. This is called __________ . Three metabolic waste materials produced by the body are water, __________ and carbon dioxide. The kidneys are responsible for excreting excess __________ and they also eliminate urea. This is produced from the __________ of unwanted amino acids. The __________ of the body is controlled mainly by the skin. *(5)*

2 Water is one of the substances that the body has to keep at a constant level.

a List all the ways that water gets into the body. *(3)*

b List all the ways that water is lost from the body. *(3)*

3 Below are six sentences about the way our kidneys filter blood, but they are in the wrong order. Write the six sentences in the correct order. *(6)*

- This solution of small molecules passes down the kidney tubule.
- Blood enters the kidney under high pressure.
- The body cannot afford to lose all of this solution so most of the water and all of the glucose is reabsorbed.
- It is periodically eliminated as urine.
- The remaining fluid is passed to the bladder for storage.
- Small molecules like urea, water and glucose are filtered out of the blood.

4 Mary has a fried egg for breakfast. She knows that when the egg cools down, it will not return to a runny consistency like a raw egg. She has been told in her science class that this is because when proteins are heated their structure changes and they cannot return to their original shape.

a Enzymes work best at a specific temperature. What is the name given to this specific temperature? *(1)*

b Enzymes are proteins. What effect does temperature have on the way enzymes work? *(2)*

c Describe what will happen to the rate of reaction catalysed by an enzyme as the temperature increases from:

i 5 °C to 37 °C *(1)*

ii 37 °C to 70 °C. *(1)*

d Enzymes can also be denatured by changes in pH. Amylase is an enzyme found in saliva. It breaks down starch into simple sugars. Explain how changes in pH during digestion may affect how the enzyme works. *(2)*

5 Neil's mother asks him what he has been doing at school. He says he has learnt about homeostasis. His mum has never heard of this and asks him what it means. He tells her that homeostasis is 'maintaining a constant internal environment'. She still does not understand. Write an explanation of homeostasis that would explain it to Neil's mum. *(2)*

6 Some mammals can tolerate losing considerable amounts of water from their blood in hot dry conditions.

mammal	water lost in cm^3 per kg of body tissue per hour
gerbil	13
rabbit	5
human	2
camel	1

fig 18

a Describe the effect of body size on the rate of water loss. *(2)*

b The camel weighs 500 kg. Use the information in fig 18 to calculate the volume of water lost per hour in order to maintain a constant body temperature. (3)

7 Peter is a diabetic. The doctor tells him that he will need regular injections of the hormone insulin because his body is no longer making any of its own.

- **a** Where in the body is insulin normally made? *(1)*
- **b** Peter has a heavy meal. Shortly afterwards he tests his blood to find the level of glucose. What would he expect to find? *(1)*
- **c** Suggest what Peter should do so that the level of glucose in his blood returns to normal. *(1)*
- **d** Explain what happens to any excess glucose found in the blood of a non-diabetic person after they have eaten a heavy meal. *(2)*
- **e** The doctor tells Peter that he should have more, regular, small meals. Explain why the doctor gave Peter this advice. *(2)*
- **f** Peter's doctor tells him that he has a new type of genetically engineered insulin.
  - **i** Explain the difference between normal and genetically engineered insulin. *(2)*
  - **ii** The following steps describe the process of transferring a gene from one organism to another. Rewrite them in the correct order. *(5)*
    - Use the same enzyme to cut open the bacterial plasmid.
    - Insert the gene and join the DNA with a ligase enzyme.
    - Remove the human gene using a restriction enzyme.
    - Extract and purify the insulin.
    - Place the microbe in a fermenter to produce insulin. *(2)*

8 Anita plays in the snow but she has forgotten to put on some gloves. Very soon her hands begin to turn white and they start to feel very cold.

- **a** Explain what is happening in her skin as she is playing with the snow. *(2)*
- **b** She notices that she always produces more urine when she is cold than when she is hot. Use your knowledge of the kidney and the skin to explain why this happens. *(2)*
- **c** Explain the part played by the brain in the changes that happen in Anita's skin. *(1)*

9 Joy's skin is an organ that helps to regulate the temperature of her body. Whilst on holiday she stays out in the sun for too long.

- **a** Explain what will happen in her skin to ensure that her body temperature does not rise above 37 °C. *(3)*
- **b** Explain why it is important that Joy's body temperature stays at 37 °C. *(2)*
- **c** Joy realises that the hot sun has made her very thirsty. Explain the role of antidiuretic hormone (ADH) in ensuring that Joy retains as much water as possible in her blood. *(3)*

10 Some animals such as the camel are adapted to live in hot, dry conditions. Explain how each of the following helps the camel to survive in the desert.

- **a** The ability to allow its body temperature to rise by up to 7 °C without any harm *(1)*
- **b** Storing fat in its hump *(2)*
- **c** Having more hair on the upper part of its body, and less on the underneath part of its body *(2)*

IDEAS AND EVIDENCE

11 Many people die each year whilst waiting for a kidney transplant. Donor organs are in short supply and are not always of a close enough tissue match to avoid rejection. Some people manage to stay alive by using an artificial kidney machine but these are very expensive and are also in short supply.

- **a** What criteria do you think should be used when deciding who should be allowed to have one of the few artificial kidney machines? *(2)*
- **b** What ethical and moral decisions must be taken by the health authorities when deciding how to spend their limited budget? *(2)*
- **c** People can survive with just one kidney. This means that people who are closely related may be able to donate one of their kidneys to a relative and still lead an active and healthy life. Suggest whether this type of organ donation is a good idea and describe some of the problems that might arise. *(2)*

Inheritance and evolution

Introduction

This Teaching block explains how we have come to be what we are today. Over millions of years of evolution, life on Earth has developed from single-celled organisms into the wonderfully varied and complex life forms that we see around us today. For this variety to have occurred, genetic information had to be passed on from parent to offspring through the genes by the process of sexual reproduction. The variation that this produces allows evolution to occur, selecting those individuals that are best suited to survive in a changing environment. The survivors then go on to have offspring of their own and pass on these successful genes to the next generation. This Teaching block explains how all this happens.

Check-up

Have a go at the following questions. They will remind you of what you should know about inheritance and evolution.

a The following are examples of variation in humans.

height • **hair length** • **eye colour** • **scar tissue** • **weight** • **blood group**

Copy the list and for each word indicate whether the variation is caused by the environment, is due to inheritance, or is due to a mixture of both.

b The following is a list of living organisms:

dog • **eagle** • **rose** • **cod** • **moss** • **slug**

From the list write down an example of each of the following:

i a fish
ii a bird
iii a non-flowering plant
iv a mammal
v a flowering plant
vi an invertebrate.

c A farmer has a herd of cows. He wants them to produce more milk. Suggest how he could use selective breeding to improve the milk yield of his herd.

If you have difficulty, ask your teacher for a Summary sheet.

Contents of the Teaching block

10.1 Genes and chromosomes – 1

This spread looks at the structure of the chromosome and the role of DNA. We will learn that DNA not only has to store vast amounts of information, but also has to make copies of itself.

10.2 Genes and chromosomes – 2

Sex is determined by the chromosomes that we inherit from our parents. We will learn why there are two sexes and why equal numbers of boys and girls are born.

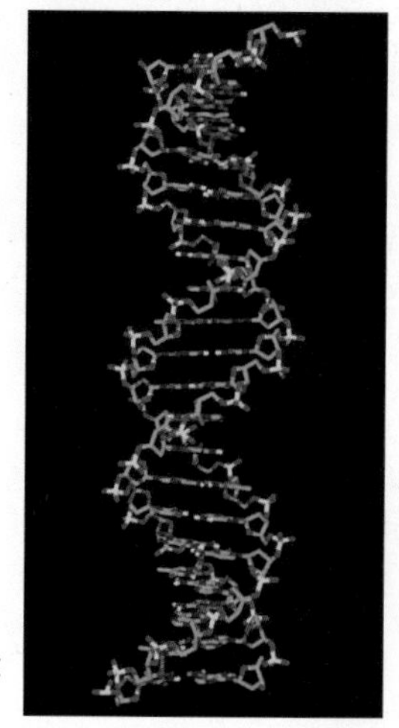

fig 1 Computer graphic showing a segment of a DNA molecule

Contents of the Teaching block (continued)

10.3 Variation – the causes

Variation within a species has several causes and it is important to allow evolution to occur. Some variation is environmental and some is genetic.

10.4 Variation – the consequences

Some variation is caused by mutations. Although mutations usually cause problems, on rare occasions they can be beneficial to a species.

10.5 Reproduction

Asexual reproduction produces identical copies of the parents; sexual reproduction does not and is a valuable source of variation for evolution.

10.6 Manipulating genes

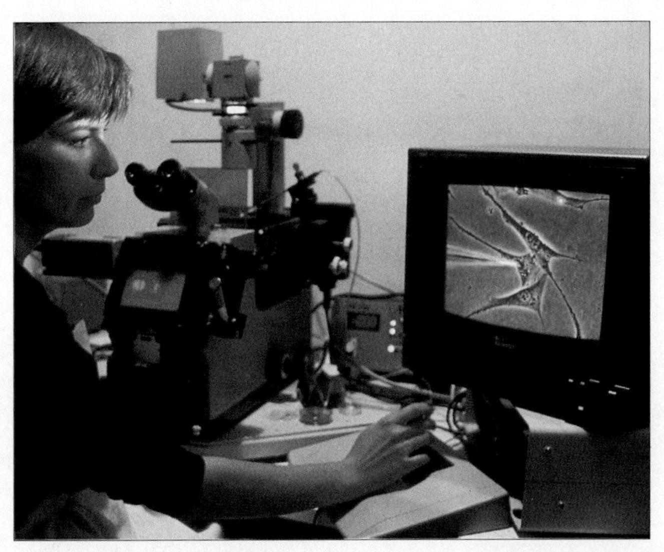

fig 2 | A gene being injected into a white blood cell nucleus

Manipulation of genes can provide massive benefits for mankind but brings with it many moral dilemmas. We will learn how genetic engineering is carried out and how selective breeding can be used to produce plants and animals with desirable characteristics.

10.7 Genetic crosses

In this spread we will learn how characteristics are inherited – passed on from one generation to the next.

10.8 Mendel and family trees

Genetic crosses work to strict rules, first discovered by a monk called Gregor Mendel. Mendel is often referred to as the father of modern genetics.

10.9 Evolution

Variation allows natural selection to occur. This ensures that organisms which best suit the environment are the ones that survive and reproduce. This is the basis of evolution.

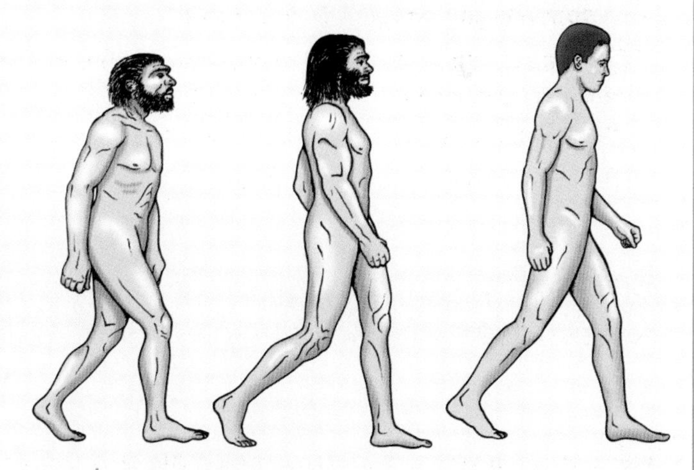

fig 3 | Human evolution

Links with other Teaching blocks

1.1 Cells
7.1 Distribution of organisms
7.6 Food production

10.1 Genes and chromosomes – 1

Key points

- The nucleus contains threads of DNA called chromosomes.
- Chromosomes are divided into sections called genes. Genes carry instructions and may be copied and passed on to the next generation.

Cell structure

Cells contain a **nucleus** that has a membrane around it. Inside the nucleus are the **chromosomes** (fig 4). The chromosomes are made from a molecule called deoxyribonucleic acid – **DNA** for short. This is a very long molecule. The DNA from one person is long enough to stretch all the way to the moon! This length of DNA fits into our cells because it is highly coiled to make it much shorter, and is divided into lengths called chromosomes.

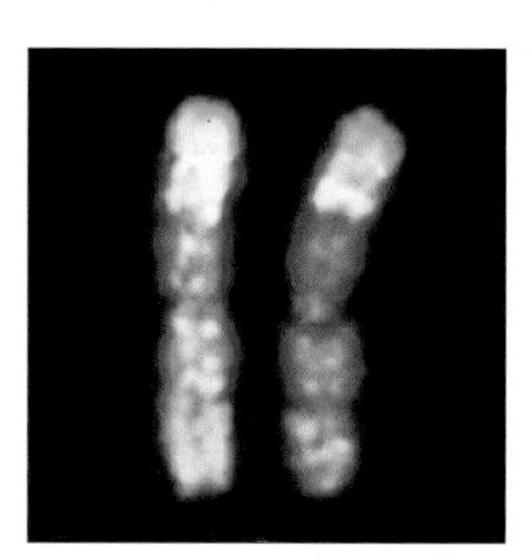

fig 4

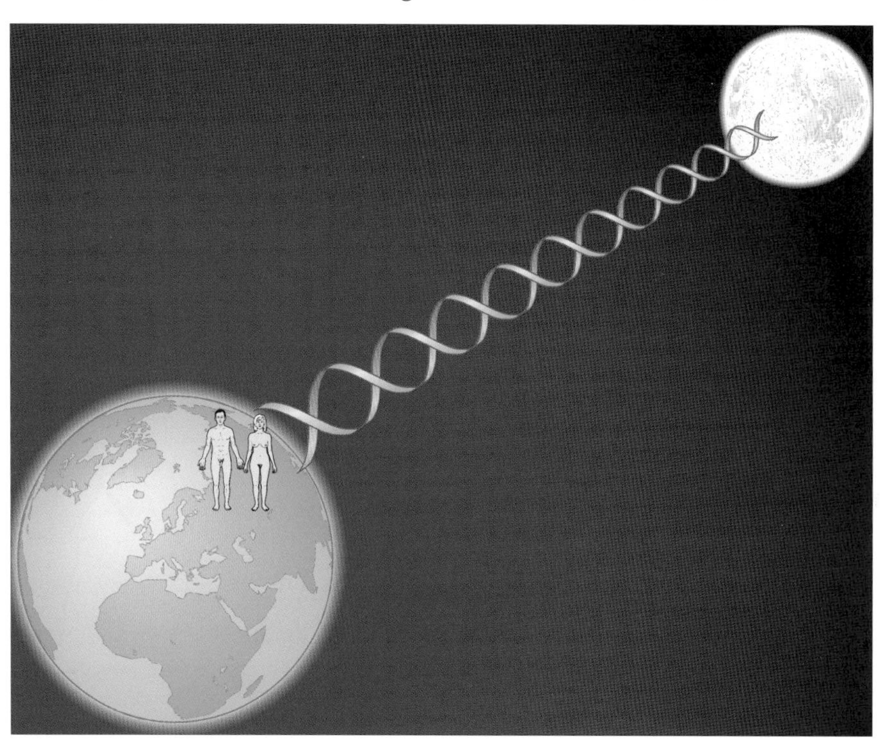

fig 5

DNA has two very important jobs to do:

- It must store a vast amount of information.
- It must be able to copy itself so that this information can be passed on to the next generation.

a Suggest why DNA has to be such a long molecule.

b Suggest why it is important that DNA makes an exact copy of itself, with as few mistakes as possible.

The DNA is divided into sections called **genes**. Each gene contains all the information for a single instruction. This instruction is how to make a single protein and is sometimes referred to as 'one gene – one protein'. The different proteins produced by the genes are used by the body in many ways.

c If all the chromosomes in a nucleus are represented by a book, and each chromosome is represented by a chapter, suggest what you think each gene is represented by.

We now know that the instruction from the gene is how to make a specific protein. Clearly the genes do not use the same language that we use to hold all this information.

We store information by using different combinations of the 26 different letters of the alphabet. Genes store information in the order of four different chemicals or **bases** which are called A, C, G and T for short.

AGCCTGAATCGAATCGGTCTCGACATGC

This language may look like gibberish but a foreign language like French looks gibberish to someone who cannot speak it!

d Suggest some other ways of storing information.

Thinking further

- **1** State two functions carried out by DNA.
- **2** Suggest why chromosomes are kept inside the nucleus, and are not allowed out into the cell where they may be damaged by all the cellular activity.
- **3** The English language has 26 letters. The DNA language has four letters. Suggest what implications this will have on the storage of genetic information.
- **4** A gene stores the information for making a protein. List three different jobs carried out by three different kinds of protein. For each, state the type of protein and the job that it does.

KEY WORDS
bases • chromosomes • DNA • genes • nucleus

Extraction of DNA.

10.2 Genes and chromosomes – 2

Key points

- Each species of organism has a specific number of chromosomes in the nucleus.
- Humans have 46 chromosomes (23 pairs) in each nucleus.
- The chromosomes that determine sex are called the X and Y chromosomes.

Chromosome number

The number of chromosomes varies from species to species. In humans there are normally 46 chromosomes (fig 6). On rare occasions there can be more than this but this always leads to health problems. Down's syndrome, for example, is caused by having an extra chromosome (see spread 10.4).

a Suggest why it is impossible for humans to have fewer than 46 chromosomes.

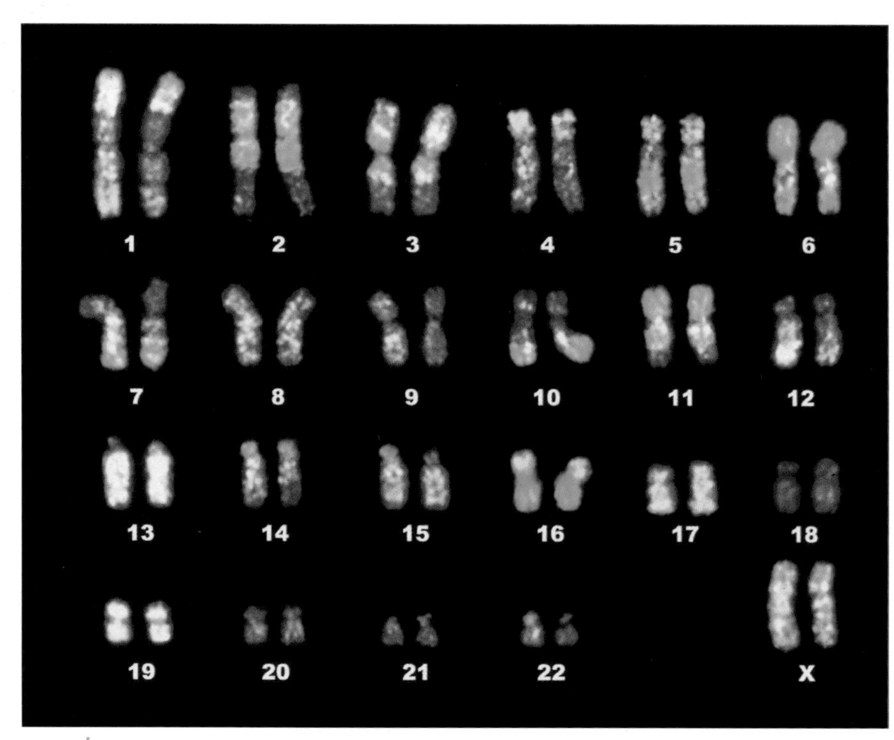

fig 6 | Human cells contain 46 chromosomes, which can be arranged in 23 pairs. These chromosomes are from a female because there are two X chromosomes.

Although different species have different numbers of chromosomes, they all have an even number. This is why in humans the **46 chromosomes** are usually referred to as **23 pairs**.

One of the pairs of chromosomes is called the **sex chromosomes**. There are two kinds of sex chromosome. One is called **X** and the other is called **Y**.

b Write down the different ways in which you can combine X and Y to make a pair of chromosomes.

You will have found that there are more than two different combinations. However, there are only two sexes: male and female. This means that only two of the possible combinations are used.

- Females have two X chromosomes and are XX.
- Males have one of each type of chromosome and are XY.

fig 7 | Males have sex chromosomes XY and females have XX

c State which chromosome is responsible for maleness. Explain your answer.

- Females inherit an X chromosome from their mother and an X chromosome from their father.
- Males inherit an X chromosome from their mother and a Y chromosome from their father.

The Punnett square in fig 8 shows how this can happen.

d What do you notice about the numbers of boys and girls that are likely to be born?

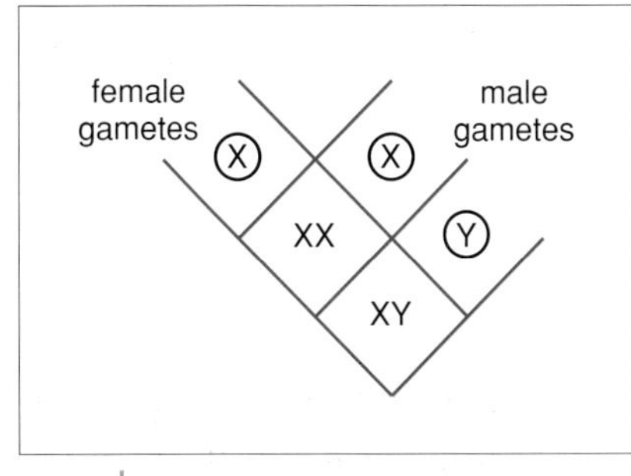

fig 8 | A Punnett square to show inheritance of sex

▷▷ Taking it further ▷▷

Sometimes things go wrong

Down's syndrome is caused when the chromosomes do not separate properly and one ovum gets an extra chromosome, making a total of 24. If the ovum is fertilised, the embryo ends up with 47 chromosomes.

This process can also happen with the sex chromosomes, so some people have an extra X or Y chromosome.

- Individuals who end up XXY look male but have small testes and are sterile.
- XXX individuals look female and are usually normal. There is, however, more chance of having a mental deficiency.
- XYY males are usually taller than normal.

It can be seen that having an extra sex chromosome usually has a less profound effect than having an extra one of the other chromosomes, as occurs with Down's syndrome.

IDEAS AND EVIDENCE

Scientists can select embryos and implant them into a mother. This could allow parents to choose the sex of their children. State, with reasons, whether you think this is a good idea.

Thinking further

■ **1** Joy inherited half her chromosomes from her mother and the other half from her father. Why is she unlikely to have an odd number of chromosomes?

■ **2** Which sex chromosomes will Joy have?

◆ **3** Joy intends to have children when she gets married. Draw a Punnett square to show the probabilities of having a boy and of having a girl.

◆ **4** Suggest why some species of organisms have more or fewer pairs of chromosomes than other species.

KEY WORDS

23 pairs • 46 chromosomes • sex chromosomes • X • Y

Other resources

Cutting up a karyotype to determine the sex of the individual.

10.3 Variation – the causes

Key points

- Variation within a species can be caused by the environment, by genetics, or by a combination of both.
- Some genetic variation can arise from mutations.
- Mutations can be caused by faulty copying of the gene, or by environmental factors that damage the gene such as harmful chemicals and radiation.

Types of variation

- Some **variation** is **inherited.** People from near the equator have dark skin whereas people from more northern countries have pale skin.
- Some variation is environmental. Hair length is often determined by the culture people live in.
- Some variation, such as intelligence, height and weight, is thought to be a combination of the two. The genes determine the range and the environment determines where in that range we will be.

fig 9 | Skin colour is inherited

a State how much of a person's intelligence you think is inherited from their parents, and how much you think is due to how well they are taught by their parents and teachers.

Explain your answer.

A scientist called Francis Galton thought that all intelligence was inherited, and that our parents and teachers had nothing to do with how intelligent we could become.

b Explain whether you think Francis Galton was right or wrong in his belief.

fig 10 | Hair length is often determined by a person's culture

Causes of genetic variation

Genetic variation can arise from **mutations**. Mutations are changes that happen to the chromosomes or to the sequence of the chemical bases. When the DNA has been copied, the cell divides and each cell has one of the copies (fig 11). Sometimes one cell will get one chromosome too few – it dies – and one cell gets one chromosome too many – a mutation.

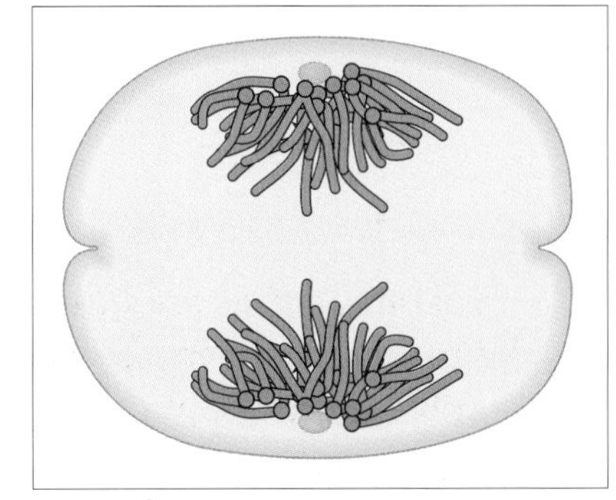

fig 11 | Chromosomes become visible during cell division

Sometimes when the DNA is being copied an error is made in one of the bases. This is like a spelling mistake.

c Copy out the three key points at the beginning of this spread but make three deliberate spelling mistakes. Give them to a friend. Does the text still make sense to your friend or is it now just gibberish? Try changing the letter 'e' to 'o' in the word gene.

If a chemical base is changed, it may make very little difference or it may have a profound effect on the organism. Radiation and certain chemicals can damage the DNA and change the sequence of the chemical bases. This can completely alter the type of protein that the gene makes.

Taking it further

Types of mutation

- **Deletion** – a single base or number of bases is removed from the DNA. It is rather like having a letter or word missing from a page of text.
- **Insertion** – a base or number of bases is inserted in the DNA. It is rather like having extra letters inserted into a page of text. It usually results in gibberish.
- **Translocation** – a section of the DNA is removed and replaced somewhere else in the DNA.
- **Inversion** – a section of the DNA is turned round to face the other direction. It is rather like having several letters or words printed back to front.

Most of these changes to the DNA usually result in the gene being unable to make the protein properly.

Thinking further

1 Describe three differences between yourself and a friend. For each difference state whether it is caused by the environment, genetics, or a combination of both.

2 Explain why an error in copying the sequence of chemical bases will lead to a mutation.

3 Intelligence is a result of both genetic and environmental factors. Studies have been done on identical twins that were separated at birth. The intelligence of each twin was measured and the findings compared. Explain how this technique could be used to find out how much of a twin's intelligence was due to the environment and how much was inherited from the parents.

KEY WORDS
inherited • mutation • variation

10.4 Variation – the consequences

Key points

- Most mutations are harmful but on rare occasions they may be useful.
- Some mutations can be inherited and passed from generation to generation.
- Sexual reproduction also produces variation.

Useful mutations

Useful mutations are very rare.
Because mutations are random events that change the structure of the DNA, it is highly unlikely that a mutation will be beneficial to the organism. Imagine a young child playing with your television and video recorder. It is possible that when they have finished playing you would have a better picture than the one you started with but the most likely event is that you would not have any picture at all!

Random changes seldom lead to improvements. When they do, however, they have a massive impact on the evolution of the species. The evolution of feathers on birds' wings possibly started with a useful mutation.

a Make a list of other useful mutations that might have occurred in the past.

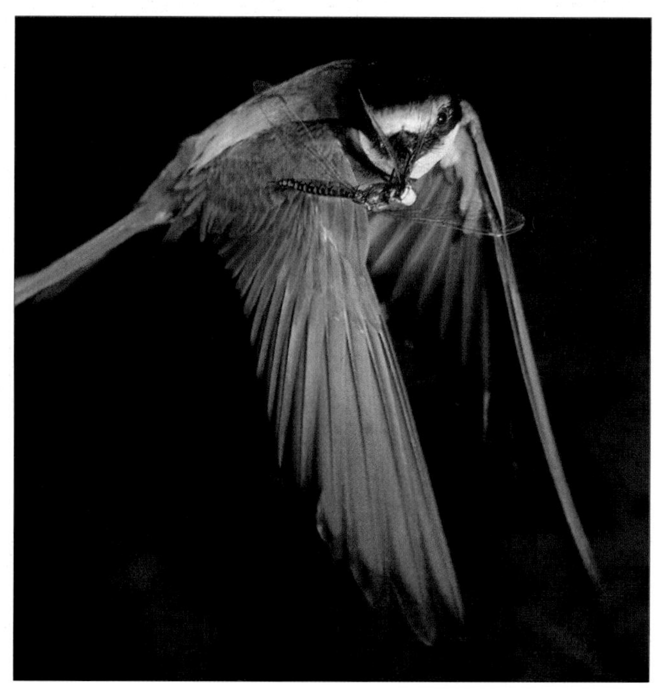

fig 12

Harmful mutations

Most mutations have harmful results and usually lead to illness or death of the person concerned.

Cystic fibrosis

Cystic fibrosis is a disease that is inherited and is caused by a single mutated gene. It affects about 1 in 2000 children. One consequence of this mutation is that secretions like mucus are much thicker and stickier than normal.

b Describe the effect this will have on the lungs.

The sticky mucus also causes blockages in the **pancreas** so that digestive enzymes are not released and food such as fat and protein cannot be digested properly.

c Suggest the kind of treatment needed by someone with cystic fibrosis.

Down's syndrome

Down's syndrome is caused when a person has an extra chromosome, making a total of 47 instead of the normal 46 (fig 13). The extra chromosome is inherited from the mother, and the chance of this happening increases with the age of the mother. The most frequent features of Down's syndrome are low intelligence and changes to facial features (fig 14). People with Down's syndrome also tend to have a kind and loving personality.

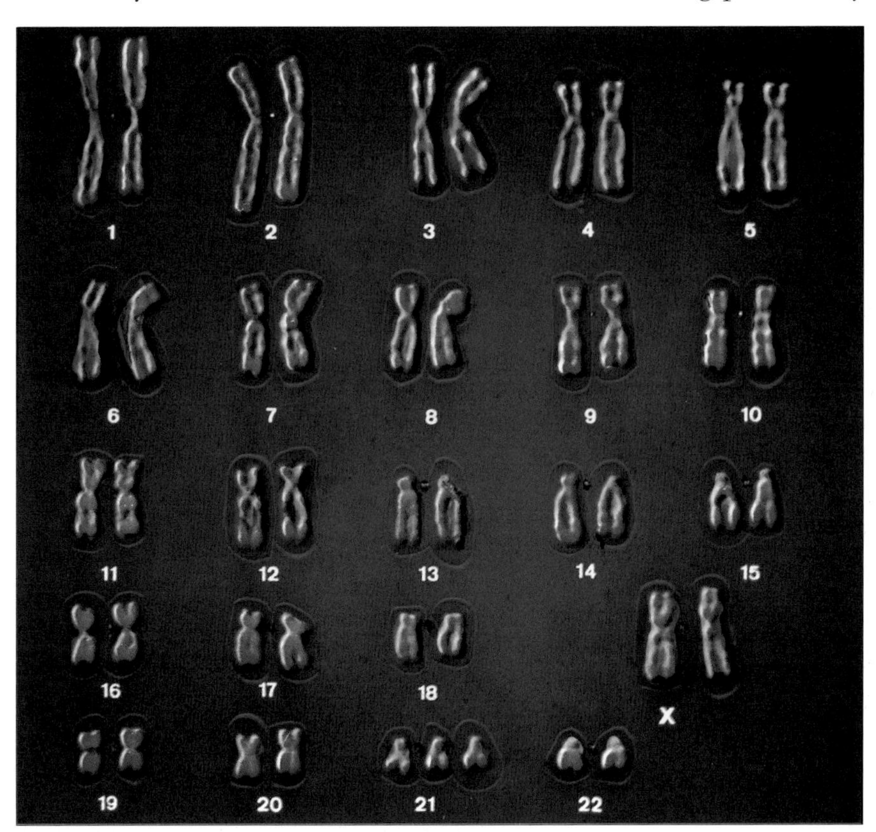

fig 13 | In a person with Down's syndrome, the cells have an extra chromosome 21, making 47 chromosomes altogether

fig 14 | A child with Down's syndrome

IDEAS AND EVIDENCE

It is possible to determine whether a pregnant mother is carrying a baby with Down's syndrome as early as ten weeks into the pregnancy. Discuss the moral dilemma the mother faces in trying to decide whether to have the pregnancy terminated if the test result is positive.

Thinking further

■ **1** Suggest why useful mutations are more likely than harmful mutations to survive and be passed on to the next generation.

■ **2** Explain why most mutations that occur are harmful and that very few will be useful.

◆ **3** Suggest a test that could be used to find out if a pregnant mother is carrying a child with Down's syndrome.

KEY WORDS

cystic fibrosis • Down's syndrome • pancreas

Other resources

Cutting up karyotype of Down's syndrome.

10.5 Reproduction

Key points

- Sexual reproduction is a source of genetic variation – all the offspring are different.
- Asexual reproduction is not a source of genetic variation – it produces identical copies called clones.

Sexual reproduction

Children, just like their parents, have 46 chromosomes in each cell. This means that they cannot receive all the chromosomes from each parent, or they would end up with 92 in each cell.

a How many chromosomes does a child inherit from each parent?

When the father's **sperm** and the mother's **ova** are made, they must each contain half the normal number of chromosomes (fig 15). This type of cell division is called **meiosis.**

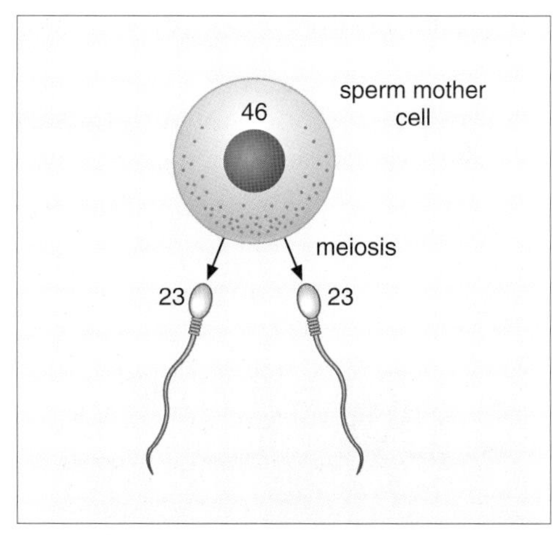

fig 15 | Sperm production – each sperm has 23 chromosomes

Each sex cell or **gamete** must have one chromosome from each pair. This ensures that each sex cell has one set of instructions for making a new baby.

b The mother and father have 23 chromosomes each. The baby gets one chromosome in each pair from each parent. How many possible combinations of chromosomes do you think there are?

When the ovum is fertilised by a sperm, the chromosome number returns to the normal 46 (fig 16). It is pure chance which sperm will **fertilise** the ovum.

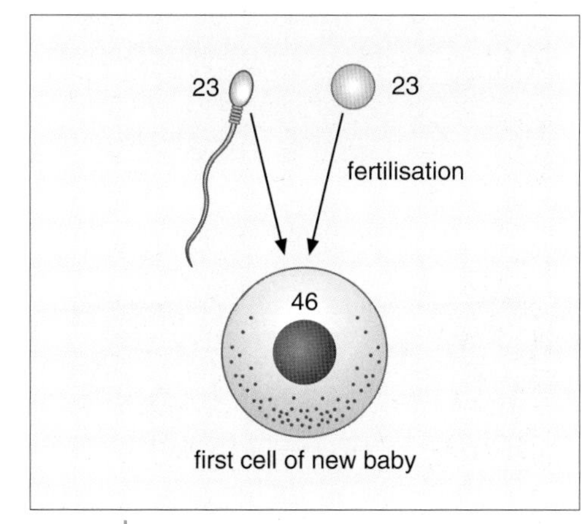

fig 16 | The sperm and ovum fuse at fertilisation, producing a cell with 46 chromosomes

How does sex lead to variation?

- Gametes are produced by meiosis and each contains a different combination of genes.
- There is the possibility that any sperm could fertilise any ovum. This leads to an enormous possible number of combinations of genes in the baby. This is why no baby looks identical to its parents, and why no two people ever look the same.

c Identical twins are the one exception to this rule. Suggest why identical twins look the same.

d Explain why non-identical twins do not look the same.

Asexual reproduction

Asexual reproduction occurs when cells divide to produce identical copies of themselves. Organisms do this when they grow. It is important to remember that all the offspring from asexual reproduction have identical gene combinations to their parents. They are called **clones**.

This type of cell division is called **mitosis**. Each new cell ends up with the full number of chromosomes (fig 17).

Some plants reproduce by asexual reproduction. Examples include bulbs, stem tubers like the potato, and runners like strawberries (fig 18). Commercial growers take cuttings of plants to make clones.

e State the advantages to the grower of taking cuttings rather than waiting for seeds to grow.

Commercial growers also use **micropropagation** of plants. Plants are grown from a few cells in a Petri dish. Vast numbers of cloned plants can be grown in controlled and sterile conditions.

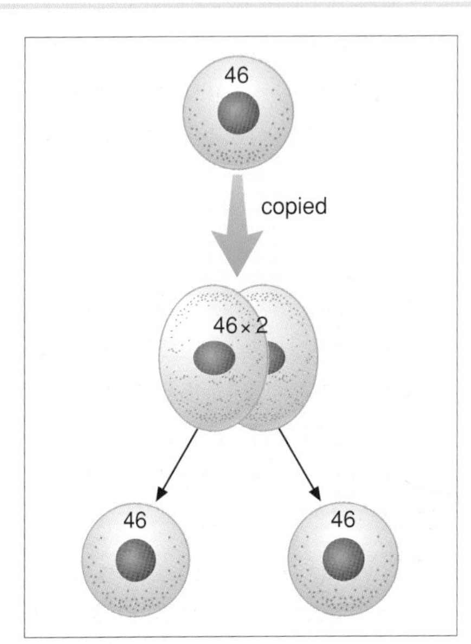

fig 17 | Cells produced during mitosis have the full number of chromosomes, which is the same number as in the parent cell

fig 18 | Potato stem tubers (left), strawberry runners (middle) and bulbs (right) are all examples of ways in which plants reproduce asexually

Thinking further

◆ **1** List the differences between sexual and asexual reproduction.

◆ **2** List the similarities between sexual and asexual reproduction.

KEY WORDS

clone • **fertilise (fertilisation)** • **gamete** • meiosis • micropropagation • mitosis • **ova/ovum** • **sperm**

10.6 Manipulating genes

Key points

- Scientists can now make clones of animals as well as of plants.
- Genes can be transferred from one organism to another.
- Genetic engineering brings major benefits, but also moral dilemmas.

What is genetic engineering?

Genetic engineering is the ability to alter **DNA**. For example, a **gene** from one organism can be transferred into the DNA of a totally different organism. In some cases, all the DNA can be removed from a cell and replaced with the DNA from another organism. This is possible because, unlike humans, who use lots of different languages and often cannot communicate with one another, DNA uses a common chemical language that is the same in all living organisms. The same language is used in a daffodil as is used in a fish.

a Suggest how someone from France could communicate with someone from China if they do not speak each other's language.

Dolly the sheep (fig 19) was the first animal to be produced by **genetic cloning** (fig 20).

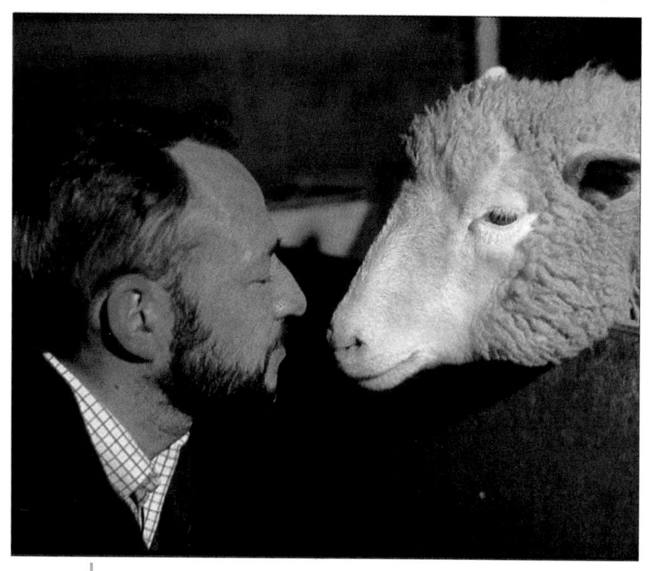

fig 19 | Dolly the sheep and her creator, Bill Ritchie

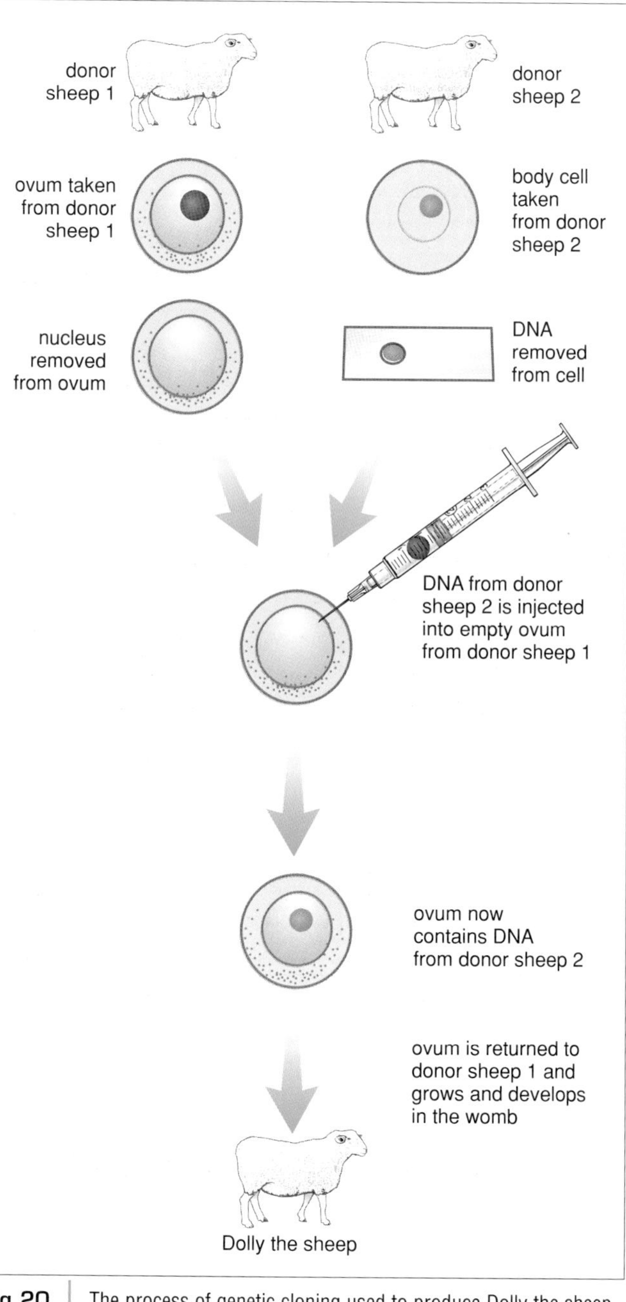

fig 20 | The process of genetic cloning used to produce Dolly the sheep

- An ovum was taken from a female donor sheep and its nucleus removed.
- The whole of the DNA was extracted from the cell of another sheep.
- This DNA was inserted into the empty ovum.
- The ovum was returned to the donor sheep and allowed to grow and develop in the womb.

In China, this technique is being done using rabbit eggs to host DNA from giant pandas. This will enable many ova to be produced and will hopefully prevent the panda from becoming extinct.

b State, with reasons, whether you think it would be a good idea to produce humans by genetic cloning.

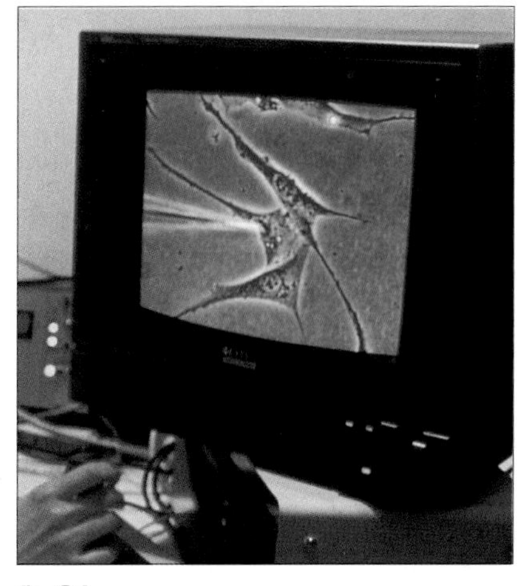

fig 21

Selective breeding

Selective breeding has been used for centuries to produce plants and animals with required traits. Fig 22 shows some examples.

organism	reason
Husky dogs	to pull sledges
wheat	greater yield
potato	more flavour
tomato	resistance to disease

fig 22 | Examples of traits that humans have bred into plants and animals

c Make a list of five more examples.

Selective breeding is done by choosing parents with the required traits. These are then bred to produce offspring. Sexual reproduction will ensure that there is variation. Some of the offspring will have better traits than their parents. Offspring with a desirable trait are then selected and bred again. The process is repeated for several generations.

Thinking further

■ **1** Some fish make a type of antifreeze which enables them to live in cold Arctic waters. Suggest how scientists might produce a lettuce plant that could grow during the winter.

◆ **2** A farmer wants his chickens to lay bigger eggs. He decides to use selective breeding to increase egg size. Only some of the chicken's genes will control the size of the egg. Use your knowledge of genetics to explain why there will be a limit to the maximum size of egg that the farmer will be able to get.

KEY WORDS

DNA • genes • genetic cloning • selective breeding

10.7 Genetic crosses

Key points

- Genes can be dominant or recessive.
- A cross between a dominant gene and recessive gene will give a ratio of 3:1 for the dominant and the recessive traits.

A monohybrid cross

Humans inherit 23 chromosomes from each parent. Each set of 23 is a complete set of instructions for making a new human being. That means that each nucleus contains two complete sets of instructions, one from the mother and one from the father.

For example, some people can roll their tongue and some cannot (fig 23). The gene for tongue rolling has two instructions or **alleles**, one from each parent. Sometimes these alleles agree about whether the person can or cannot roll their tongue – no problem! Sometimes, however, these alleles disagree about whether a person can roll their tongue – problem! When the two alleles disagree, they cannot both be right. However one of them is **dominant** and the other is **recessive**.

fig 23 | A tongue roller and a non-tongue-roller

allele from mother	allele from father	baby
✓	✓	David ✓✓
✗	✗	Mary ✗✗
✓	✗	Peter ✓✗
✗	✓	Joan ✓✗

✓ = tongue roller
✗ = non-tongue-roller

fig 24

In the example we are using about tongue rolling, the allele for tongue rolling is dominant, and the allele for non-tongue-rolling is recessive.

Instead of using ✓ and ✗, it is more usual to use a capital letter for dominant (in this case, T) and a lower-case letter for recessive (**t**).

a Look at fig 24. State which of David, Mary, Peter and Joan will not be tongue rollers.

b State which babies in fig 24 will be tongue rollers.

When the alleles are the same, the gene is **homozygous**. When the alleles are different the gene is **heterozygous.**

c State which two babies in fig 24 are heterozygous for tongue rolling.

The expression of the gene is called the **phenotype**. The phenotype of David is that he can roll his tongue.

d State the phenotype of Peter in fig 24.

The combination of alleles in the gene is called the **genotype**. The genotype of David for tongue rolling is **TT**.

e State the genotype of Joan in fig 24.

The inheritance of tongue rolling

Let us assume that the mother is homozygous for tongue rolling – she has genotype **TT** – and that the father is homozygous for non-tongue-rolling – genotype **tt.** The mother will only be able to produce gametes with the tongue-rolling allele **T** and the father will only be able to produce gametes with the non-tongue-rolling allele **t.**

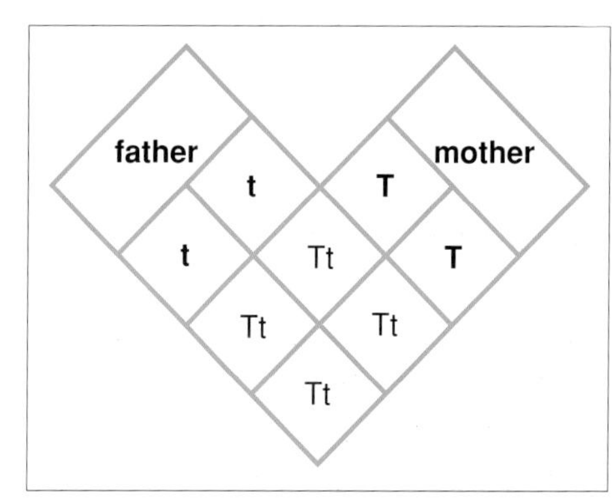

fig 25

The first generation of any cross is called the **F1 generation.** When two offspring of the F1 generation are crossed (which can occur in animals or plants, but not in humans) the offspring are called the **F2 generation.**

When each parent is homozygous for one of the alleles, all the F1 generation are heterozygous (fig 25). Human brothers and sisters cannot marry and have children to produce an F2 generation. However, if two heterozygous adults have children, the offspring shown in the Punnett square in fig 26 (continuing the example above) are possible.

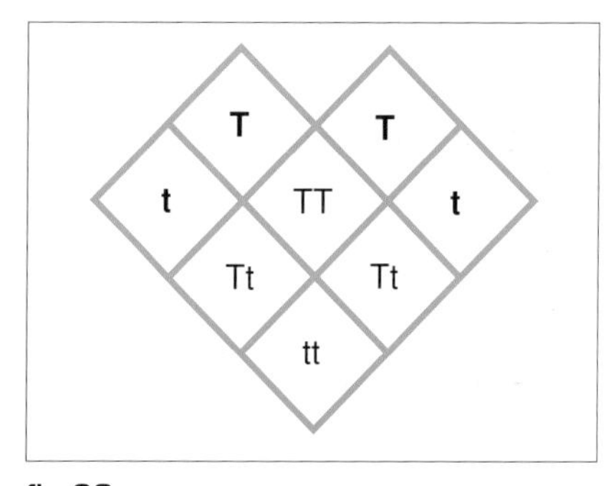

fig 26

The ratio of offspring with the dominant and the recessive trait is 3:1. This means that, on average, three-quarters of the offspring will have the dominant phenotype – tongue rolling in the example – and one-quarter will have the recessive trait – non-tongue-rolling.

Thinking further

■ **1** Explain what you notice about the phenotype of an F1 generation from two parents who are homozygotes.

◆ **2** Explain why the phenotypes in the F2 generation from two heterozygotes are always in a 3:1 ratio.

KEY WORDS

allele • dominant • F1 and F2 generation • genotype • heterozygous • homozygous • phenotype • recessive

10.8 Mendel and family trees

Key points

- Gregor Mendel was a monk who investigated inheritance by doing experiments with garden peas.
- Later, when science appreciated the data that he collected, his efforts led to an understanding of modern genetics.
- Mendel's laws of inheritance can be used to work out the genotypes of organisms.

Gregor Mendel

Mendel was an Augustinian monk who lived at the monastery at Brno in the Czech Republic. He collected thousands of seeds from several varieties of garden peas. From his breeding experiments he concluded that individual characteristics were passed from generation to generation as discrete packets of inheritance. Much later these discrete packets of inheritance were called genes.

fig 27 | Gregor Mendel (1822–1884)

Mendel produced two laws of genetics.

- The **law of segregation** – this simply means that when gametes are produced, the two alleles will separate. One allele will go into one gamete and the other allele into another.
- The **law of independent assortment** – this simply means that any gamete from the father can fertilise any gamete from the mother.

a Look at the Punnett squares on spread 10.7. How do they show that Mendel's two laws are true?

Mendel was fortunate that he chose to study peas. The genetics of many other plants is much more complicated. Some people think that his results were too good to be true; however, the more likely explanation is that Mendel was a very observant man with lots of spare time (and patience!) to do the laborious work required.

He presented the results of his work to the Natural History Society in 1865. However, he was so far ahead of his time that no one could explain his results. It was not until much later, when good quality microscopes were available and Watson and Crick had discovered DNA, that Mendel's work could finally be explained.

IDEAS AND EVIDENCE

Explain the difficulties faced by Mendel in performing experiments that at the time could not be explained by scientific discovery.

Family trees

Family trees (fig 28) are a useful way of working out the genotypes of individuals.

b State the genotype of Maurice. Remember that Helen must have inherited one allele from each parent.

c State the genotypes of Lynne's three children: Russell, Robin and Rebecca.

d State why Rachel must be heterozygous for tongue rolling.

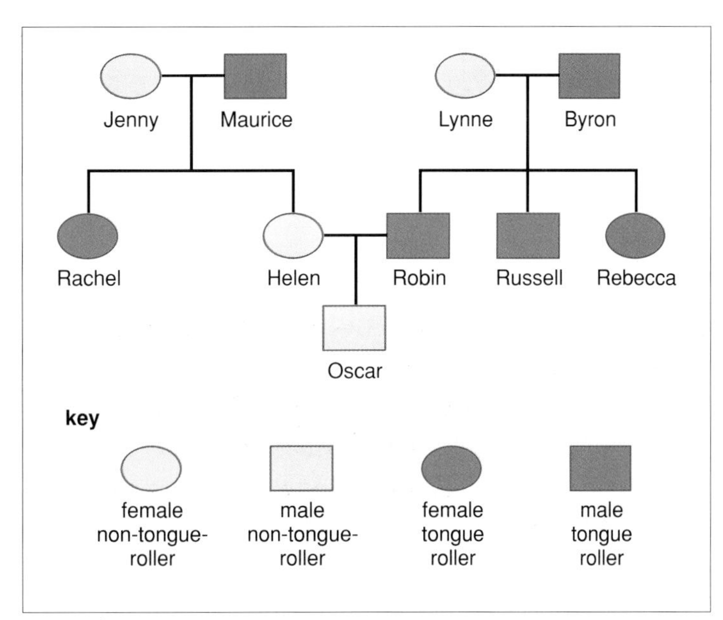

fig 28 | A family tree to show the inheritance of tongue rolling

Test crosses

Information about family trees is not usually available in biology, particularly when looking at organisms other than humans. However, it is still possible to work out the genotype of an organism. If the unknown genotype is crossed with a homozygous recessive individual, the resulting offspring will indicate the genotype of the unknown parent. This is called a recessive backcross.

e Draw two Punnett squares to show the genotypes of the children produced if the genotype of one parent was ✗✗ and the genotype of the other parent was either ✓✗ or ✓✓.

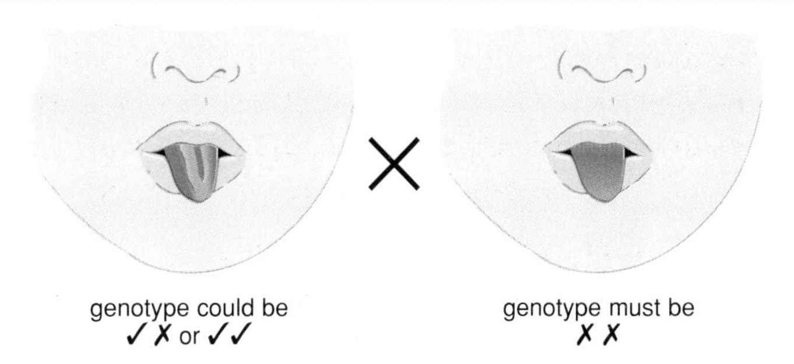

fig 29

f What do you notice about the phenotypes of the children if the genotype of the unknown parent was ✓✗ or ✓✓?

This means that if you can roll your tongue and one of your parents cannot, you must be heterozygous – ✓✗ – and not homozygous – ✓✓.

Thinking further

1 Try to produce a tree of your own family to show the genotypes of those who are tongue rollers and those who are not.

KEY WORDS

law of segregation • law of independent assortment • Mendel

10.9 Evolution

Key points

- Evolution occurs as a result of the variation produced by sexual reproduction.
- Natural selection ensures that those individuals that best suit their environment are the ones that survive.
- Evolution occurs when the environment changes.
- Fossils provide us with a record of past evolution.

fig 30 | Charles Darwin (1809–1882)

Charles Darwin

Darwin lived from 1809 to 1882. He worked as a naturalist on board the ship HMS Beagle. He spent many years observing the organisms living on the Pacific Islands. He noticed four things.

1. Most organisms produce large numbers of offspring, most of which die or get killed. For example, a frog lays about 2000 eggs, but only a few of these will end up as mature adult frogs.
2. Population numbers tend to remain fairly constant over long periods of time.
3. Sexual reproduction ensures that all the offspring are slightly different from each other. This is called **variation**.
4. These variable characteristics are inherited from the parents.

From these four facts Darwin produced his *theory of* ***evolution*** *by* ***natural selection*** which attempted to explain the wonderful variation and complexity that we find in all living things.

If Darwin tried to explain the evolution of the peppered moth, his thinking would go something like this. Before the Industrial Revolution, which began in the late eighteenth century, the peppered moth had excellent camouflage on the bark of trees. You can see from fig 31 how hard it would be for birds to spot the moths.

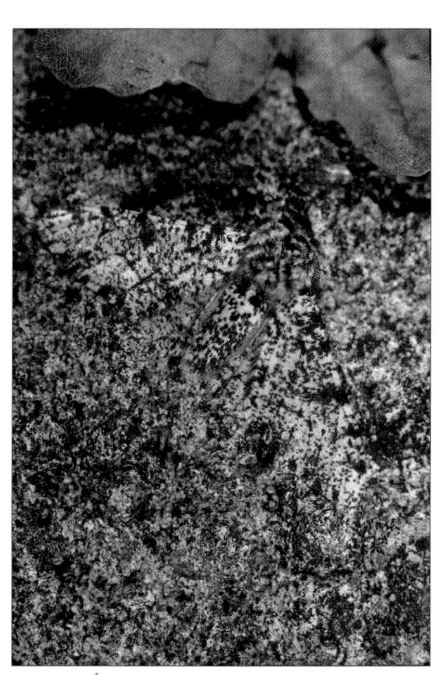

fig 31 | Before the Industrial Revolution, the peppered moth was well camouflaged on tree trunks

During the Industrial Revolution, pollution from factory chimneys turned the bark of trees almost black. The pale moths were no longer camouflaged (fig 32) and were more likely to eaten by birds. However, the darker moths survived to reproduce and some of their offspring were even darker. This is what Darwin called **survival of the fittest**. It was not long before the peppered moth had become almost black, and once more had perfect camouflage (fig 34).

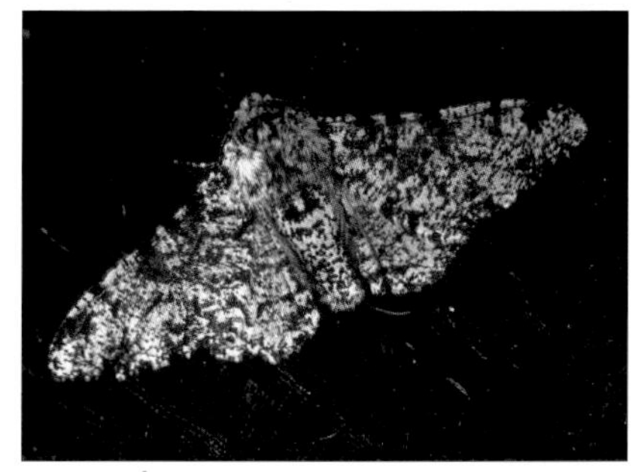

fig 32 | When soot turned the tree trunks black, the peppered moth was no longer camouflaged

Extinction of a **species** occurs when it fails to change to fit in with its new environment. Fortunately for the peppered moth, it managed to evolve and survive.

During the Industrial Revolution, soot turned tree trunks black. The pale peppered moths were spotted by birds and eaten.

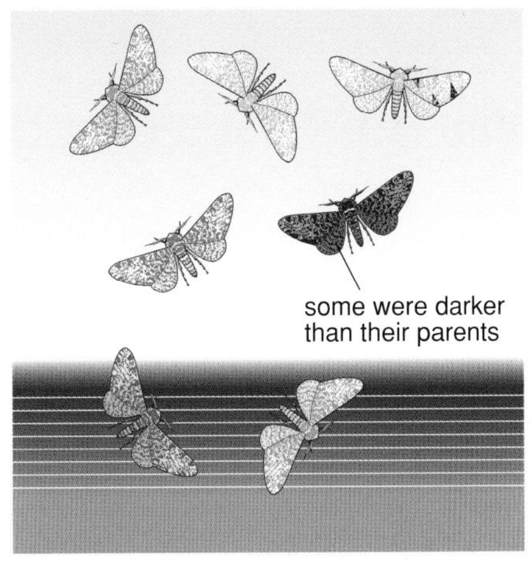

But the peppered moth produced a large number of variable offspring.

The darker moths were less likely to be spotted by the birds and be eaten.

fig 33 | The process of evolution enabled the peppered moth to survive the effects of the Industrial Revolution

New species

Sometimes a species gets separated into two groups, perhaps by a physical barrier such as a sea, desert or mountain range. When this happens, natural selection ensures that the two groups evolve independently. If the two groups ever change so much that they can no longer reproduce with each other, they have evolved into two new species. This may be how all the different species that we have today came into existence.

fig 34 | Dark moths were well comouflaged on soot-covered tree trunks and so survived to reproduce

Evidence for evolution

Because we cannot travel back in time, we cannot prove that evolution actually happened. However, the circumstantial evidence for it is overwhelming. One area of evidence can be found by looking at **fossils**. Fossils have two big advantages.

- They are the preserved remains of organisms that lived millions of years ago.
- They can be dated.

This means that we can look at fossils and build up a picture of what happened to the organisms over a long period of time. We can see how they changed to be best suited to their environment.

Thinking further

■ **1** Describe, using ideas gained from the peppered-moth example, how the leopard could have got its spots.

■ **2** Find out and write about how fossils are formed.

◆ **3** State the links between the structure of DNA, Mendel's laws of genetics and Darwin's theory of evolution.

KEY WORDS

evolution • extinction • fossil • natural selection • species • survival of the fittest • variation

Questions on inheritance and evolution

1 Mary and Anita are identical twins. Fig 35 gives some information about some of their characteristics.

characteristic	Mary	Anita
height	1.62 m	1.62 m
interests	pop music	films
hair style	long	short
eye colour	blue	blue

fig 35

State which characteristics are controlled by genetics, and which are a result of the environment. *(4)*

■ **2** A farmer wants to increase the amount of milk produced by his cows.

a Explain what is meant by selective breeding. *(2)*

b Suggest how the farmer might introduce a selective breeding programme to improve the milk yield of his cows. *(2)*

■ **3** The cells in John's skin each contain 46 chromosomes. State how many chromosomes you would expect to find in John's:

a sperm *(1)*

b white blood cells *(1)*

c children's white blood cells. *(1)*

■ **4** Copy the paragraph below and use words from the following list to fill in the blank spaces. Each word may be used once, more than once, or not at all. *(6)*

allele • genotype • heterozygous • homozygous • phenotype • recessive

Mendel experimented on pea plants. He found that when he crossed a __________ tall plant with a homozygous short plant, all the plants had a tall __________ . However, the __________ of the plants was **Tt**. The __________ **T** was therefore dominant and **t** was __________ . When he crossed two __________ plants, the seeds produced plants with a ratio of three tall to one short.

5 The Jones family have the DNA fingerprint shown in fig 36.

band	child	mother	father
1			■
2	■	■	
3	■		■
4		■	
5	■	■	
6	■		■
7			■

fig 36

● **a** State which bands are the same in the mother and the child. *(2)*

■ **b** State how you know that these are the child's biological parents. *(2)*

◆ **c** State which bands would be found in the child's father's sperm. *(2)*

6 In the 1950s, a new disease called myxomatosis killed large numbers of rabbits. Only a few rabbits survived.

■ **a** Why did some rabbits survive? *(1)*

◆ **b** Rabbits now exist in large numbers again. Explain why this is an example of natural selection. *(3)*

◆ **7** During the Second World War, many soldiers died of infected wounds. When penicillin was discovered it was called a wonder drug because it saved so many lives.

a Explain why nowadays many bacteria are resistant to penicillin. *(3)*

b Explain why, when a new antibiotic is discovered, it is a good idea for doctors to restrict its use to the most serious infections. *(1)*

c Explain why you should always finish a prescribed course of antibiotics. *(2)*

8 Joan keeps guinea pigs. In guinea pigs the allele for black coat, **B**, is dominant and the allele for brown coat, **b**, is recessive. When Joan mated two of her black guinea pigs, some of the babies were black and some were brown.

a Copy fig 37 and fill in the boxes to show the genotypes of the offspring. *(3)*

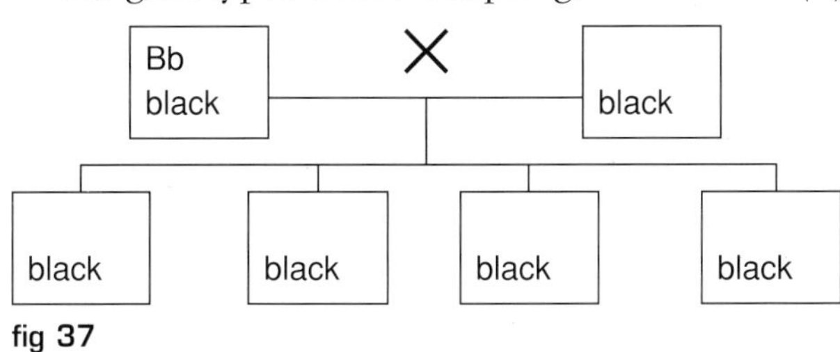

fig 37

b What proportion of a heterozygous male guinea pig's sperm contain a **B** allele? *(1)*

c State the expected ratio of black and brown offspring. *(2)*

d State and explain which crosses would always produce brown guinea pigs. *(2)*

9 John and Mary have a baby daughter called Jill.

a Draw a Punnett square to show how Jill inherited her sex chromosomes from her parents. *(3)*

b Explain why in a large population equal numbers of boys and girls are born. *(2)*

c Suggest what might have happened to Jill if she had been conceived with:

i an extra chromosome. *(1)*

ii a chromosome missing. *(1)*

10 When developing his theory of evolution, Darwin noticed the following facts:

- Populations produce large numbers of offspring – more than survive.
- Sexual reproduction ensures that offspring vary.
- Characteristics are inherited from parents.

Explain how the facts enabled Darwin to produce his theory. *(3)*

11 Rita and Paul have a child called David who has Down's syndrome. He has 47 chromosomes instead of 46.

a When the sperm and ovum fertilised to make David, state how many chromosomes were in:

i the sperm **ii** the ovum.

b Some plants also have an extra chromosome.

i Copy fig 38 and write a number in each of the pollen grains and in each of the ovules to show how many chromosomes each one should have. *(2)*

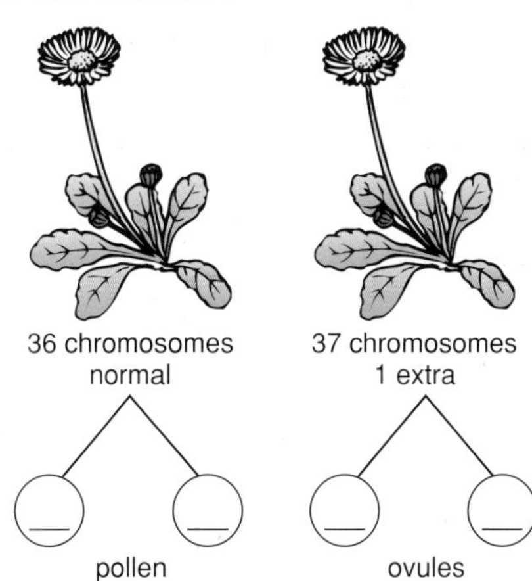

fig 38

ii Copy the Punnett square in fig 39 and transfer the numbers from fig 38 to show the number of chomosomes in the pollen and ovules. Complete the square to show how many chromosomes each of the four possible types of offspring would have. *(2)*

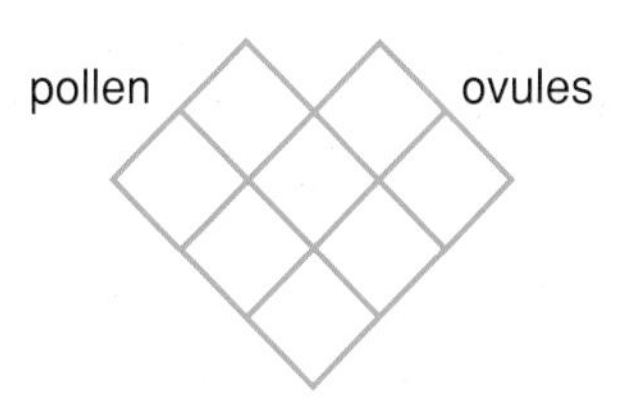

fig 39

IDEAS AND EVIDENCE

12 Charles Darwin produced the theory of evolution. Whereas Mendel's laws can be proved, Darwin's ideas still remain theoretical.

a Evaluate all the evidence that you can find and state, with reasons, whether you think Darwin's theory will ever become Darwin's law. *(3)*

b Darwin had a cousin called Francis Galton. Galton believed that intelligence was inherited and that human stock could be improved by using a selective breeding programme called eugenics. Describe the moral implications of Galton's ideas. *(3)*

c Genetic engineering can be used to provide many benefits for humanity. Explain why some people think that advances in genetic engineering should be carefully monitored and controlled. *(3)*

Extension A1 Human physiology

Links to Double Award

2 Digestion
3 Respiration
4 Breathing
6 Transport
8 Response to stimuli
9 Homeostasis

Introduction

Physiology is the study of the processes and activities that occur in living organisms. Physiologists study how the different organs in the body work and how they are controlled.
Human physiology concentrates on the organs of the human body.
These studies form an important part of any medical training course.

Sometimes physiologists study an organ that has been removed from an animal's body, for example a muscle. In the 1950s Hugh Huxley and Jean Hanson used this approach to work out how muscles contract.

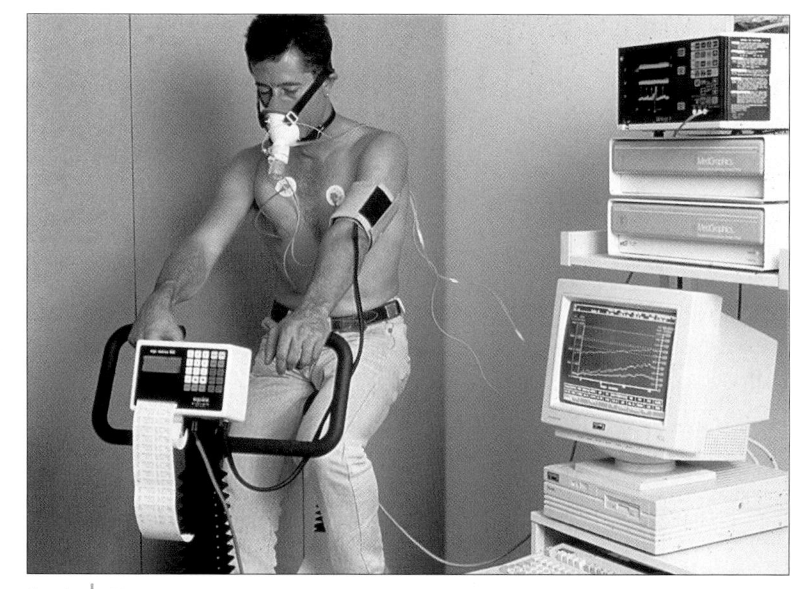

fig 1 The electrodes on the chest monitor the heart, the mask over the mouth monitors the breathing, and the cuff on the arm monitors the blood pressure

It is also important to study how different organs work together in the body. For example, physiologists may study how the body responds to exercise (fig 1). This could involve studying the nervous system, muscles, breathing system, heart and circulation. The nervous system causes the muscles to contract, the muscles bring about movement, and the breathing system, heart and circulation maintain a supply of oxygen and nutrients for these processes.

Many physiological studies concentrate on the ways in which the body manages to keep the internal environment of the body constant despite changes in activity and external conditions.
This idea – called homeostasis – was first suggested by the French physiologist Claude Bernard in 1859. The excretory system plays an important role in homeostasis.

In order for the organs of the body to work correctly, they need to be supplied with an appropriate selection of food molecules.
This is provided by a balanced diet.

fig 2 Claude Bernard (1813–1878)

Check-up

Have a go at the following questions. They will remind you of what you should know about human physiology.

a What is meant by the term balanced diet?

b Why does the concentration of carbon dioxide in the blood increase during exercise?

c During exercise, the muscles increase their requirements for certain substances. Name two of these substances.

d The various organs in the body are affected by nerves and hormones. What is a hormone?

e The central nervous system is the main control centre of the nervous system. What is the central nervous system?

f What is a reflex?

g What do the kidneys remove from the blood?

h How do the kidneys control the concentration of the blood?

Contents of the Teaching block

A1.1 A balanced diet

The diet must provide the body with fats, proteins, carbohydrates, fibre, vitamins and minerals. These food molecules must be in the correct amounts if the body is to function correctly. The importance of many of these substances can be seen by studying people who have not received the correct amounts.

A1.2 Diets and requirements

The amounts of the different chemicals needed in the diet vary at different times in a person's life. Sometimes people decide to alter the types of food they eat. They might put themselves on a particular diet.

A1.3 Physiology of exercise

Exercise can make considerable demands on the heart and breathing system. The body needs to meet these demands and ensure that the systems return to normal after exercise.

A1.4 Excretion

The kidney contains over one million tiny tubes called nephrons. These nephrons control the composition of the blood. Sometimes this system fails and the person has to use a kidney dialysis machine.

A1.5 The brain and responses

Many areas of the brain bring about responses without conscious thought. These responses are reflexes. The cerebrum, however, receives sensory information and uses conscious thought to decide on an appropriate response.

A1.1 A balanced diet (1)

Key points

- To function correctly, the body needs substances from the seven different types of food molecules.
- The need for many of these substances can be demonstrated by studying deficiency diseases.
- Other diseases can be caused by the intake of too much of a certain food substance.

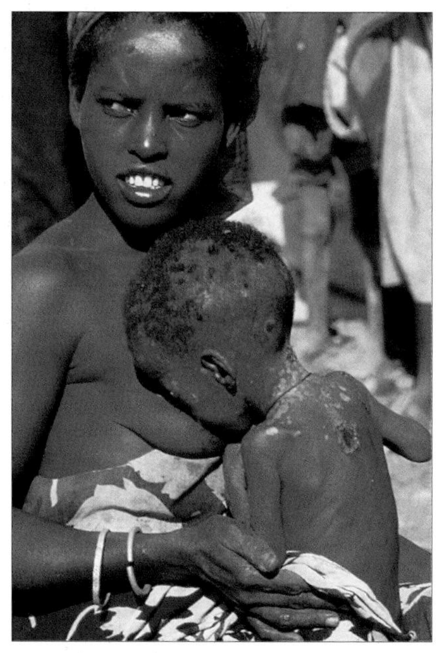

fig 3 | This child shows signs of kwashiorkor: thinning of the hair and skin lesions

Proteins

If all the water is removed from a cell, proteins make up the majority of what is left. Protein in the diet is broken down into **amino acids** which are absorbed into the blood stream. They can then be used to make the enzymes and other proteins needed by cells.

People who do not receive enough protein suffer from the disease kwashiorkor (fig 3). These people have flaky skin, pale thin hair, muscles that are wasting away and an abdomen that is swollen with fluid.

Different proteins contain different amounts of the various amino acids. The body can make some of these amino acids. However, there are some amino acids that the body cannot make. These must be obtained from the diet and are called essential amino acids. They are more common in some proteins than in others.

Foods are given a quality rating on the basis of the variety of essential amino acids that they contain. The higher the rating, the greater the variety of amino acids present. If a food contains only a small amount of a particular amino acid, this will reduce the quality rating. This amino acid is said to be limiting.
Fig 4 shows the protein quality rating of some foods.

food	protein quality rating	limiting amino acid
egg	0.98	none
beef	0.77	none
wheat	0.62	lysine
peas	0.49	methionine

fig 4

a What do the data in fig 4 indicate about the differences between animal and plant proteins?

b Suggest why it is a good idea to eat peas and wheat together.

Fat

Fats are used in the body as a rich supply and store of energy. They are also needed to produce cell membranes. The most common fats are made up of fatty acids and glycerol. Fatty acids that are found in animal fats do not usually contain double bonds and are called **saturated fatty acids**. Plant fats contain more **unsaturated fatty acids**. These do have double bonds.

Animal fat also contains another type of fat called **cholesterol**. Cholesterol is an important component of cell membranes but too much of it in the diet can cause health problems.

Fats are stored around the body, under the skin and around the organs. Sometimes cholesterol is deposited in the arteries. This can occur in the **coronary arteries**, which supply the heart muscle with blood. These deposits gradually increase in size and may block the artery (fig 5), which can prevent the heart muscle from contracting.

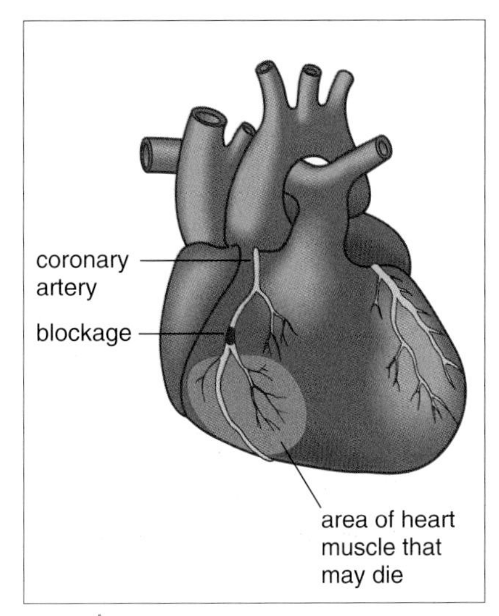

fig 5 | A blockage in a coronary artery can lead to a heart attack

c Why might a blockage in the coronary artery stop the heart muscle from contracting?

d Why is a blockage at the start of a coronary artery likely to cause more damage than a blockage further down the artery?

If a large area of heart muscle is affected, this could lead to a heart attack. Such blockages are most likely to occur in people who eat a lot of cholesterol and saturated fats.

Digestible carbohydrate

The main digestible carbohydrates are various sugars and starch. Starch is converted into sugars during digestion and the sugars are absorbed into the bloodstream. They are used as an immediate supply of energy, although small amounts can be stored as glycogen.

The trouble is that sugars are added to many foods. This sugar is not held in cells and is called **extrinsic sugar**. Bacteria in the mouth feed on these sugars and turn them into various acids. The acid damages the enamel of the teeth, which leads to **dental decay**.

Fibre

Dietary fibre is mainly made up of the cell walls of plants. Although it cannot be digested by human enzymes, dietary fibre is important in the diet because it adds bulk to the food so that it can be moved along the gut by **peristalsis**. This helps to prevent constipation, which might lead to straining and haemorrhoids (piles). Fibre may also help to dilute poisonous chemicals, possibly preventing bowel cancer.

e Why does wholemeal bread contain more fibre than white bread?

Continued

A1.1 A balanced diet (2)

Vitamins

Vitamins are a wide range of organic chemicals needed in the diet for the correct functioning of the body. They cannot be produced by the body.

It was well known for many years that certain foods could prevent certain diseases. However, the fact that these deficiency diseases were caused by lack of vitamins was not shown until the start of the 20th century. The importance of vitamins was first demonstrated by Gowland Hopkins in 1910. Now, many vitamins are known about.

Some vitamins, such as vitamins A and D, are soluble in fat and so are often found in foods with a high fat content. Some of the vitamins are described in fig 6.

vitamin	good food source	function in the body	deficiency disease
A	fish oil, liver, butter, (carotene in vegetables can be converted into vitamin A)	needed to make the light-sensitive pigment found in the rods of the retina	night blindness
C	citrus fruit, green vegetables	making connective tissue	**scurvy**, which results in bleeding gums and poor wound healing
D	fish oils, milk, can be made in the skin by the action of sunlight	aids absorption of calcium from the intestine	rickets

fig 6

Minerals

In addition to the elements found in proteins, carbohydrates and fats, the body needs to take in various other elements, called minerals.

f Which elements are found in proteins, carbohydrates and fats?

The two minerals that are needed in the largest amounts are calcium and iron. Other minerals are needed in very small or trace amounts.

A healthy body contains 3–4 grams of iron. Iron is needed to make the haemoglobin in red blood cells. Lack of iron is thought to be the most common deficiency disease in the world, affecting 500 million people. It causes **anaemia** – a reduction in the number of red blood cells. A person with anaemia is pale, tired and easily becomes short of breath. They can take iron tablets to increase their iron intake. However, the absorption of iron is inefficient – the body only absorbs about 10% of the iron in food. The amount absorbed can be increased by the presence of vitamin C.

Calcium is needed to harden bones and teeth and is involved in clotting of the blood. About 99% of the calcium in the body is in the skeleton. The bones of a newborn baby are relatively soft but they gradually become hardened by calcium. A lack of calcium in children causes **rickets**, in which the bones do not harden properly and so become weak and bent.

IDEAS AND EVIDENCE

James Lind was the ship's doctor on board the *Salisbury* in 1747. He decided to conduct a test on a number of sailors who were suffering from a deficiency disease. They all had bleeding gums, sores and weak joints.

g What disease were the sailors suffering from?

h Why did so many sailors suffer from this disease during long voyages at sea?

He gave all the sailors the same basic diet but different groups of sailors had in addition one of the following: cider, vinegar, sea water, oranges, or nutmeg. One group received only the basic diet.

He found that the sailors who received the oranges recovered very quickly and were fit to return to duties in six days.

i Why did the sailors who received the oranges recover rapidly from the disease?

j Why did the addition of vinegar to the diet of one group of sailors provide a useful comparison?

fig 7 James Lind (1716–1794)

Thinking further

■ **1** Fat is stored under the skin. What other function, apart from storage of energy, does this have?

■ **2** Why do people with anaemia get very tired and short of breath?

■ **3** Boiled eggs contain iron. Why are they more useful as a source of iron if they are eaten in a meal along with orange juice?

◆ **4** Why does lack of vitamin D have a similar effect to lack of calcium?

◆ **5** Why do some people think that vitamin D should not be classed as a vitamin?

◆ **6** Sailors aboard ships found that dogs that accompanied them on voyages did not get the same disease as the sailors on the *Salisbury*. Suggest why.

KEY WORDS

amino acids • anaemia • cholesterol • coronary arteries • dental decay • extrinsic sugar • peristalsis • rickets • saturated fatty acids • scurvy • unsaturated fatty acids

A1.2 Diets and requirements

Key points

- A person needs different amounts of the various food molecules at different times in their life.
- Sometimes people change their food intake by putting themselves on a particular diet.

RNI

In 1991, the Department of Health issued sets of figures giving the amounts of various food molecules that are needed per day by most people. These figures are called the **reference nutrient intake (RNI)**. Some RNIs for females of different ages are shown in fig 8.

age	protein in g	calcium in mg	iron in mg	vitamin C in mg
3 months	12.5	525	1.7	25
6 months	12.7	525	4.3	25
3 years	14.5	350	6.9	30
6 years	19.7	450	6.1	30
10 years	28.3	550	8.7	30
14 years	41.2	800	14.8	35
20 years	45.0	700	14.8	40
20 years (pregnant)	51.0	700	14.8	50

fig 8 | Reference nutrient intakes (RNIs) for females of different ages

Childhood

Breast milk is an ideal food for babies. It has all the necessary nutrients to meet the RNI of the baby. It lacks iron but a baby usually has plenty stored in its liver when it is born.

a How does the baby get this iron?

As the baby gets older, its requirement for iron increases and the baby is moved on to solid food, or **weaned**. The baby needs large amounts of calcium because its bones are growing and hardening.

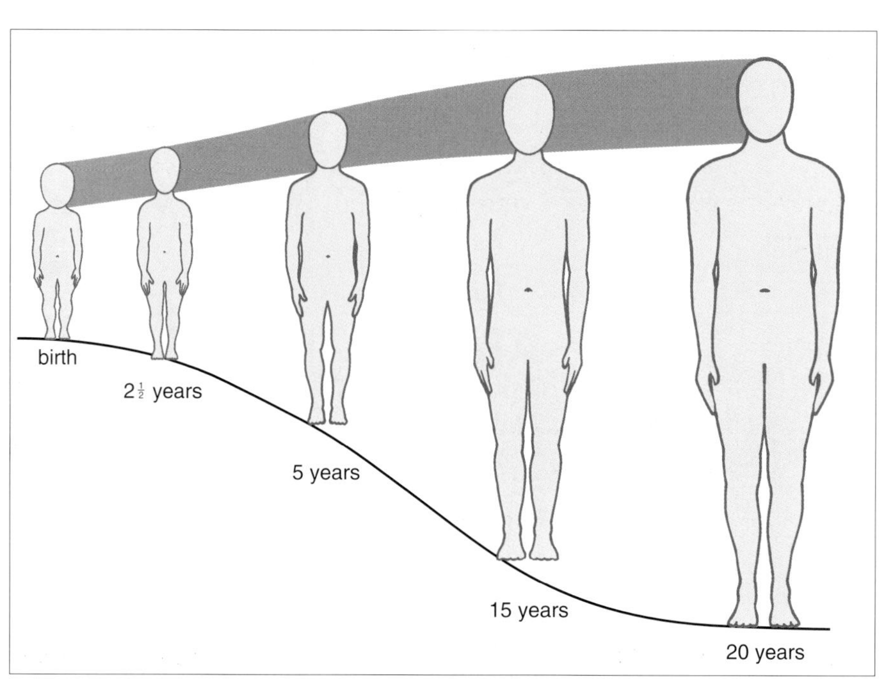

fig 9 | Human growth

Adolescents

During puberty, children undergo a **growth spurt.** This usually occurs earlier in girls than in boys. The need for protein, calcium and iron all increase rapidly. The needs of boys and girls are similar but boys do not need as much iron.

b Why do adolescent boys need less iron than adolescent girls?

If adolescents eat a balanced diet, then the RNI should be met. However, vitamin supplements may be useful.

Pregnancy

A woman needs to increase her intake of many nutrients during pregnancy. She needs to provide nutrients for the baby to use for growth and also needs more nutrients for herself. She lays down fat reserves for use when she is breast-feeding, and needs more energy.

c Why does a pregnant woman need more energy?

During pregnancy, a woman's blood will be tested to make sure that it contains enough haemoglobin. If this is too low, she may need to take iron supplements.

Special diets

People put themselves on different diets for a number of reasons. Some of these include:

- an attempt to lose weight
- religious reasons
- because of illnesses or allergy
- for ethical reasons, such as vegetarians.

It is important for all of these people to ensure that their diet is not deficient in any essential nutrient. This may particularly be the case with people who are trying to lose weight by going on a very restricted diet.

Vegetarians do not eat meat and many do not eat fish. They do eat animal products such as milk. **Vegans**, however, do not eat any food that comes from animals. They must make sure that they eat a good variety of plant proteins. This is because plant proteins contain less variety of amino acids than do animal proteins. Vegetarians may also lack vitamin B12 but they can get this from yeast extracts.

fig 10 Yeast extract is an important source of B vitamins

Thinking further

1 Using the data in fig 8, plot a line graph of the RNI for protein against age.

2 Explain the shape of the graph.

3 What other factors might affect the RNI of a person, apart from their age or sex?

4 A mother provides the raw materials for a fetus to make its own red blood cells. Why does she do this rather than making the red blood cells for the fetus?

KEY WORDS

growth spurt • reference nutrient intake (RNI) • vegan • vegetarian • weaned

A1.3 Physiology of exercise

Key points

- The heart rate is adjusted in order to keep the blood pressure as constant as possible.
- During exercise, the heart rate and breathing rate increase in order to meet the extra demands of the muscles.
- These changes are brought about by nerves and hormones

Control of heart rate

The heart muscle has its own in-built ability to contract. Unlike the muscles of the skeleton, it does not need to receive impulses from nerves in order to contract. The heart rate is, however, affected by nerves and hormones. These include:

- **adrenaline**, a hormone that is released from the adrenal glands, which are small organs above the kidneys
- nerves that are connected to the heart – these carry impulses from an area of the brain called the **medulla**.

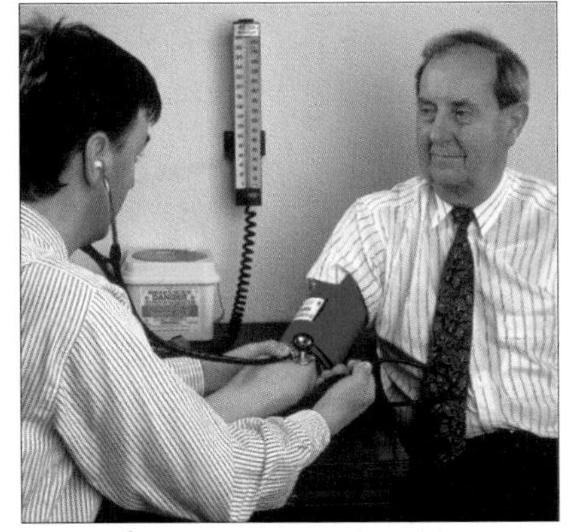

fig 11 Blood pressure is measured using a cuff inflated around the upper arm

Regulating blood pressure

It is vital for the blood pressure to be as constant as possible. If it is too high, the person could suffer a **stroke**. This may be the result of a blood vessel bursting in the brain. Low blood pressure may mean that the kidney loses its ability to filter the blood.

The blood pressure is measured in one of the main arteries of the body, usually the one in the arm. The pressure in these arteries varies in time with the heart beat.

a Why does the pressure in the arteries vary in time with the heart beat?

There are pressure receptors in the walls of some of the main arteries. If the blood pressure rises then these receptors send impulses to the medulla. The medulla then sends impulses to the heart to decrease the heart rate and bring the blood pressure back to normal. If blood pressure falls below normal, impulses are sent from the medulla to increase the heart rate and blood pressure.

b What name is given to this type of control mechanism?

High intake of salt in the diet can increase the blood pressure. This could be particularly dangerous for people whose blood pressure is already high. These people are usually advised to reduce their salt intake by avoiding salty foods and using 'low-sodium' salt in place of ordinary salt.

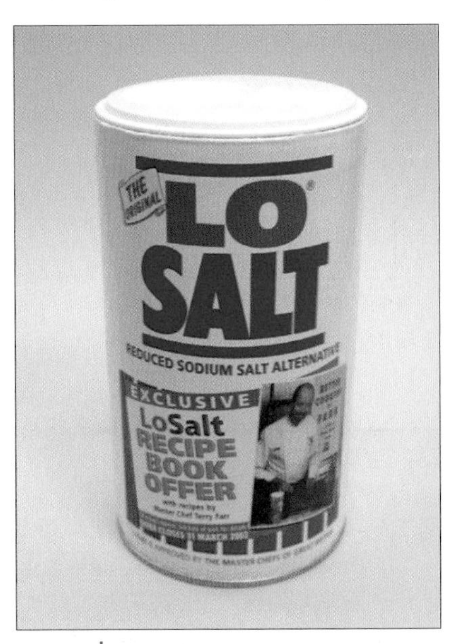

fig 12 Salt that has a low sodium content is often recommended to people with high blood pressure

Preparing for action

When a person is preparing to undertake some activity, changes happen in their body before they actually do anything. These changes are mainly caused by the hormone adrenaline. Fig 13 shows some of the actions of adrenaline on the body.

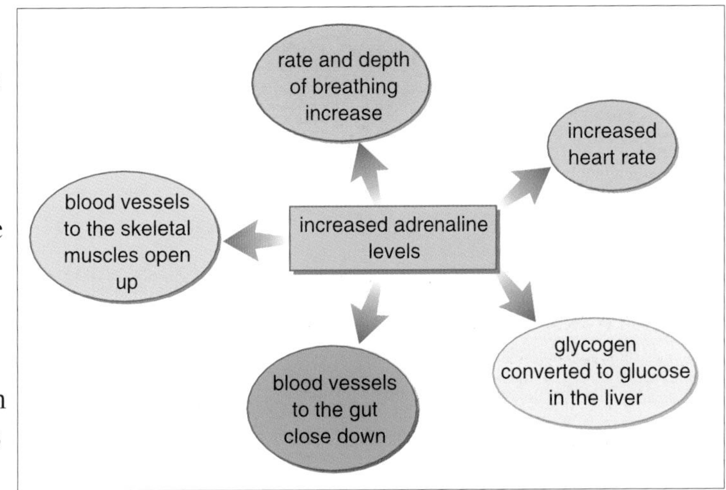

fig 13 | The actions of adrenaline in the body; adrenaline is sometimes called the 'fight or flight' hormone because it prepares the body for action

Changes during exercise

During exercise, the muscles need extra oxygen and glucose for respiration and the body needs to remove the extra carbon dioxide that is produced. Adrenaline and nerves will bring about the following changes:

- The rate and depth of breathing increase in order to draw more air in and out of the lungs.
- The heart rate increases so that more blood can be pumped to the lungs and muscles. This can be detected as an increase in blood pressure and pulse.
- The distribution of blood to different organs changes.

c Which organs will receive more blood and which will receive less blood?

These changes can be detected by studying a person on an exercise bike (see fig 1 on the introductory spread in this Teaching block). Fig 14 shows some of the effects of work rate on the body.

work rate in watts	heart rate in beats per minute	volume per beat in cm^3	breathing rate in breaths per minute	volume of air exchanged per breath in litres
0	86	65	10	0.6
60	106	84	11	0.8
100	122	120	13	1.0
140	143	130	16	1.2
160	156	125	30	0.7

fig 14

d Look at fig 14. Why are the values for before the cyclist started pedalling (work rate 0 watts) likely to be different from his normal resting values?

The changes are controlled by the medulla in the brain. This time, it is the increased acidity of the blood reaching the hypothalamus in the brain that causes the medulla to bring about these changes. When the carbon dioxide level returns to normal, the medulla sends appropriate signals to return the breathing rate and heart rate to normal.

Thinking further

■ **1** The amount of blood pumped by the heart in a minute can be calculated by multiplying the heart rate by the volume per beat. Work this out for each work rate shown in fig 14.

■ **2** Plot your results against work rate on a line graph.

■ **3** Describe the pattern shown on your graph.

◆ **4** Why does the volume of air exchanged per breath go down during heavy exercise?

KEY WORDS
adrenaline • medulla • stroke

A1.4 Excretion

Key points

- The kidney contains millions of units called nephrons.
- Each nephron consists of a blood supply and a long tubule that filters the blood and then reabsorbs certain substances according to the body's needs.
- People whose kidneys fail to work properly may have to use a kidney dialysis machine.

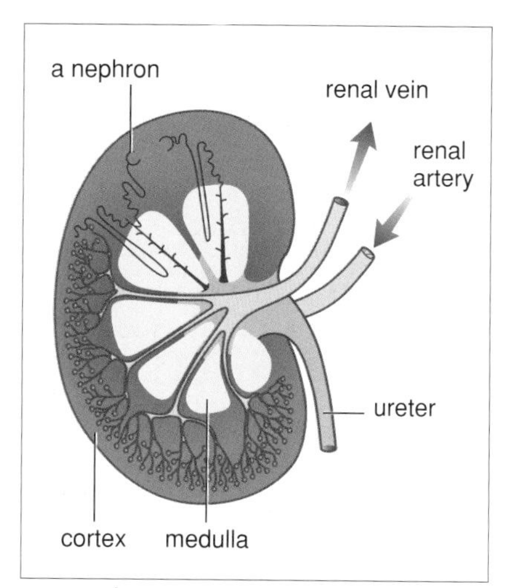

fig 15 | A section through a human kidney – just two nephrons are shown but in reality there are at least a million

The nephron

Each human kidney contains at least a million individual units called **nephrons**. Each nephron contains a very narrow tube called a **kidney tubule** which is about 3 cm long. The nephrons are arranged in the kidney in a special way (fig 15). They start in the outer region – the cortex – and then pass into the inner region – the medulla – before returning to the cortex. The tubules empty into collecting ducts, which join together and pass the urine into the pelvis of the kidney. The urine is then carried along the ureter to the bladder.

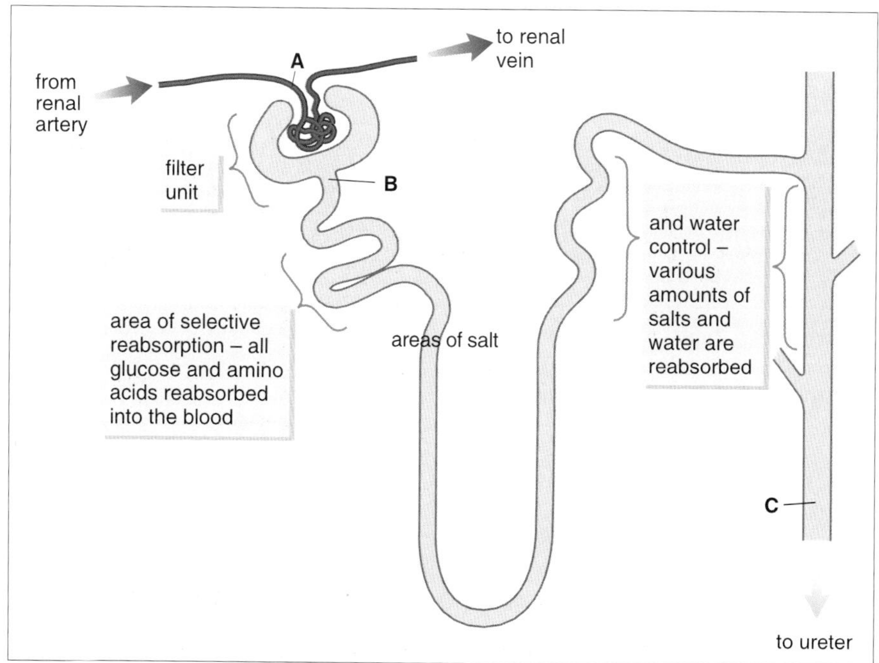

fig 16 | The three main areas of the nephron. The composition of the fluid in the different regions is shown in fig 17.

The way in which the kidneys work is described in Teaching block 9. Briefly, the kidneys filter the blood and then take useful chemicals back into the bloodstream. The amounts of water and salts that are taken back can be adjusted according to how concentrated the blood is. The hormone ADH (antidiuretic hormone) controls this process.

The nephron can be divided into three different regions. A particular process occurs in each region. This is shown in fig 16. The composition of fluid in each of the three regions in fig 16 is shown in fig 17.

	percentage of substance in		
substance	**blood plasma at A**	**filtered fluid at B**	**urine at C**
water	90	99	97
proteins	9	0	0
glucose	0.1	0.1	0
urea	0.03	0.03	2.0

fig 17 | Composition of fluid in the areas marked on fig 16

a What substances, in addition to those shown in fig 17, are found in blood plasma?

b What effect does ADH have on the percentage of water in the urine?

Kidney failure

Kidney failure may have a number of causes. These include:

- bacterial infection
- mechanical injury
- extremes of blood pressure.

The kidneys can work successfully using only about 50% of their nephrons. If failure is worse than this, a person may need to use a **dialysis machine**. This is a device that is used to regulate the composition of the person's blood.

A join is made between an artery and vein in the patient's arm. Blood is taken from the arm and is passed through a long, selectively permeable dialysis tube, as shown in fig 18.

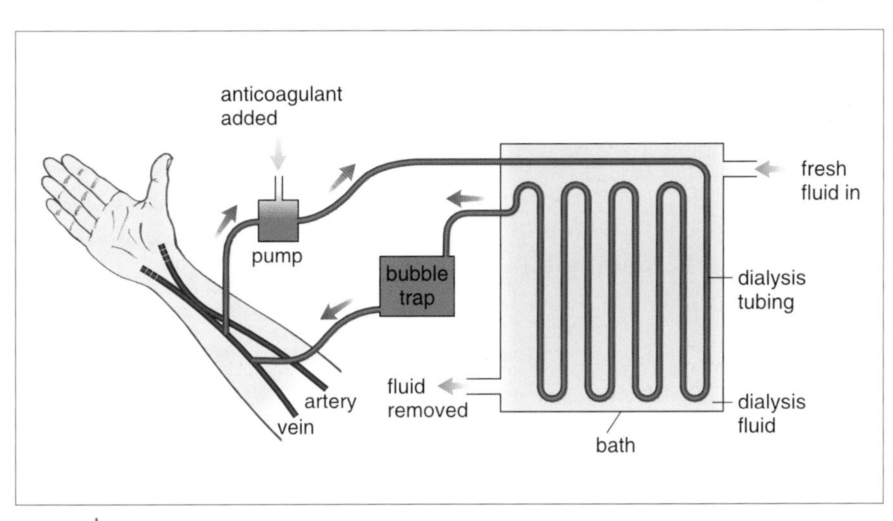

fig 18 | A dialysis machine

c Suggest why a join is made between the artery and the vein.

The dialysis tube is surrounded by fresh dialysis fluid which contains the ideal concentration of glucose, amino acids, water and salts for the body, but no urea. Urea will therefore diffuse out of the blood in the tube into the bath.

d Why is there no net movement of glucose and amino acids out of the tube, even though they are small enough to pass through the membrane?

A person may have to be connected to a dialysis machine for 6–10 hours at a time, three times a week. The alternative treatment is a kidney transplant. Although two thousand kidney transplants are carried out a year in the United Kingdom, many more people who need a transplant have to wait because of a lack of donors.

Thinking further

◆ **1** Why is glucose found in the fluid filtered into the kidney tubule but not in the urine?

◆ **2** Why is there no protein in the urine?

◆ **3** Although no glucose is found in the urine, why is there less glucose in the renal vein than in the renal artery?

KEY WORDS
dialysis machine • kidney tubule • nephron

A1.5 The brain and responses

Key points

- Sensory neurones enter the spinal cord through the dorsal root of the spinal nerves; motor neurones leave through the ventral root.
- Some responses are reflexes, which may or may not involve the brain.
- The brain has many different regions which are responsible for different functions.
- The muscles are the main effectors in the body.

Input of information to the brain

Much of the information from the sense organs enters the spinal cord along sensory neurones. The sensory neurones are in spinal nerves that divide just before they enter the cord (see fig 10 on spread 8.3). They pass through a pathway called the **dorsal root** (fig 20). Other sensory information passes through neurones in nerves that go straight to the brain, such as the optic nerve.

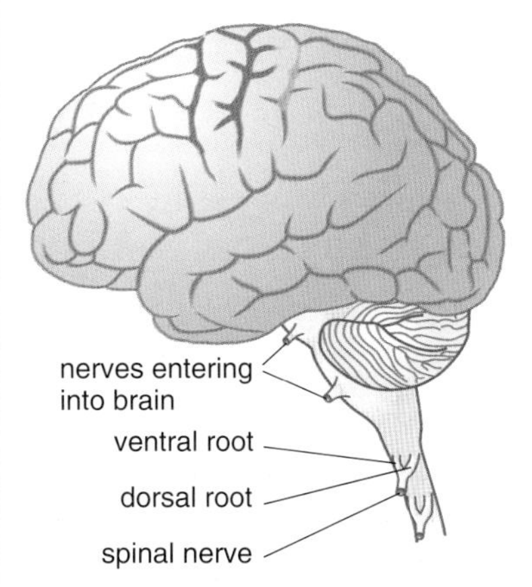

nerves entering into brain
ventral root
dorsal root
spinal nerve

fig 19 Entry of nerves into the central nervous system

Different areas of the brain

The human brain has a mass of about 1.3 kg and contains about a million, million neurones. It can be divided into different regions (fig 21), each of which carries out different functions.

a Why is the brain enclosed in the skull?

b The brain is surrounded by membranes called the **meninges**. Which disease leads to an infection of these membranes?

Functions of brain areas

Scientists have found that different areas of the brain are responsible for different functions. Three types of investigations have helped scientists to allocate functions to different brain areas. These are:

- studying people who have suffered damage to particular parts of the brain
- taking electrical measurements from parts of the brain during brain surgery on humans or animals
- measuring the amount of respiration or electrical activity in different areas of the brain whilst the subject carries out different actions.

These studies have shown that the medulla is responsible for many reflex actions. These include the control of blood pressure, heart rate and breathing rate, as covered in spread A1.3.

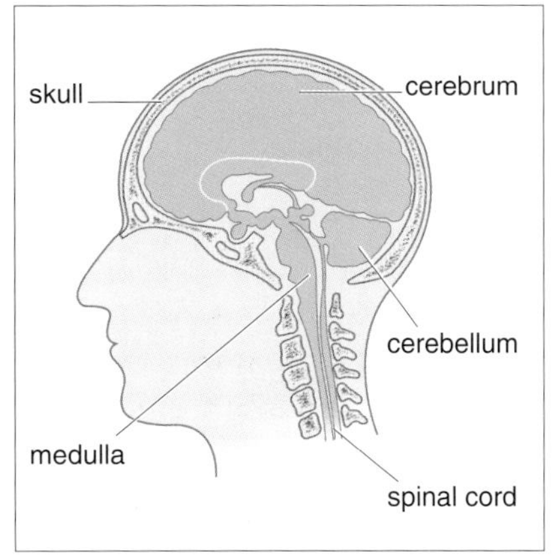

fig 20 A section through a human brain to show the main areas

Other reflexes include swallowing, vomiting and sneezing.

The **cerebellum**, which is at the back of the brain, also carries out actions below the level of consciousness. It controls balance and posture, co-ordinating voluntary movements to make sure they occur smoothly. The cerebellum does not initiate the movement – this is the responsibility of the **cerebrum**. The cerebrum is a large thin sheet of cells that is deeply folded. It covers the top of the brain. Certain areas in the cerebrum receive information from the sense organs such as the eyes and skin receptors. Another area is responsible for initiating voluntary actions such as movement. The front areas of the cerebrum seem to be concerned with personality, memory and intelligence. The cerebrum is therefore involved in conscious thought.

c Suggest why the cerebrum is so highly folded.

Conditioned reflexes

So far two types of responses have been discussed.

- Simple reflexes do not involve conscious thought and are rapid simple responses.
- Voluntary actions are complicated responses involving conscious thought.

During his experiments on dogs, Ivan Pavlov (see Question 7 on the question spread at the end of Teaching block 7) rang a bell immediately before feeding the animals. He found that, after a while, the dogs would produce saliva just on hearing the bell, without food being provided. He called this type of 'learnt' response, which does not involve conscious thought, a **conditioned reflex**. Many of our responses, such as walking and food aversions, are thought to involve this type of reflex.

d How might conditioned reflexes help to protect animals from being stung by insects such as wasps and bees?

Thinking further

■ **1** Explain why blinking is a simple reflex and why it does not involve conscious thought.

◆ **2** Why do different species of animals have different sized cerebrums?

◆ **3** The cerebrum receives information from skin sense receptors and has different sized areas for different parts of the body. Which parts are likely to have the largest areas allocated to them in the cerebrum?

KEY WORDS

cerebellum • cerebrum • conditioned reflex • **dorsal root** • end plate • **meninges** • skeletal muscles • ventral root

Muscle contraction

In simple reflexes, conditioned reflexes or voluntary actions, the most common effectors are the muscles that move the skeleton – the **skeletal muscles**. The motor neurones leave the spinal cord by the **ventral root** of the spinal nerve and travel to the muscles. They form structures called **end plates** at the end of their axons (fig 21). These structures are similar to synapses. A transmitter substance is released when an impulse reaches the end plate. The transmitter substance diffuses across the small gap to the muscle fibre and causes the fibre to contract.

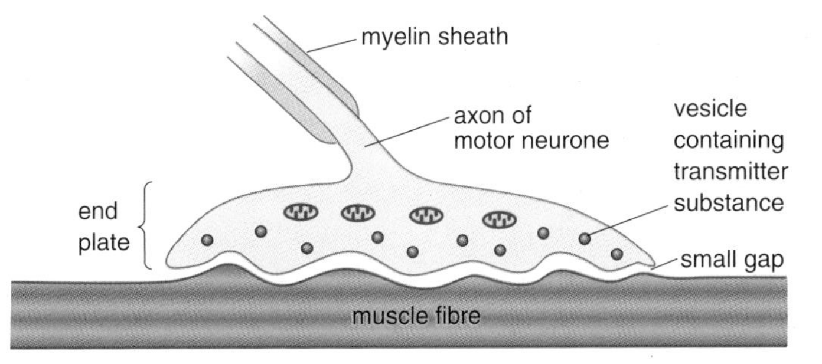

fig 21

Questions on human physiology

● **1** Copy the list of various food molecules and the list of different functions. Draw lines to link the correct molecule to its function in the body. The first one has been done for you. *(3)*

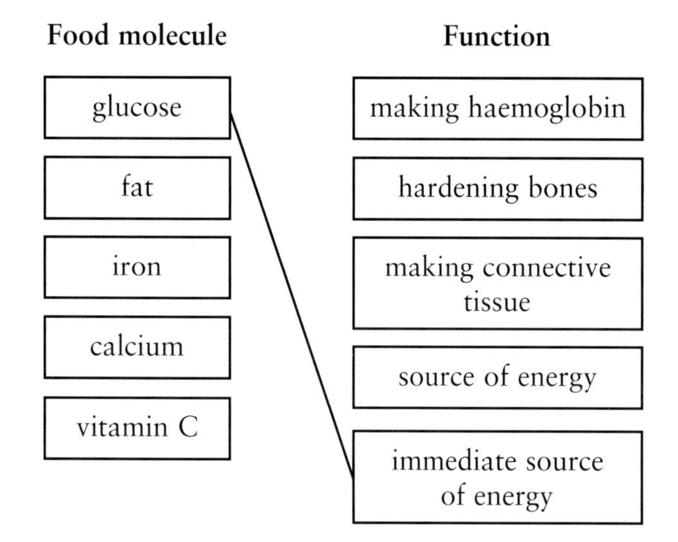

■ **2** Copy and complete the sentences below using words from this list. *(5)*

dorsal root • spinal cord • spinal nerve • ventral root • vertebral column

The __________ is a large collection of nerve cells that runs all the way up the back to the brain. It is protected by the bones of the __________ . At regular intervals along its length __________s enter; these contain motor neurones and sensory neurones. The sensory neurones enter by the __________ and the motor neurones leave by the __________ .

■ **3** Explain the scientific reasoning behind each of the following statements.

a During the Second World War, fighter pilots were given extra rations of carrots. *(2)*

b Rickets is more likely to occur in northern than in southern countries. *(2)*

c Certain types of margarine are advertised as being healthier to eat than butter because they are low in saturated fatty acids. *(2)*

d Eating a peach that contains sugar is less likely to cause tooth decay than sucking a mint that contains sugar. *(2)*

e Being vegetarian reduces your risk of getting bowel cancer. *(2)*

■ **4** Refer to fig 18 on spread A1.4 to answer the following questions.

a The anticoagulant stops the action of platelets. Why is it necessary to add this chemical? *(2)*

b Why is the dialysis fluid replaced regularly? *(2)*

c The dialysis tubing is in a coil. Why is this? *(2)*

d Why is it important to stop air bubbles from entering the person's bloodstream? *(2)*

◆ **5** Fig 22 shows a section through the human brain. Copy the diagram and on it write the letters **A, B, C and D** to show in which area each of the following processes occurs: *(4)*

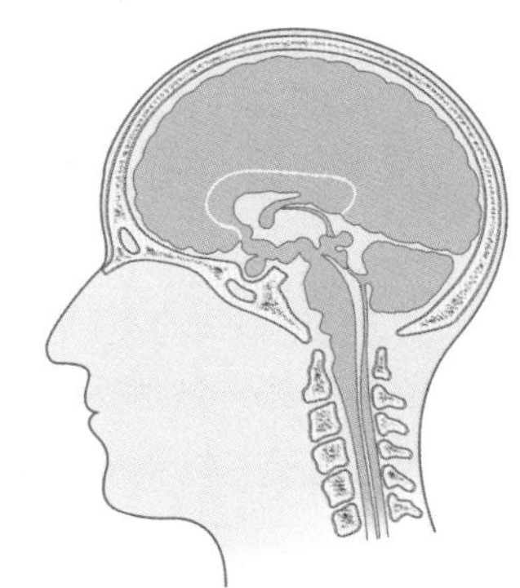

fig 22

A control of heart rate

B initiation of a voluntary action

C control of balance and posture

D control of breathing rate.

6 Fig 23 shows the blood flow to different parts of the body whilst at rest and during exercise.

	blood flow in cm^3 per minute	
body region	**at rest**	**during exercise**
brain	750	750
heart	250	1000
skeletal muscle	1300	21 150
skin	500	500
rest of the body	3100	600

fig 23

■ **a** Display the data in fig 23 as a bar graph. *(3)*

■ **b** Which part of the body shows the greatest increase in blood flow during exercise? *(1)*

◆ **c** Calculate the percentage increase in blood flow to this region of the body during exercise. *(2)*

◆ **d** The heart muscle receives 1000 cm^3 of blood per minute during exercise. Through which blood vessel does this blood reach the heart muscle? *(1)*

◆ **e** Using these data, what conclusions can you draw about the total blood flow around the body during exercise? *(2)*

◆ **f** Explain the mechanisms that occur in the body during exercise to cause these changes in blood flow. *(6)*

IDEAS AND EVIDENCE

7 Frederick Gowland Hopkins carried out the first thorough scientific study on vitamins, in 1910. He took a number of closely related young rats and divided them into two groups. He fed group **A** on pure protein, fats, carbohydrates, salts and water. Group **B** received the same diet but with the addition of a small amount of whole milk.

Gowland Hopkins measured the masses of the rats in each group for 18 days and then he swapped over the diets of the two groups. The results are shown in fig 24.

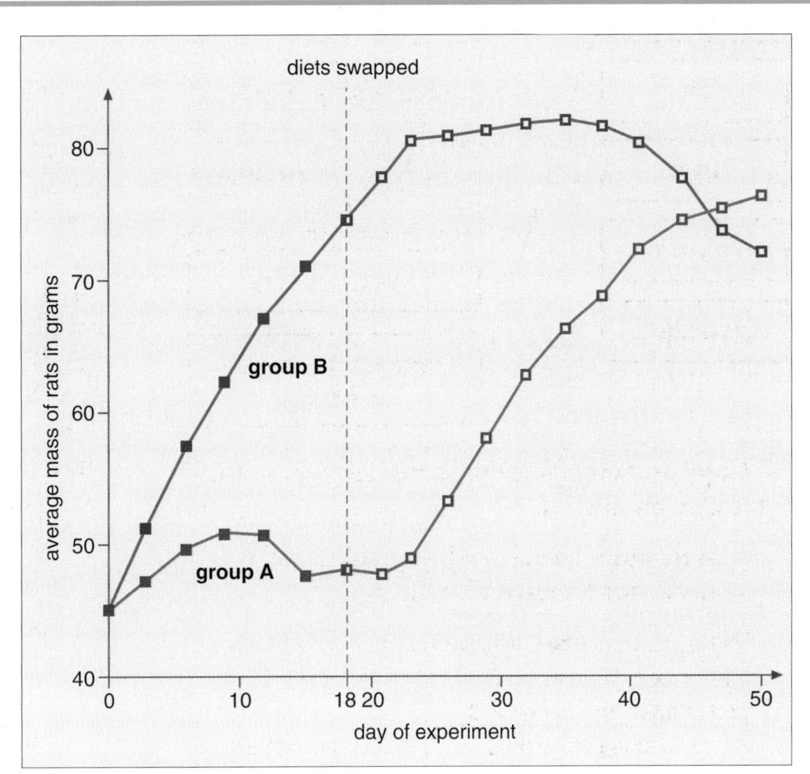

fig 24

a ■ **i** Describe what happened to the mass of group A rats for the first 18 days of the experiment. *(2)*

◆ **ii** Explain why the mass of these rats changed as it did. *(2)*

■ **iii** What happened to the mass of group A rats after day 18? *(2)*

◆ **iv** Explain these changes. *(2)*

b Read through the details of James Lind's investigation (spread A1.1), which took place more than 150 years before Gowland Hopkins' experiments.

◆ **i** Both scientists used a similar approach to try to make their experiment a fair test. Explain how they did this. *(2)*

◆ **ii** Describe two differences between the experiments that made Gowland Hopkins' results more valid. *(2)*

◆ **iii** Very soon after Gowland Hopkins' experiment, vitamins were identified in milk. Suggest why vitamins were not identified in oranges after Lind's experiment. *(2)*

A2 Diversity and adaptation

Links to Double Award

Introduction

Ever since the time of Aristotle in Ancient Greece, mankind has been classifying organisms. Aristotle classified about 500 different organisms, but now millions of types of organism are known.

To classify organisms, we need to look at their characteristics and use these to divide the organisms into groups. For example, the pupils in a town could be divided into two schools according to sex, boys in one school and girls in another. Each school is then divided into years according to the age of the pupils. Each year may then be divided into classes or sets, which could be based on ability in a subject. This is the principle of a modern classification system. As you move down the system, there are more and more groups. There are fewer and fewer members in these groups but the members have more in common with each other.

The huge number of different organisms on Earth has been produced by the process of evolution. There is such a great variety because of the large number of different habitats on the planet. Each species has developed as a result of natural selection. Mutations produce variation, and natural selection allows those that are best suited to each environment to survive. Sometimes the result of evolution is that organisms look very different even though they might be quite closely related. This is the case with some of the mammals. Their limbs have evolved to help them survive in different habitats. Although they carry out different jobs, the limbs are built to the same pattern (fig 1).

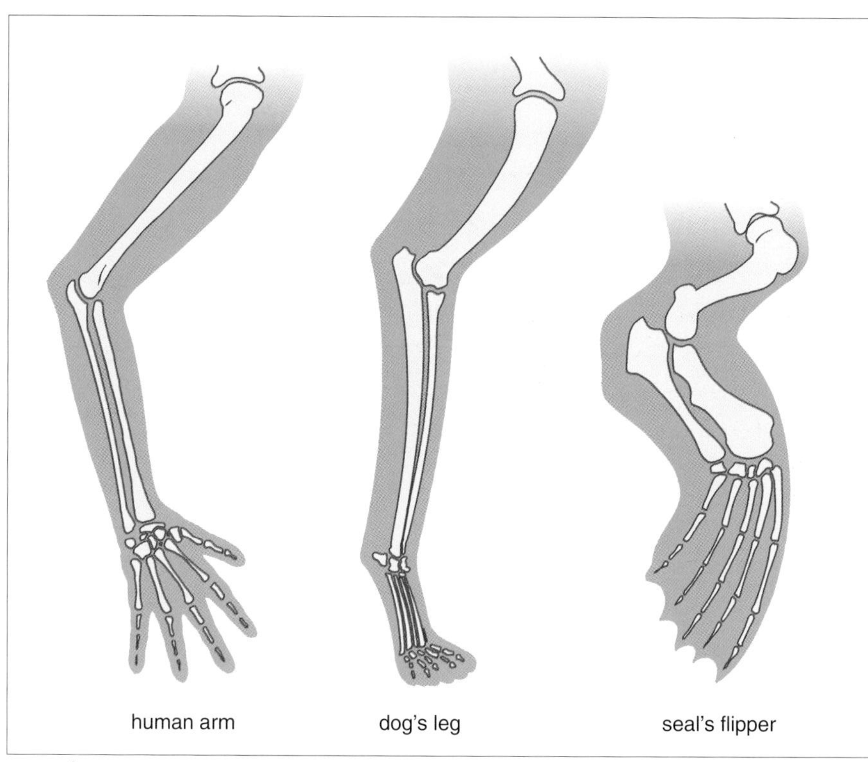

fig 1 Mammalian limbs all have the same basic structure but the limbs have evolved to perform different functions

Some groups of animals, such as the reptiles and insects, have become very well adapted to living in dry places by the process of natural selection. Many flowering plants have also achieved this. They have all developed ways of minimising their loss of water.

Check-up

Have a go at the following questions. They will remind you of what you should know about diversity and adaptation.

a Why have people found it useful to classify organisms into groups?

b What is a habitat?

c How do mutations occur?

d Name the scientist who put forward the idea of natural selection.

e Briefly explain how natural selection can cause a group of organisms to become better suited to their environment.

f Describe two similarities between a human arm and a seal's flipper.

g How do plants lose water?

Contents of the Teaching block

A2.1 Classification

The type of classification system that we use today was first developed in the 17th century by an Englishman called John Ray. The system was enlarged and improved by a Swedish scientist called Carl Linnaeus. Linnaeus also developed a method of naming organisms – the binomial system.

A2.2 Diversity and adaptation in plants

The first step in classifying organisms is to place them into one of five kingdoms. These include the plant and the animal kingdoms. The main difference between plants and animals is their method of feeding; this leads to other differences. The flowering plants are one of the largest groups in the plant kingdom and they have a number of adaptations for living on dry land.

A2.3 Diversity and adaptation in animals

The animal kingdom contains many groups, the largest of which are the arthropods and the vertebrates. The vertebrates include fish, amphibians, reptiles, birds and mammals. Fish are restricted to living in water; amphibians need damp conditions, whereas reptiles are adapted to living in much drier habitats. Arthropods can find a suitable habitat by simple responses to stimuli. Many also have complex life cycles that reduce competition with each other.

A2.1 Classification (1)

Key points

- Artificial classification systems are based on single characteristics.
- Modern classification systems are natural systems and often provide information about evolutionary pathways. They were first developed by John Ray.
- The first step in classifying an organism is to place it into a kingdom, of which there are five.
- Organisms are named using the binomial system that was introduced by Carl Linnaeus.

fig 2 | John Ray (1627–1705)

Why classify organisms?

At present about five million different living organisms have been identified as being alive today. For convenience, we place these organisms into groups. This makes it much easier to identify and compare organisms. The process of classifying organisms into groups is called **taxonomy**.

a Why might a current classification system actually have more than five million organisms in it?

b Give two reasons why a classification system of the future may have to classify many more than five million organisms.

fig 3 | Carl Linnaeus (1707–1778)

Methods of classifying

For hundreds of years, organisms were put into groups according to a single characteristic. This is called an **artificial system.** For example, poisonous plants would be put into one group whilst plants used for medicines would be in another group. This system meant that very different organisms were classified together in the same group. It also made it very difficult to make predictions about organisms. For example, a locust and a bird may have been placed in the same group because they could both fly. There are, however, big differences in all the major systems of their bodies.

Modern scientists use a **natural system** of classifying organisms. In this system, organisms that have the most common characteristics are put together in a group. This system also provides some information about evolution. If organisms are classified together, it is likely that they evolved from the same type of ancestor and so are closely related.

IDEAS AND EVIDENCE

Aristotle was the first person to try to carry out a scientific classification of living organisms. He classified about 500 different animals on the basis of a number of features such as structure, behaviour and ecology. His system often classified an organism on the basis of a single characteristic.

c Suggest why Aristotle classified only 500 animals.

Aristotle's classification system remained in use for nearly 2000 years. However, in the seventeenth century, explorers were beginning to travel much further afield and Aristotle's system was starting to prove inadequate.

d Suggest why the travels of explorers made Aristotle's system appear inadequate.

John Ray was born in England in 1627 and devoted much of his life to studying plant physiology. He was the first person to classify organisms according to a large number of characteristics, such as the type of flowers, seeds, fruits and roots. Until this time most people still used the system put forward by Aristotle in Ancient Greece.

e What is the name for the type of system devised by Ray?

Carl Linnaeus was born in Sweden two years after Ray died. He was inspired by Ray's work and made many improvements to Ray's classification system. He wanted to construct a system of classification that would be 'the plan for nature used by God the Creator'. Linnaeus believed that since the creation of the world, no new species had been created and none had become extinct.

f What type of evidence may have made Linnaeus question the idea that no organisms had become extinct?

Linnaeus started a new system of naming organisms that avoided using common names. This is called the binomial system, and is described in more detail overleaf.

How many groups?

Organisms are placed into groups, which in turn are divided into smaller and smaller groups. This produces a system of classification in which the smaller the groups become, the more similar are its members to each other.

The largest group is a **kingdom;** the kingdoms are subdivided into phyla (singular: **phylum**) followed by **classes, orders, families, genera (singular: genus)** and **species.**

Kingdoms may contain millions of different types of organisms but the number in each group decreases as the groups are divided further. Fig 4 shows how humans are classified.

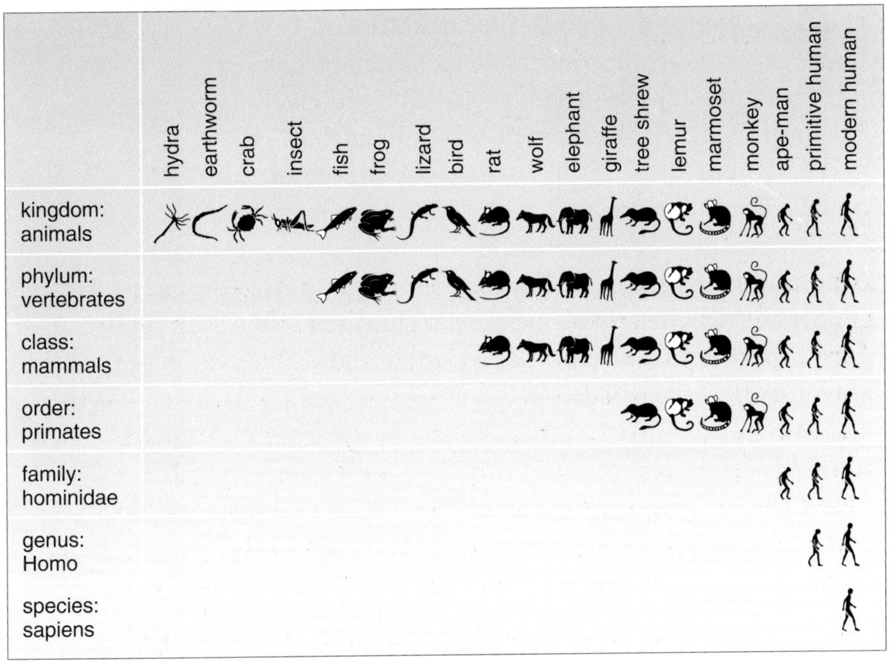

fig 4 Classification of man

Continued ▶

A2.1 Classification (2)

What is a species?

The smallest group in classification contains only one type of organism and is called a species. Sometimes it is quite difficult to tell if two organisms are members of the same species. This is because even members of the same species may look different from each other because of variation.

The most common definition that is used for a species is:

> a group of similar organisms that can breed with each other to produce fertile offspring.

g Why does this definition make it difficult to place organisms such as bacteria into species?

Some closely related species can breed and produce offspring but the offspring are infertile (sterile). These offspring are called hybrids. For example, a horse and a donkey can mate to produce a mule. Different species of plants can also reproduce to produce infertile offspring.

Naming organisms

Fig 5 shows a photograph of a wild flower and includes some of the names that it has in different parts of the country. This situation can be very confusing and so all organisms are given a scientific name. This system was introduced by Carl Linnaeus in 1735. It is called the **binomial system** of naming because it gives every species a name made up of two parts. The name is in Latin and is unique. The first part of the name is the genus that the species belongs to and the second part is the species. For example the flower in fig 5 is called:

Arum maculatum

Arum is the name of the genus containing similar plants	*maculatum* comes from the Latin for spotted

Note that the name is always in italics when it is typed and that the genus name starts with a capital letter but the species name starts with a lower-case letter.

fig 5 | The plant *Arum maculatum* has many different common names

Taking it further

New species can be formed when two groups of organisms of the same species become separated for a long period of time. This is discussed on spread 10.9. Sometimes, however, a new species is formed when two different species interbreed. If the two species are closely related, they may breed and form a sterile hybrid. This happened in the case of a type of grass called *Spartina* that lives in salt marshes. In 1870, a hybrid appeared that was the result of a cross between a British species and a species that had been introduced from America. The hybrid, called *Spartina townsendii*, was infertile but spread rapidly.

More recently, *S. townsendii* has formed a new species by doubling its chromosome number. This hybrid is fertile and is now a new species called *Spartina angelica*. Scientists think that many plant species may have developed in this way.

h The sterile hybrid reproduced for many generations before becoming fertile. How did it do this?

i Why is it less likely that new animal species evolved in this way?

Thinking further

1 Which of the following is the correct scientific name for our species?
   a *homo habilus*
   b *Homo sapiens*
   c *Homo erectus*
   d *Homo Sapiens*

2 Write down four characteristics that might be useful in classifying animals in a natural classification system.

3 Size is not always a useful way of classifying organisms. Why is this?

4 Suggest why the scientific names in the binomial system are in Latin.

5 Different members of the same species may look very different.
   a Why is this?
   b How could you tell that they belonged to the same species?

KEY WORDS

artificial system • **binomial system** • **class** • **family** • **genus** • **kingdom** • natural system • **order** • **phylum** • **species** • **taxonomy**

A2.2 Diversity and adaptation in plants

Key points

- The modern classification system that is usually used today has five kingdoms, one of which is plants.
- The most advanced phylum of plants is the flowering plants; they are well adapted to living on dry land.

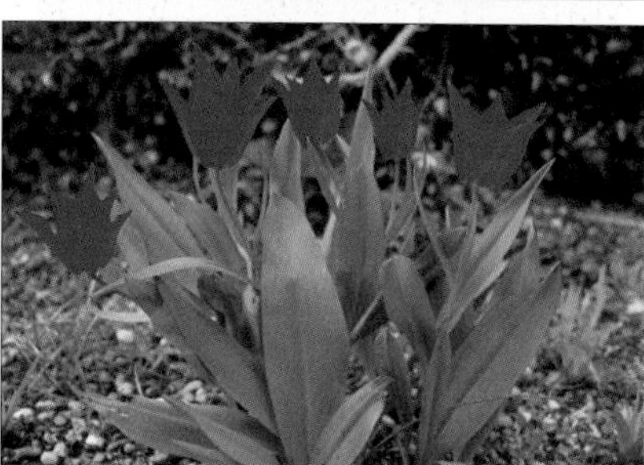

fig 6 Examples of plants (from top to bottom): moss – the stalked capsules above the plants contain the reproductive spore; ferns; conifers – the Scots pine, showing the young male cones; a flowering plant – tulips

Plant or animal?

Most scientists now use a scheme of classification put forward by Margulis and Schwatz in 1988. Their scheme divides organisms into five kingdoms: bacteria, protoctista, fungi, plants and animals.

It is usually obvious whether an organism is a plant or an animal but sometimes it can be difficult to tell. The main difference between animals and plants is their method of feeding. Plants are **autotrophic** – they make their own food from simple chemicals by photosynthesis. Animals take in their food as complex ready-made chemicals. They are **heterotrophic.** Many of the other differences between plants and animals are a result of the difference in feeding method. These include their speed of responding to stimuli and their degree of movement. Plants tend to respond more slowly and move only by growing in a particular direction. There are also important differences in the structure of their cells (see spread 1.1).

a What do plant cells possess that animal cells lack?

The other three kingdoms are the bacteria, fungi and protoctista. The bacteria and fungi are discussed on spread A4.1. The protoctista are a kingdom that contains the protozoa. These were originally classified as single-celled animals. The kingdom also contains the algae, which used to be classified as plants. Some of these algae are single celled whereas others, such as the seaweeds, are relatively simple groups of cells. Many of the protoctista share some of the characteristics of plants and animals and so it is convenient to place them in their own kingdom.

Colonising the land

Four main phyla of plants have evolved. These are the bryophytes, ferns, conifers and flowering plants (fig 6).

- Bryophytes include the mosses. These are small plants that need to live in damp conditions. This is because they do not have xylem vessels to transport water and they produce gametes that need water to swim and meet.

- Ferns have developed xylem vessels and so can grow tall but they still produce gametes that swim. They therefore need damp conditions.
- Conifers and flowering plants have broken this need for damp conditions and can live in much drier areas.
- Enclosing the male gamete in a pollen grain eliminates the need for water for reproduction. In many flowering plants the pollen is transferred from plant to plant by insects. Some flowering plants such as cacti have adaptations that enable them to grow in the driest conditions.

Adaptations for pollination

Many flowering plants are adapted for pollination by a particular insect. In some, the relationship is very close and neither organism could survive without the other. The deadnettle flower is usually pollinated by bees. The lower petal of the flower acts as a landing platform for the bee. The weight of the bee causes the stigma to jerk down. The bee is then in the correct position so that any pollen on its back will rub onto the stigma. When the bee withdraws from the flower, the stamens rub pollen onto its back (fig 7).

b What is the bee searching for when it lands on the flower?

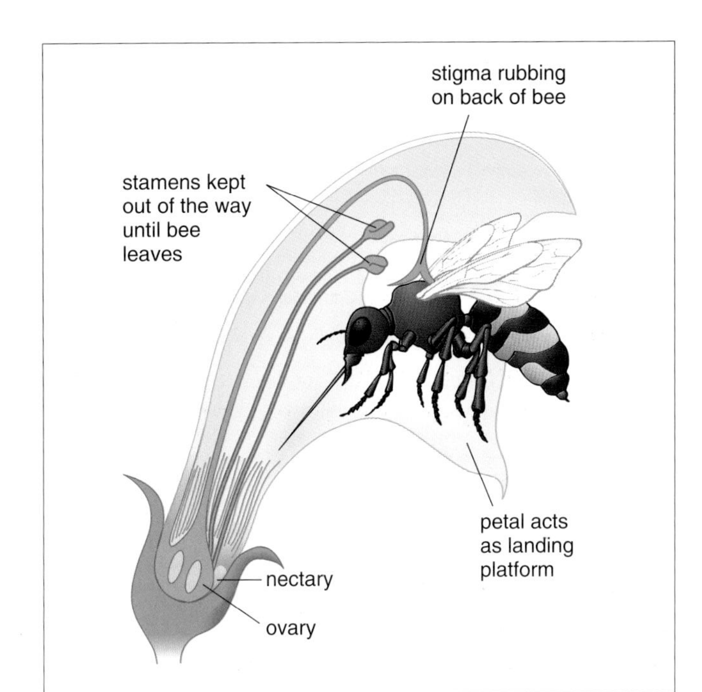

fig 7 | A bee entering a deadnettle flower

Living in dry conditions

Cacti are flowering plants that are very well adapted for growing in dry or **arid** conditions. Many of these adaptations are shown in fig 8.

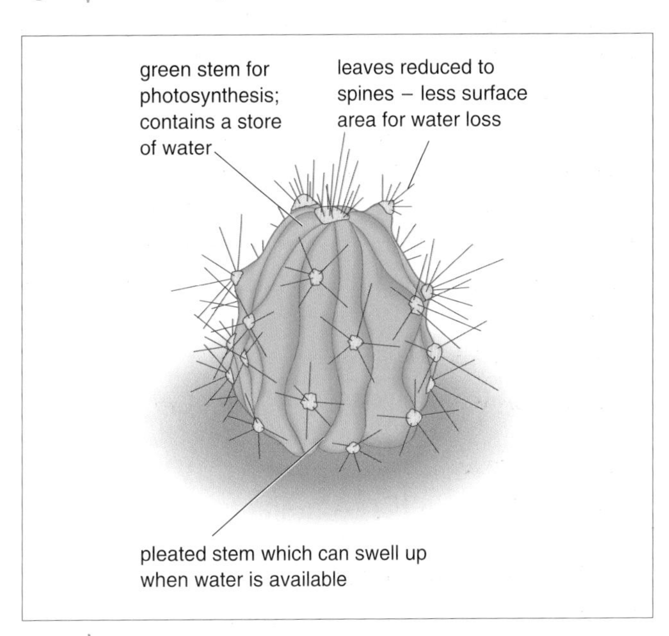

fig 8 | Adaptations of cacti to living in dry conditions

Thinking further

1 Unlike animals, plants have no need for quick responses and tend to move only by growing in a particular direction. Explain why this is.

2 Suggest why the water that is stored in the stem of a cactus contains various poisonous chemicals.

◆ **3** Explain how the shape of the deadnettle flower (fig 7) tends to prevent the flower from being pollinated by its own pollen (self-pollination).

KEY WORDS
arid • autotrophic • heterotrophic

A2.3 Diversity and adaptation in animals

Key points

- Most habitats on Earth have been colonised by animals and these animals have become adapted to the conditions found in these habitats.
- These adaptations include differences in the structure of their bodies, their body processes and their life cycles.

Classifying animals

Once an organism has been placed in the animal kingdom it can be classified into one of a number of phyla. A full classification system has a large number of phyla. Two of the major phyla are the arthropods and the vertebrates.
The vertebrates are then further divided into five classes, shown in fig 9. All of these classes of vertebrates include animals that are adapted in different ways. Some, like the mammals, can live in a number of different habitats whereas fish are much more restricted in where they can live.

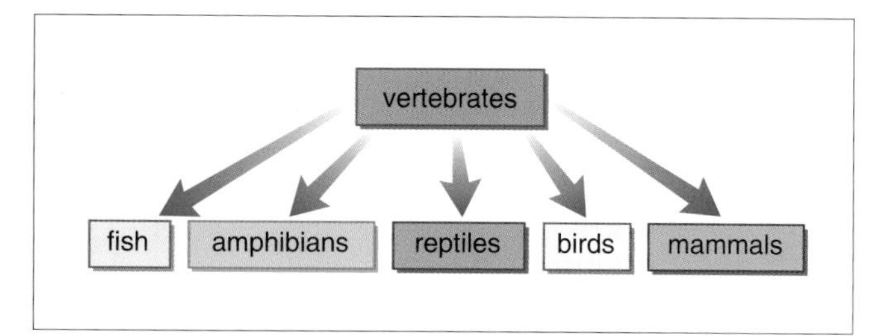

fig 9 | Classification of vertebrates

Gaseous exchange in fish

Fish are restricted to living in water because of their method of gaseous exchange. Fish obtain oxygen from water using **gills**. Bony fish have four gills on each side of the body. Water is drawn in through the mouth and passes over the gills (fig 10). It leaves the fish through a flap called the operculum.

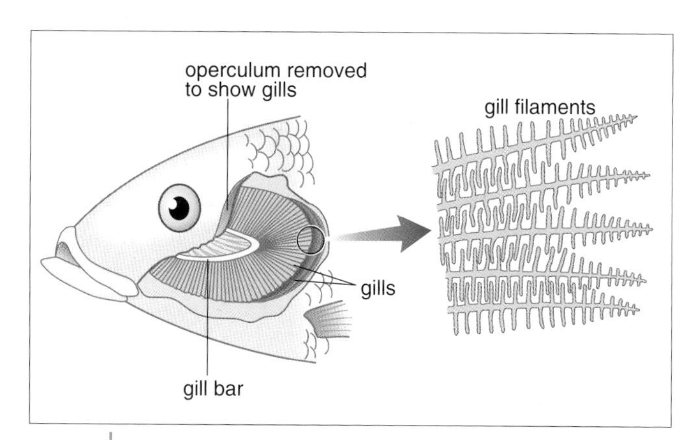

fig 10 | Flow of water over the gills

The gills (fig 11) are made up of three main parts:

- The **gill rakers** filter out small stones and other particles that may damage the gills.
- The **gill bar** carries blood vessels and supports the gill.
- The many **gill filaments** are branched and contain small capillaries.

The water flows over the gill filaments.
Oxygen diffuses into the capillaries and carbon dioxide passes into the water.

a The gill filaments look very pink. Explain why?

b Why do the filaments have many branches?

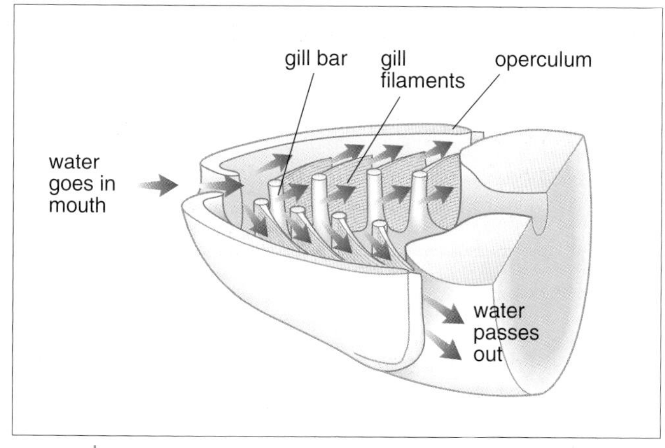

fig 11 | Structure of the gills (the gill rakers are not shown)

Adaptations of amphibians and reptiles

Unlike fish, amphibians such as frogs and toads do not have to live in water because the adults possess lungs rather than gills. They do, however, need to live in damp places for a number of reasons:

- Amphibians breed by **external fertilisation** in which the sperm and eggs are released outside the body into water.
- The eggs are covered in jelly and would easily dry out on land.
- The eggs hatch into **larvae**, such as tadpoles, which have gills and so need to live in water.
- The skin of the adult amphibian is not waterproof.

Reptiles, however, are well adapted to living on land and can live in some of the driest areas. They have a waterproof, scaly skin. Reptiles breed by **internal fertilisation**, in which the sperm are placed inside the female, and they lay eggs which have a tough, waterproof, leathery shell.

Some adaptations of arthropods

Arthropods have adaptations in their behaviour and life cycles that have enabled them to live in almost every habitat on the planet. Many arthropods have behaviour patterns that help them to find the habitat that they prefer. One type of response is called a **kinesis**. This involves the organism moving more quickly when it is in an area where conditions are unfavourable and slowing down when conditions are suitable. The organism therefore spends most of its time in suitable conditions. These responses can be investigated using a **choice chamber** (fig 12). This simple apparatus gives the organism a choice of conditions and then at any one time the number of organisms in each area can be counted. This gives an idea of the preferred habitat.

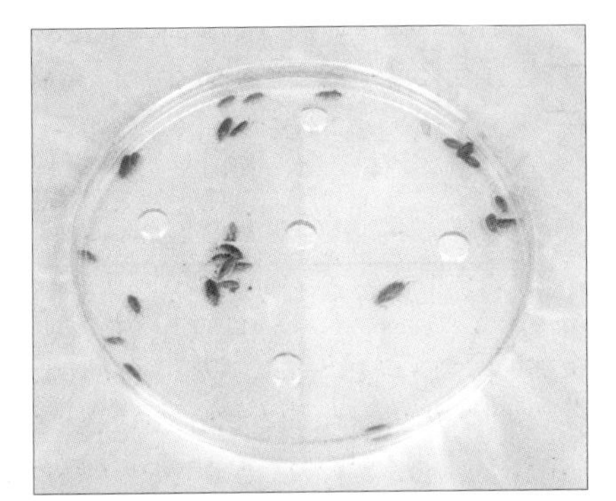

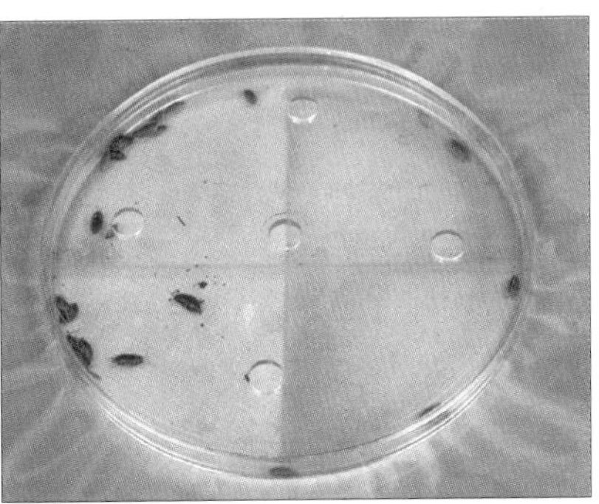

fig 12 | Choice chambers are used to find out the conditions that arthropods such as woodlice, prefer

The insects are the largest class in the arthropod phylum. Many insects, such as the blowfly, undergo a complete change in body form at some stage of their life cycle. This is called **metamorphosis**. The stages for the blowfly are shown in fig 13.

The larvae and adult insects usually feed on different foods in different habitats. This means that they are not competing directly with each other for food.

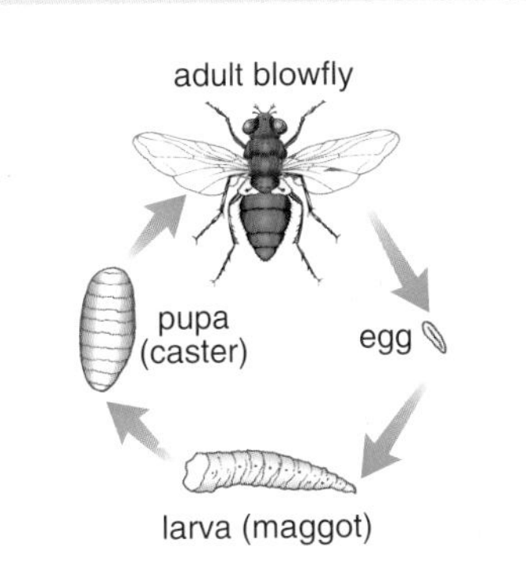

fig 13 | Life cycle of the blowfly

KEY WORDS

choice chamber • external fertilisation • gill bar • gill filaments • gill rakers • gills • internal fertilisation • kinesis • larva(e) • metamorphosis

Thinking further

■ **1** In a choice-chamber some blowfly larvae were given the choice between light and dark. Which condition do you think the larvae would prefer?

■ **2** How would these responses help the larvae to find their usual habitat?

◆ **3** The characteristics needed by a respiratory surface are described on the introductory spread of Teaching block 4. How do the gills fulfil these characteristics?

Questions on diversity and adaptation

● **1** Copy the sentences below, filling in the gaps using words from the following list. You may use each word once, more than once or not at all. *(8)*

animal • aquatic • arthropod • carbon dioxide • class • gill filaments • gill rakers • gills • nitrogen • order • oxygen • terrestrial • vertebrate

The group containing fish is a __________ belonging to the __________ phylum. The phylum is part of the __________ kingdom. Fish have respiratory surfaces called __________ . They extract __________ from the water and release __________ . They are able to do this because they have a large number of __________ that increase the surface area. This system of gaseous exchange restricts them to __________ habitats.

2 The modern system of classification places organisms into groups of decreasing size. The groupings are genus, family, order, class, kingdom, species, phylum.

● **a** Put these groups in order starting with the largest. *(6)*

● **b** **i** How many kingdoms are there? *(1)*

ii What are the names of these kingdoms? *(2)*

● **c** **i** If you discovered a strange new organism, how would you decide whether it was an animal or a plant? *(2)*

ii If the organism showed some plant and some animal characteristics, which kingdom would you place it in? *(1)*

■ **d** The binomial name for man is *Homo sapiens*. What does this indicate about its classification? *(2)*

■ **3** Fig 14 shows an apparatus used to investigate the conditions that woodlice prefer.

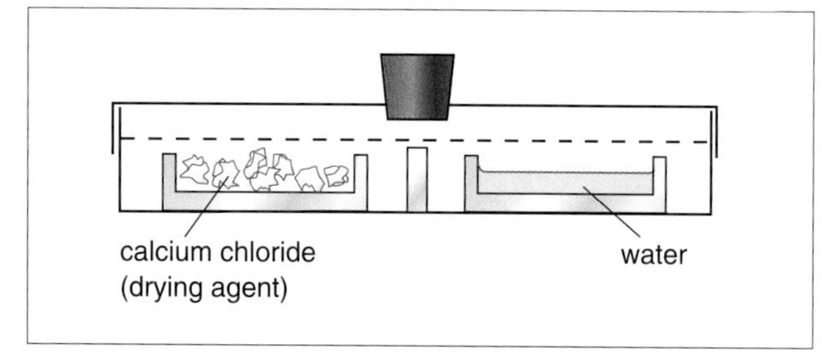

fig 14

a **i** What is the name given to this type of apparatus? *(1)*

ii The apparatus is set up to investigate responses to a certain environmental condition. What is this condition? *(1)*

b Twenty woodlice were placed in the apparatus. The number of woodlice found in each half was counted every minute for eight minutes. The results are shown in fig 15.

	number of woodlice	
time in mins	**in left side**	**in right side**
1	8	12
2	6	14
3	3	17
4	2	18
5	1	19
6	0	20
7	1	19
8	1	19

fig 15

i Plot a line graph to show how the number of woodlice on each side varied with time. Draw the two sets of results on the same pair of axes. *(6)*

ii Which environmental condition did the woodlice prefer in this experiment? *(1)*

iii What name is given to the type of response shown by the woodlice in this experiment? *(1)*

iv How does this response help the woodlice survive? *(2)*

v How would you adapt this experiment to investigate whether the woodlice favour damp conditions or dark conditions? *(3)*

4

■ **a** Each of the features in the list below applies to fish, amphibians or reptiles.

- lay eggs with a leathery shell
- smooth permeable skin
- adults have lungs but larvae have gills
- internal fertilisation
- adults have gills

- body covered in moist scales
- body covered in waterproof scales

Copy and complete fig 16 by placing each feature in the correct column. *(7)*

fish	amphibians	reptiles

fig 16

◆ **b** Reptiles are better adapted than fish and amphibians to living on land. Use the features listed above and your biological knowledge to explain how they achieve this. *(4)*

◆ **5** The life cycle of insects such as the blowfly consists of four main stages:

adult • pupae • larvae • eggs

a Arrange these stages in the order in which they occur in the life cycle of the blowfly. *(1)*

b The larva and pupa stages of the blowfly are often given specific names. Write down these names. *(2)*

c **i** Explain what is meant by the term metamorphosis. *(2)*

ii Explain how metamorphosis has enabled insects to colonise a wide range of habitats. *(2)*

6 Each of the following adaptations helps the plant species to survive. In each case explain how.

■ **a** Cacti have leaves that have been reduced to spines. *(3)*

◆ **b** Some cacti have very deep roots whereas others have shallow roots that spread out over a long distance. *(3)*

◆ **c** A deadnettle flower produces nectar. *(2)*

◆ **d** The male gametes of flowering plants are enclosed in pollen grains. *(2)*

◆ **e** The shape of the deadnettle flower encourages cross-pollination and prevents self-pollination. *(3)*

IDEAS AND EVIDENCE

7 Read the following passage about John Ray and answer the questions below.

John Ray was the first person to develop a natural classification system. He used this system to investigate how different organisms are adapted to their environment. He believed that this was due to God's design.

Ray also had a number of theories about fossils. Many people at the time would not believe that fossils were once living organisms. Ray believed that they were but did not understand why some fossils did not look like any organisms that still existed. He could not believe that God would let any organisms that had been created become extinct.

◆ **a** What is a natural classification system? *(2)*

■ **b** How were fossils formed? *(2)*

◆ **c** John Ray lived about 200 years before Charles Darwin. If Ray had lived after Darwin, how might this have changed his ideas on:

i why organisms are adapted to their environment *(3)*

ii why some fossils do not look like organisms that are alive today? *(2)*

A3 Micro-organisms and food

Links to Double Award

2 Digestion	Chemistry 4 Rates of reaction
10 Inheritance and evolution	Physics 5 Radioactivity

Introduction

We normally think of micro-organisms as organisms that can cause disease. However, they are also responsible for the decay of food. Food that has gone off is more than just a minor inconvenience. It can cost millions of pounds in lost revenue and can cause untold misery to people who contract food poisoning from the toxins produced by the microbes.

fig 1 Contaminated food can make you ill ...

Micro-organisms, like most living organisms, prefer warm, moist conditions and reproduce rapidly when these conditions exist. Just a few bacteria can reproduce to produce tens of thousands in only a few hours. If these bacteria happen to be on food that has been left out after a meal, they could cause food poisoning in anybody who eats the food.

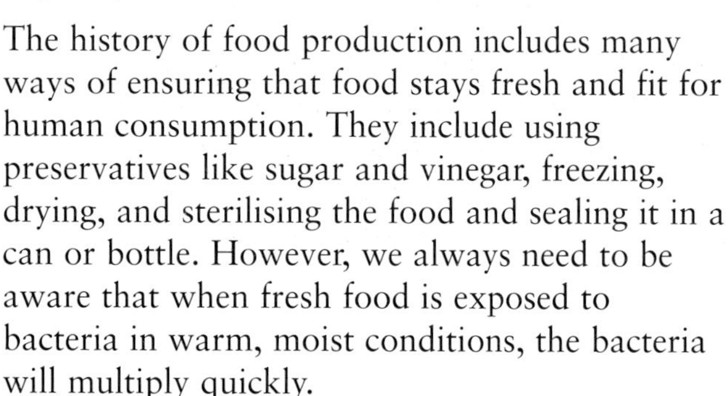

The history of food production includes many ways of ensuring that food stays fresh and fit for human consumption. They include using preservatives like sugar and vinegar, freezing, drying, and sterilising the food and sealing it in a can or bottle. However, we always need to be aware that when fresh food is exposed to bacteria in warm, moist conditions, the bacteria will multiply quickly.

fig 2 Micro-organisms are essential for the production of a variety of foods

The story of micro-organisms and food is not all bad news. Some micro-organisms are used in the manufacture of certain types of food. Without micro-organisms we would not have cheese, bread, yoghurt or alcohol, and our diet would be far less interesting and varied.

Genetic engineering has taken the role of micro-organisms in food production even further, and we can now buy items such as vegetarian cheese which were not available a few years ago.

Check-up

Have a go at the following questions. They will remind you of what you should know about micro-organisms and food.

a John eats a bacon sandwich. It contains carbohydrate, protein and fat. Explain what will happen to these substances when they are digested.

b Mary tries to eat a balanced diet. Explain what is meant by the term balanced diet.

c During digestion, food is broken down by enzymes. Choose one of the enzymes that you have studied and explain what it does.

d Explain what the purpose of digestion is and how the process works.

e The gut has a large surface area with a good blood supply. Explain how these two factors aid the process of digestion.

Contents of the Teaching block

A3.1 Food poisoning

Food poisoning is caused by eating food contaminated with micro-organisms. It causes illness ranging from an upset stomach to prolonged and serious vomiting and diarrhoea, and can sometimes lead to death. Good hygiene is extremely important in reducing the possibility of food poisoning.

A3.2 Making food

Micro-organisms are used to make foods such as bread, yoghurt and cheese.

A3.3 Enzymes

Enzymes are biological catalysts.
They speed up the rate of a chemical reaction. This spread looks at how enzymes work and what can affect them.

A3.4 DNA makes protein

DNA codes for all of the proteins that make a human being. This spread looks at how the chemical code of DNA is translated and how this results in a single gene being responsible for making a single protein.

A3.5 Biotechnology and food

Biotechnology has now become extremely important in the manufacture of modern foods. This spread looks at how the biotechnology revolution had given us products such as vegetarian cheese.

A3.1 Food poisoning

Key points

- Micro-organisms can cause food to go bad, which can lead to food poisoning.
- Hygienic practices can prevent food poisoning.
- Food can be preserved in a variety of ways.

The growth of micro-organisms

Micro-organisms can grow very quickly. Some bacteria can multiply every twenty minutes.

a If one bacteria divides into two every twenty minutes, how many bacteria would there be after ten hours?

Like all living organisms, in order to multiply bacteria need:

- **warmth**
- **moisture**
- **food.**

These are exactly the conditions found in most kitchens. If just a few bacteria get onto food, in a few hours they will have multiplied into tens of thousands (fig 3).

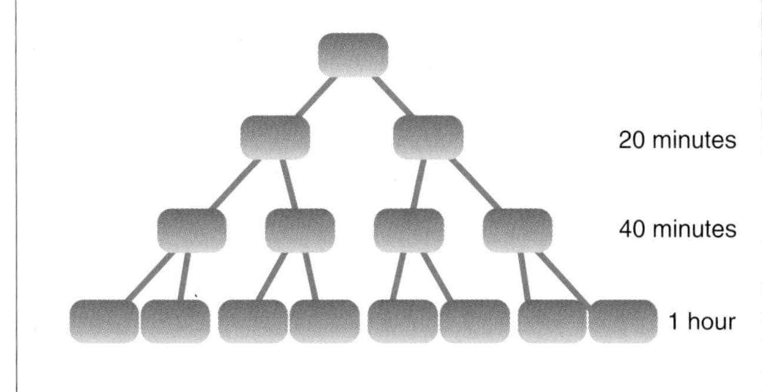

fig 3 | Micro-organisms reproduce very quickly

Keeping food safe

Some foods such as raw meat can contain large quantities of bacteria such as ***Salmonella*** which can cause food poisoning. These bacteria can be transferred to our hands while handling meat. Anything we touch after that will become **contaminated** with the bacteria.

b Explain why we should not handle cooked food after touching raw meat.

c Explain why we should not put cooked food on a work surface that has just been used for raw meat.

Preserving food

Fig 4 shows ways in which food can be preserved.

d Give one example of a food preserved by each of the different methods listed in fig 4.

canning	sterilised food is sealed away from bacteria
freezing	food is too cold for bacteria to grow
drying	bacteria need water to live
ultra-heat treatment	bacteria are killed but without spoiling the taste of the food
irradiation	bacteria are killed but without spoiling the taste of the food
chemical preservatives	bacteria are killed but without spoiling the taste of the food

fig 4

Some foods, for example jams, are preserved by adding substances such as sugar. Although this does not remove the water from the food, it lowers the **water potential** or water concentration of the food (fig 5). The high solute concentration of sugar causes water to leave any bacteria by osmosis. The bacteria die and the food stays fresh.

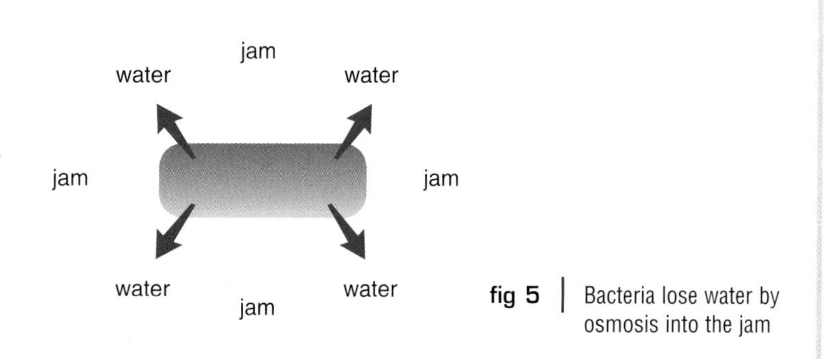

fig 5 Bacteria lose water by osmosis into the jam

IDEAS AND EVIDENCE

Some people are concerned that preserving food by irradiation or using chemical preservatives may not be safe. They think that radiation is dangerous, even though it does not make the food radioactive. They also think that the chemicals may cause damage to the body if eaten over long periods of time.

Other people think that these methods of preserving food are safe. They say that radiation only kills bacteria, and passes straight through the food without harming it. They also say that some natural foods contain high levels of harmful chemicals. They feel that it is much better to use preservatives than to risk catching (and possibly dying from) food poisoning.

e What do you think?

Thinking further

■ **1** State why some butchers have different staff and use different counters for serving fresh and cooked meat.

■ **2** Suggest why it is best to keep cooked food at the top of the fridge and fresh meat at the bottom.

■ **3** State five different ways of preserving food and explain how each of them works.

◆ **4** Explain how adding sugar to fruit will keep the food fresh, even though water is not removed from the food.

◆ **5** Suggest why the term 'water potential' is now used instead of the term 'water concentration'.

KEY WORDS

canning • chemical preservatives • contaminated • drying • food • freezing • irradiation • moisture • *Salmonella* • ultra-heat treatment • warmth • water potential

A3.2 Making food

Key points

- Micro-organisms are involved in the production of many foods.
- Micro-organisms can themselves be used as a food source.

The role of micro-organisms in making food

Cheese

Milk is mixed with the starter culture of *Streptococcus*. → **Chymosin** is added to make the milk clot into solid **curds** and liquid **whey**. → Solid curds are removed, placed in a press and dried to form cheese.

a Suggest how the process could be varied to make cottage cheese.

Yoghurt

Skimmed milk powder is added to the milk to concentrate it. → Milk is **pasteurised** to kill the bacteria. → *Lactobacillus* is added, which produces **lactic acid** when cultured at 46°C.

b State two differences between the production of yoghurt and the production of cheese.

Bread

A culture of **yeast**, sugar and water is added to baking flour. → The yeast respires to release carbon dioxide gas. This makes the dough rise. → The risen dough is baked in a hot oven to make bread.

c Explain why the bread will not rise if it is baked too soon.

Ethanol (alcohol)

A mixture of sugar, water and yeast is placed in a fermentation vessel. → The mixture is kept warm and anaerobic respiration occurs. → Carbon dioxide is released through the air lock and ethanol (alcohol) is produced by the yeast.

d Describe one similarity and two differences between bread making and ethanol (alcohol) production.

Vinegar

Beer, wine or pure ethanol (alcohol) is mixed with nutrients. → The mixture is trickled over wood shavings coated with a bacteria called *Acetobacter*. → The bacteria convert the ethanol (alcohol) into vinegar.

Single-cell protein (SCP)

A **fungus** is mixed with a sterilised source of carbohydrate, for example the whey from cheese production. → The fungus grows very rapidly in warm conditions. → The fungus is separated, dried and is ready for use.

SCP is also called **mycoprotein**. It is used as cattle food and is also used to make *Quorn*, a meat-free protein substitute for vegetarians. SCP is very high in protein and its production is a highly efficient process. When compared with cattle grown to produce meat, SCP:

- produces four times as much protein from the same food source
- uses a food such as whey that would often be thrown away
- produces protein more quickly and uses far less space.

Thinking further

■ **1** Describe the role played by three different types of micro-organism in making food.

■ **2** Suggest what manufacturers do to single-cell protein to make it into meat-free substitutes such as *Quorn*.

◆ **3** Suggest the environmental conditions that need to be carefully monitored and controlled when using micro-organisms to make food.

◆ **4** Suggest how food manufacturers reduce the risk of contamination by unwanted micro-organisms.

KEY WORDS

Acetobacter • chymosin • curds • fungus • *Lactobacillus* • lactic acid • mycoprotein • pasteurised • *Streptococcus* • whey • yeast

A3.3 Enzymes

Key points

- Micro-organisms use enzymes.
- Enzymes are sensitive to temperature and pH.
- Enzymes are substrate specific.
- A lock-and-key model can be used to explain how enzymes work.

What are enzymes?

Enzymes are biological **catalysts**. They speed up a chemical reaction without being changed or used up by it. Sound too good to be true? Read on …

Lock and key

The best way to describe how enzymes work is to use the lock-and-key model (fig 6). Some of the features of a lock and key are:

1. One key fits only one lock. To open a different lock, you need a different key.
2. A key can be used over and over again. It is not used or changed when it opens a lock.
3. A key can do two things: it can open a lock and it can close a lock. It works both ways.
4. The important part of a key has a fixed shape and must not change. It does not matter what shape the handle of the key is.

fig 6 | The working of an enzyme can be likened to a lock and key

Enzymes have a lot of similarities to the lock and key:

1. One enzyme does one job and reacts with one **specific substrate**. The shape of the enzyme is specific for that substrate and will not fit any other (fig 7).

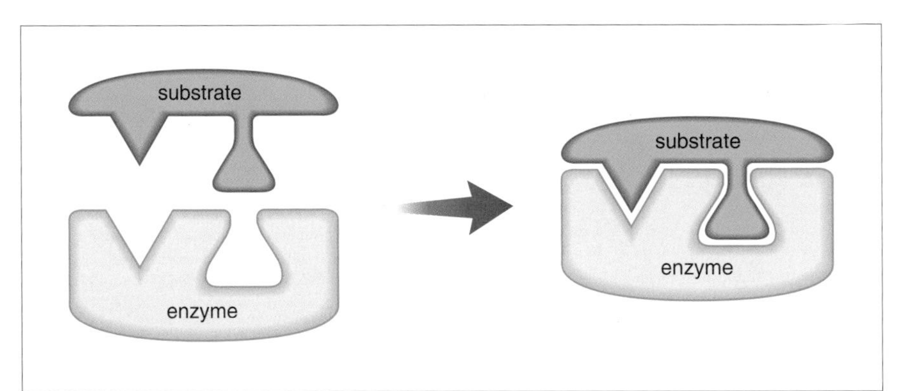

fig 7

2. Once an enzyme has reacted with a substrate it releases the products (fig 8) and repeats the process again with another substrate molecule. It does not get used up.
3. An enzyme does one of two things. It either splits a complex molecule into two simpler ones, or joins two simpler ones to make a larger more complex molecule.
4. The part of the enzyme that reacts with the substrate molecule is called the active site. It is important that this part of the molecule does not change its shape. If the shape is changed, it will not work. The lock will not fit the key.

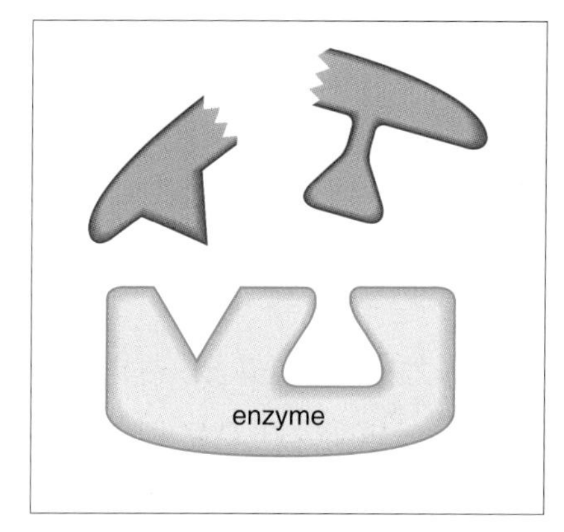

fig 8

The effect of temperature and pH

Both temperature and pH affect the way enzymes work because they can both change the shape of the enzyme. When the enzyme changes shape, it will not work as well. The greater the change in shape, the more likely that the enzyme will not work. Each enzyme has an **optimum** temperature and pH at which it works best (fig 9).

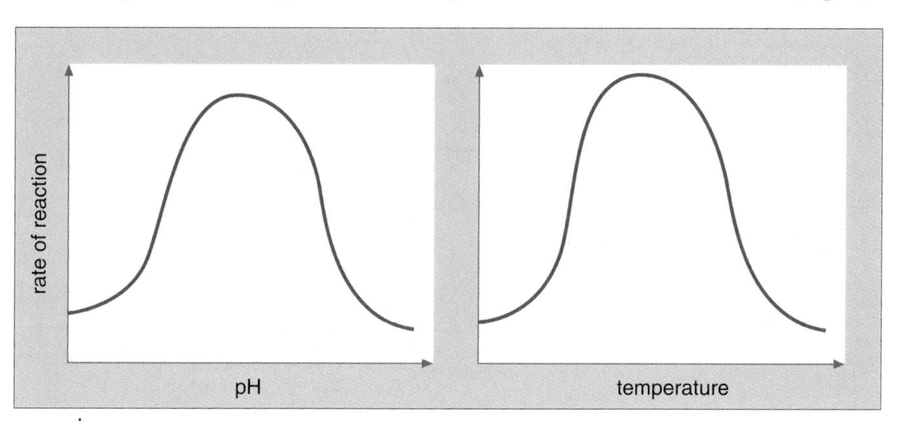

fig 9 | Each enzyme has an optimum pH and temperature at which it works best

Thinking further

1 Explain why enzymes are sometimes described as biological catalysts.

2 Explain why an enzyme works specifically with one substrate, and no other.

3 Explain how temperature and pH both affect the way that enzymes work.

4 Describe how the lock-and-key model shows how enzymes work.

KEY WORDS
catalyst • enzyme • optimum • specific • substrate

A3.4 DNA makes protein

Key points

- Each gene on the DNA codes for a specific protein.
- DNA makes a template of the gene as RNA.
- RNA constructs the protein from amino acids.
- DNA from different sources can be recombined by genetic engineering. This is called recombinant DNA.

One gene – one protein

DNA is divided into sections called **genes.** One gene codes for a specific **protein.** This is sometimes called the *one gene – one protein* law.

The DNA does not make the protein itself. Instead it makes a template of the gene using a substance called **RNA** (fig 10). The DNA stays safe and sound inside the nucleus, while the RNA moves out into the hurly-burly of the cytoplasm to make the protein.

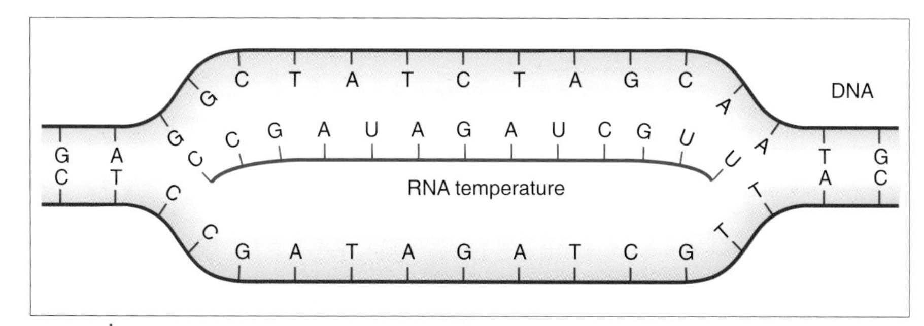

fig 10 | An RNA template is made of the gene; the RNA then leaves the nucleus

RNA is different from DNA in that:

- it is a single strand rather than a double strand
- the **base** T (thymine) is replaced with the base U (uracil).

a Suggest why it is important that the DNA stays inside the nucleus.

How RNA makes the protein

Proteins are made from amino acids. There are more than twenty different amino acids. You will recall that DNA has only four chemical bases. Problem! How do the four chemical bases of A, T, G and C code for over twenty amino acids?

The answer is just the same as the English language in which twenty-six letters code for thousands of words. The four bases are put together in different combinations.

b State how many different combinations could be made if two bases were used for each amino acid.

In fact to get sufficient combinations, three bases must be used to code for one amino acid (fig 11).

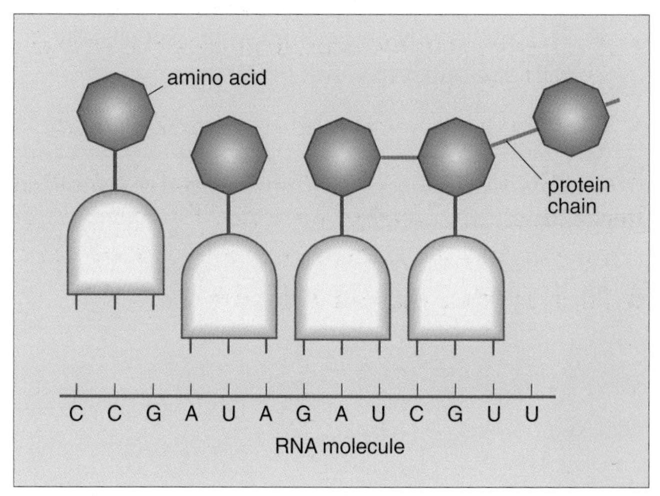

fig 11 | The RNA is used as a template to build a protein from a chain of amino acids

Recombinant DNA

The language of DNA is universal to all living things. This means that all living things use DNA, and that the same four bases code for genes in all living organisms. It is therefore possible to take a gene from one organism and place it in the DNA of a totally different organism. This is called **recombinant** DNA.
The instructions of the gene will be understood and the protein will be made from the gene.

The process of recombining DNA is done using enzymes.
One enzyme is used to cut the DNA and another enzyme is used to join the DNA (fig 12).

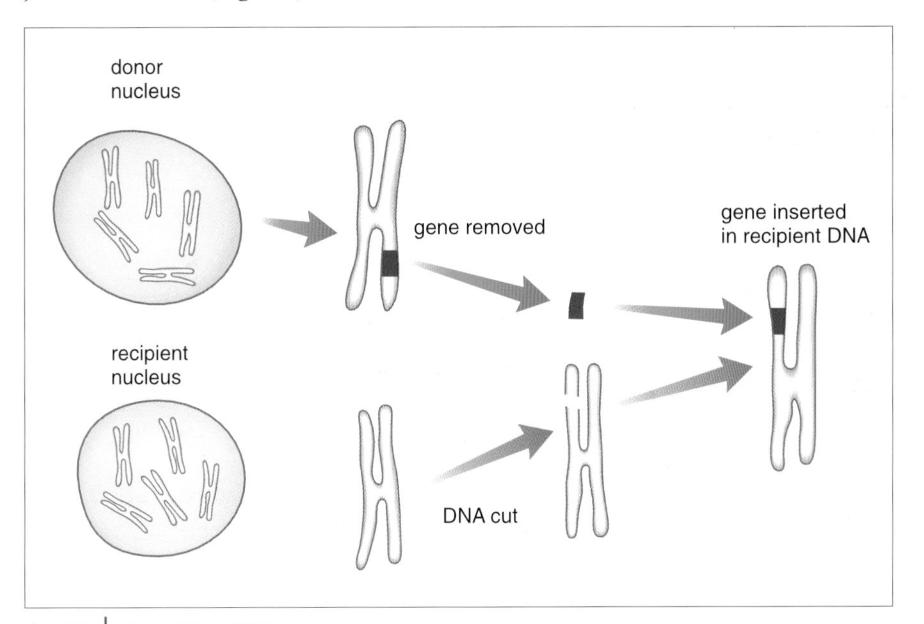

fig 12 | Recombinant DNA

The process goes like this:

- A cutting enzyme is used to remove a gene from the donor DNA.
- The same enzyme is used to cut open the DNA of the host cell.
- The gene is placed in the nucleus of the host cell.
- A different enzyme is used to stick the new gene into the DNA of the host cell.
- The new gene works and its protein is made.

The technique has been used to insert the human gene for making insulin into the DNA of bacteria. The bacteria are grown in a fermenter and the human insulin produced can be harvested.

c Suggest other uses for recombinant DNA.

Thinking further

◆ **1** Explain the term 'one gene – one enzyme'.

◆ **2** Explain how a language with only four letters can code for over twenty different amino acids.

◆ **3** Explain how DNA can be recombined from one organism to another.

KEY WORDS
bases • DNA • gene • protein • recombinant • RNA

A3.5 Biotechnology and food

Key points

- Industrial enzymes are produced from micro-organisms by fermentation.
- These micro-organisms can be genetically manipulated to improve the production of enzymes.
- Vegetarian cheese can be made using enzymes from micro-organisms instead of enzymes from animals.

Enzymes and food

The food industry uses **enzymes** in many of its production processes. In the past, enzymes were expensive because they were present in only small quantities and were difficult to extract. In 1880, a Japanese scientist called Dr Takamine developed a method for producing the enzyme diastase from a mould growing on rice. This technique is still in use today. A large range of micro-organisms is now used to produce many different enzymes.

Pectinase

Pectinase is an enzyme used in very large quantities by the food industry. It is used to break down a substance called pectin. Pectin is the substance that makes jam set, but it makes fruit juices cloudy. Uses of pectinase include:

- extracting oil from olives
- clarifying fruit juices – making them clear.

a Explain why it would not be a good idea to use pectinase when making jam.

Pectinase is made by a fungus called *Aspergillus niger*. The fungus can be grown in a **fermentation vessel** using sugar as a source of food (fig 13). It is kept at a temperature of 37 °C for about 60 hours. During this time the fungus produces large amounts of pectinase, which can then be extracted.

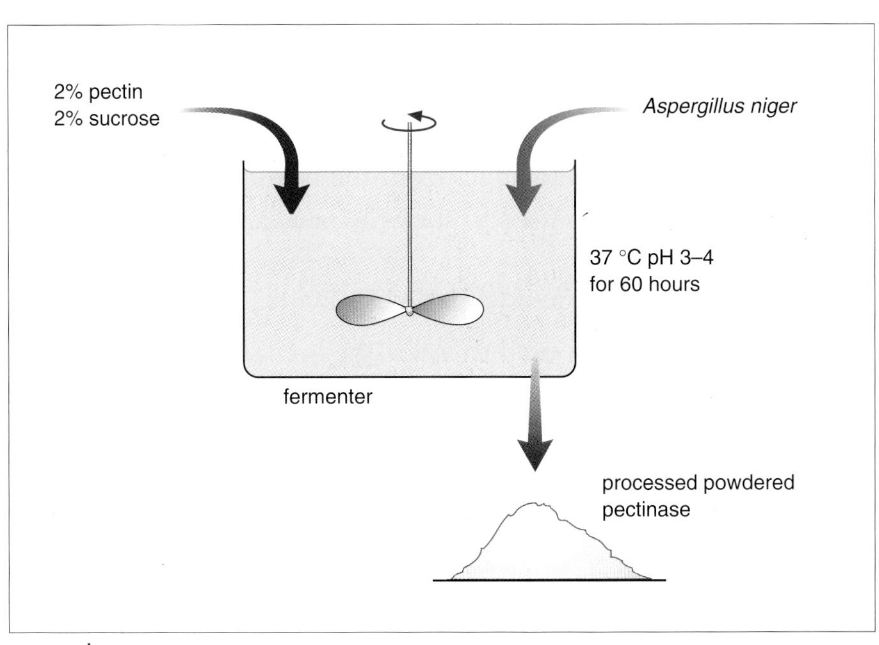

fig 13 | Production of pectinase

Vegetarian cheese

Cheese is made using the enzyme **chymosin** to clot milk. This enzyme is normally obtained from the stomach lining of calves, which means that it is unsuitable for vegetarians. Now, however, the enzyme can be made using biotechnology. The mould ***Mucor mieleli*** is grown in a fermenter and produces chymosin. Because the chymosin has not been produced from an animal, it can be used to make vegetarian cheese.

b Explain the differences in the making of normal cheese and vegetarian cheese.

Other enzymes can be used to speed up the ripening of cheese. This process can take up to a year for hard cheeses like cheddar, but can be reduced to only a few months using enzymes.

c Explain whether you think it is a good idea to use enzymes to speed up the ripening of cheese.

Improving the yield

Recent advances in genetic engineering have produced a whole new range of micro-organisms to make chymosin. DNA for the chymosin gene can now be **encoded** (built) in the laboratory without the need to extract it from calf stomach cells. The new manufactured gene has been inserted into a range of different micro-organisms, including yeast, fungi and bacteria. All these micro-organisms can now be used in fermenters to make vegetarian chymosin.

All three types of micro-organism have been approved for this use and, as yet, there is no legal requirement for the food to be labelled to show that it contains a genetically engineered product.

Thinking further

◆ **1** Suggest how recombinant DNA technology could be used to improve the yield of pectinase by the fungus *Aspergillus niger*.

◆ **2** Explain the benefits of using genetically engineered products in food.

◆ **3** Explain the potential dangers of using genetically engineered products in food.

IDEAS AND EVIDENCE

◆ **4** Explain whether you think that genetically engineered food should be labelled, and the moral implications of not doing so.

KEY WORDS

chymosin • encoded • enzyme • fermentation vessel • *Mucor mieleli* • pectinase

Questions on micro-organisms and food

1 David works in a butcher's shop. He knows that he should always wash his hands after handling raw meat. Copy the passage below about the butcher's shop and use words from the following list to fill in the gaps. You may use each word once, more than once or not at all. *(6)*

bacteria • contaminated • multiply • poisoning • raw • washed

David was serving a customer. He picked up some raw meat and placed it on a cutting board. He cut the meat, wrapped it and handed it to the customer. The board was now __________ with bacteria. He foolishly placed some cooked meat on the board. This meat now became contaminated. The __________ would __________ rapidly and could cause food __________ . David should have kept the two meats apart and __________ his hands between handling the __________ and cooked meats.

2 John is making a meat pie in a food technology class. He is going to take it home for his family's tea. Suggest how John can ensure that his pie will be safe to eat when he gets it home. *(4)*

3

a Mary is making yoghurt. The process involves the following three steps but they are written in the wrong order. Write the steps in the correct order. *(1)*

- The milk is pasteurised to kill unwanted bacteria.
- Skimmed milk powder is added to the milk.
- *Lactobacillus* is added to the liquid.

b Suggest why Mary needed to add only a small amount of *Lactobacillus* to the milk. *(1)*

c Mary heated the liquid to 75 °C. Explain why it is unlikely to turn into yoghurt. *(2)*

4 Microbes can be used to make food. Name three different kinds of food made by micro-organisms. For each one, explain the role played by the micro-organism. *(3)*

5 Richard likes to make bread. He mixes yeast into the dough to make it rise.

a State what type of respiration will take place in the dough. *(1)*

b Copy and complete the word equation for this type of respiration. *(2)*

Glucose → __________ + __________

c After mixing the yeast into the dough, Richard immediately put the dough into a hot oven. He was surprised to find that the bread had not risen at the end of the cooking time. Explain why Richard's bread did not rise. *(2)*

d Richard made a second batch of bread. This time the bread did rise. He decided to keep some for future use. Suggest and explain a method that Richard could use to store his bread. *(2)*

6 Reshma did an experiment to find the temperature at which yeast worked the best. She plotted a graph of her results (fig 14).

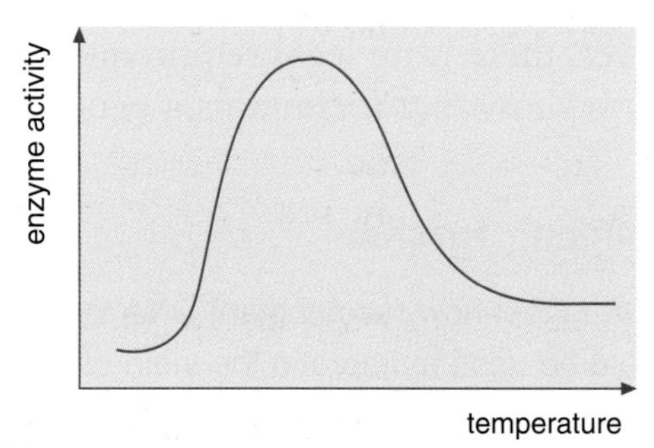

fig 14

Reshma knew that the reaction was controlled by enzymes in the yeast. Use your knowledge of enzymes to explain the following:

a The graph line rises steadily at low temperatures. *(2)*

b The graph line reaches a peak. *(2)*

c The graph line drops at high temperatures. *(2)*

d State one other factor that affects the way enzymes work. *(1)*

◆ **7** Enzyme theory is often described using the model of a lock and a key. List three ways in which the lock and key idea is similar to the way enzymes work. *(3)*

8 The police arrest a suspect for a crime. They take a DNA sample from the suspect.

◆ **a** State two roles of the DNA molecule. *(2)*

◆ **b** Explain how the police might use the DNA to evaluate whether the suspect was guilty of the crime. *(2)*

c A section of a DNA molecule contains the following sequence of bases.

AGGTACTGATTCGCATCG

■ **i** Write down the sequence of bases found on the complementary strand of the DNA molecule. *(2)*

◆ **ii** An RNA copy is made of this section. Write down the sequence of bases found in the RNA copy. *(2)*

◆ **iii** How many amino acids would this section of DNA code for in a protein? *(1)*

d A mutation occurs when part of the DNA molecule is damaged or changed.

■ **i** State two different causes of mutations. *(2)*

◆ **ii** Explain the consequences of a mutation that removed the **GG** sequence from the following strand of DNA. *(2)*

AGGTAC

◆ **9** Steven is a diabetic. He needs injections of insulin. Insulin is now produced by genetically modified bacteria.

a Explain how a human insulin gene can be placed inside a bacterium. *(4)*

b Explain the advantages of producing insulin in this way. *(2)*

10 Biotechnology is now used to produce food. During cheese making, the enzyme chymosin is used to clot milk. Chymosin is obtained from the stomach lining of calves.

● **a** Explain why some vegetarians would not want to eat this cheese. *(1)*

■ **b** Scientists can transfer the chymosin gene from a calf cell to a bacterial cell. The chymosin would then be made by the bacteria. Explain whether this would make the cheese acceptable to vegetarians. *(1)*

◆ **c** The latest scientific advances mean that scientists can build the chymosin gene in the laboratory by joining DNA bases together. This artificial gene can then be inserted into bacteria. Suggest how this might encourage even more vegetarians to eat cheese. *(1)*

IDEAS AND EVIDENCE

◆ **11** Food can be genetically engineered to make it taste better and also so that its stays fresh for longer. Some food retailers have banned genetically modified (GM) food from their shelves. This has come about because a small group of protestors were successful in portraying GM food as 'Frankenstein' food.

Suggest whether such retailers have made the right decision, or whether they should have waited until a full public debate about the issues had taken place.

◆ **12** There are many ways in which food can be genetically modified.

Example 1: crops can be made resistant to a particular weedkiller. The company that produces the modified seed can then make additional profits when the farmer buys its brand of weedkiller. This approach could also encourage the farmer to use more weedkiller because he knows that it will not harm his crops.

Example 2: rice does not usually contain vitamin A. Eye disease and blindness, caused by a lack of vitamin A, are common in parts of the world where rice is the main food. A scientist has now genetically engineered a variety of rice that produces vitamin A. This could help prevent blindness in millions of people.
The scientist has given the modified seed away free of charge.

a Explain whether your views about genetically modified food have changed after reading the two examples above.

b Suggest what laws could be put in place to protect the public, but that also allow the public to benefit from this new science.

A4 Micro-organisms and disease

Links to Double Award

6 Transport

10 Inheritance and evolution

Introduction

Disease has been a constant problem for mankind, and it is only in recent years that medical advances have allowed us to lead relatively disease-free lives. This has led to an increase in life expectancy. In the Middle Ages people would not expect to live much beyond their mid-thirties whereas these days we can expect to live twice as long.

Disease is never far away, however, and there has only ever been one example of a disease that has been totally eliminated from the face of the Earth. This disease is smallpox, and it was eradicated by a massive vaccination programme co-ordinated by the World Health Organization (WHO). The disease was spread by a virus that caused pustules all over the skin (fig 2). Most people who caught the disease died.

Diseases fall into three main groups:

- diseases caused by another biological agent such as bacteria, fungi and viruses
- diseases caused by a faulty gene that is inherited from one of our parents
- diseases caused by something in the environment such as asbestos (fig 3) or cigarette smoke (fig 4).

fig 1

fig 2 An historical photograph of a smallpox victim showing the pus-filled blisters that covered the hands and face

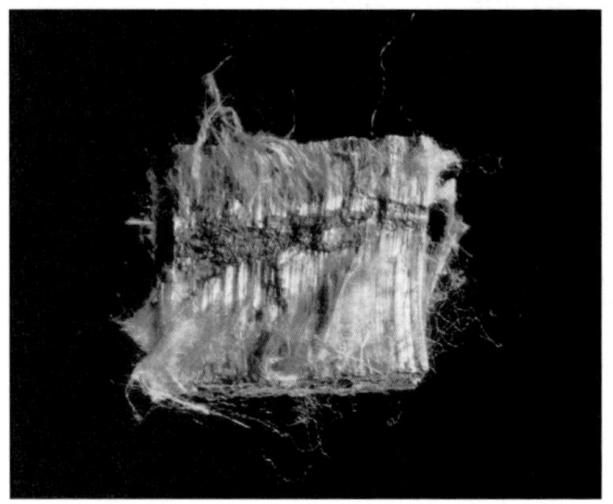

fig 3 Asbestos is a naturally occurring fibrous material that was used for fire proofing and insulation until it became known that exposure to the dust and fibres can cause cancer and asbestosis (inflammation of the lungs)

fig 4 Lungs from a healthy person (left) and a smoker (right) – the smoker's lung is darker, rougher and misshapen

Medical advances in recent years include better surgical techniques, with improved anaesthetics and painkillers. Drugs have been developed to combat disease, and antibiotics have saved the lives of millions. Science has won many battles against bacterial disease but the war has not been won. More and more bacteria are developing multiple antibiotic resistance and we can only hope that new sciences such as genetic engineering will enable us to keep one step ahead.

Check-up

Have a go at the following questions. They will remind you of what you should know about micro-organisms and disease.

a Joy catches a cold. Explain how the cold virus could have entered her body.

b Joy recovers after a few days. Explain how Joy's white blood cells helped her to get better.

c David cuts himself. Explain how his body will attempt to prevent micro-organisms from entering through the cut.

Contents of the Teaching block

A4.1 Types of disease

Although many diseases are infectious and are caught from someone else, some diseases can be inherited. Yet other diseases are caused by our environment. This spread looks at the causes of disease and, in particular, various agents that cause infectious diseases.

A4.2 HIV, AIDS and parasites

This spread explains the difference between infection with human immunodeficiency virus (HIV) and the resulting acquired immune deficiency syndrome (AIDS). It explains how HIV exists inside the very white blood cells that are supposed to destroy the virus. This is why HIV infection is so difficult to treat. The spread then looks at some of the larger parasites that can be found both in and on the human body.

A4.3 Antiseptics and antibiotics

The differences between antiseptics and antibiotics are described in this spread. Antibiotic resistance is then examined and the way in which the rapid evolution of bacteria has led to the emergence of antibiotic-resistant strains is explained.

A4.4 Immunisation

We can use vaccinations to protect ourselves from many diseases. This has led to a massive reduction in the incidence of childhood diseases such as mumps and diphtheria.

A4.5 Plants and disease

Plants are also affected by disease; this spread looks at the disease of potato blight. Farmers are constantly trying to increase the yield of their crops. Yields are reduced by diseases, and farmers can do various things to reduce the impact of disease on their crops.

A4.1 Types of disease

Key points

- Non-infectious diseases can be caused by our genes or by the environment.
- Infectious diseases are caused by micro-organisms.
- Bacteria, fungi and viruses are examples of micro-organisms that cause disease.

Non-infectious disease

Some diseases are non-infectious and cannot be caught from someone else. Some diseases such as cystic fibrosis are inherited and are caused by faults in our DNA. Other diseases such as cancer are caused partly by our environment, for example smoking causes lung cancer.

a List some other examples of non-infectious diseases.

Infectious disease

Infectious diseases are caused by micro-organisms. These include **bacteria, fungi** and **viruses.**

Bacteria

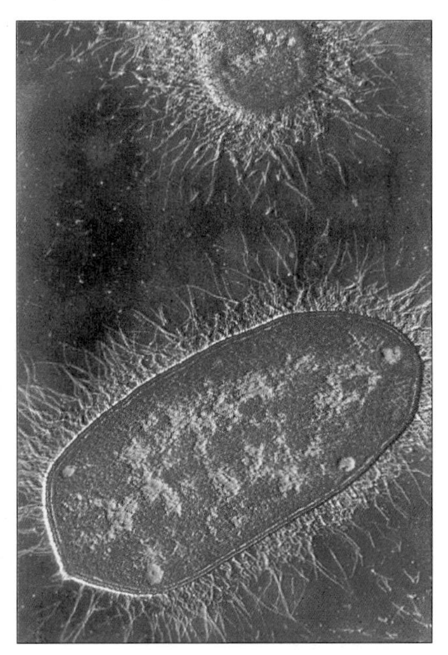

fig 5 | False-colour transmission electron micrograph of two bacteria (Calymmatobacterium species), which in reality are 1–1.5 μm in size

Bacteria are microscopic single-celled organisms (fig 5). They have no cell wall and no nucleus. The DNA is found as a long strand in the cytoplasm. Bacteria reproduce by binary fission (splitting into two; fig 6) and rapidly form colonies on solid material or turn clear liquids cloudy as they multiply.

Examples of diseases caused by bacteria include whooping cough and **tetanus**. In tetanus, the bacteria produce a toxin that causes paralysis of the jaw and the muscles that control breathing.

b Suggest how bacteria may be spread from person to person.

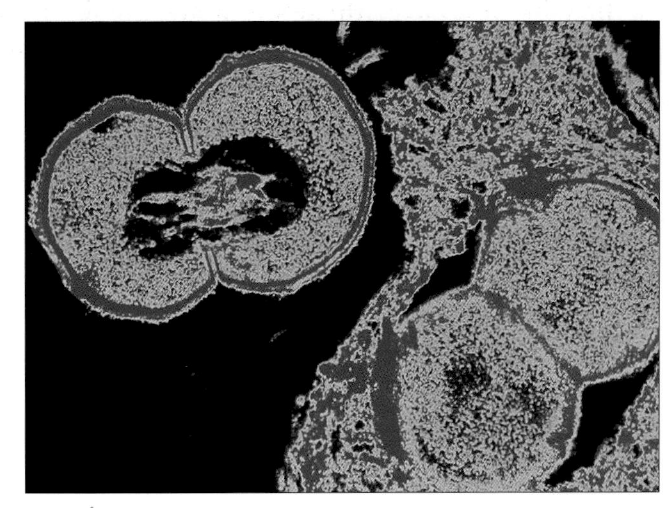

fig 6 | False-colour transmission electron micrograph showing bacteria undergoing cell division by binary fission

Fungi

Fungi are similar to plants but they do not contain any chlorophyll so they cannot photosynthesise. They therefore have to grow directly on a food source. The fungus (fig 7) consists of fine threads called **hyphae** which grow into a mass called a **mycelium**.

Fungi reproduce by means of asexually produced spores that are carried away by insects or the wind.

Athlete's foot is an example of a disease caused by a fungus. The fungus grows and feeds on warm, moist tissue such as that found between the toes. It causes the skin to crack and become sore.

c Suggest what people can do to avoid catching athlete's foot.

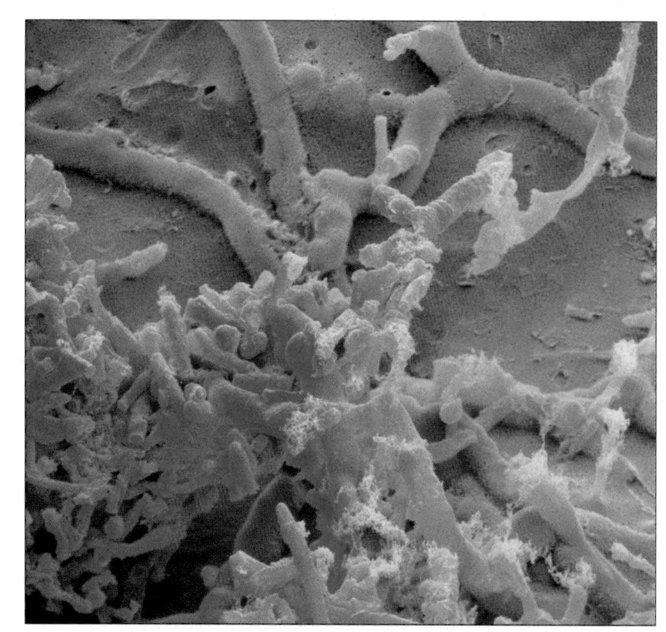

fig 7 Coloured scanning electron micrograph of the fungus that causes athlete's foot (*Trichophyton mentagrophytes*), showing the hyphal threads of the fungal mycelium and the rounded single-cell spores

Viruses

Viruses (fig 8) are very different from bacteria and fungi. They are much smaller and cannot be seen with an ordinary microscope. Viruses are considered to be non-living organisms because they cannot do the things that living organisms can do (see spread 1.2).

A virus consists of a protein coat which contains DNA or RNA. When the virus comes into contact with a cell, it injects its DNA (or RNA) into the cell and takes control of the cell. The viral DNA provides a new set of instructions, which the cell follows. These instructions are basically: 'stop what you are doing – make copies of me'. The cell makes hundreds of copies of the virus and then dies, releasing the viruses, which go on to invade other cells.

The common cold is an example of a disease caused by a virus.

d Suggest why bacteria were discovered long before viruses.

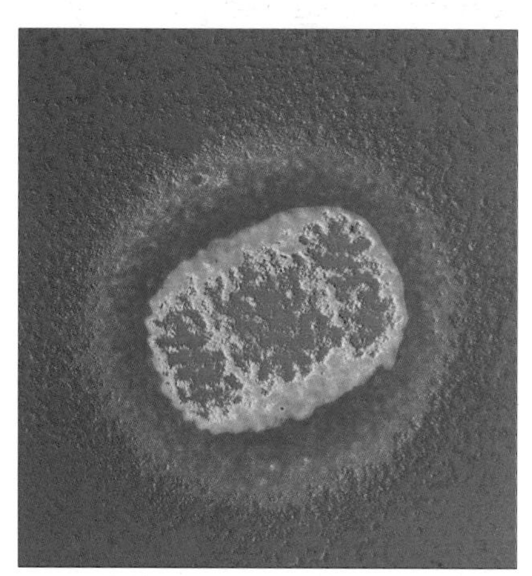

fig 8 False-colour transmission electron micrograph of the vaccinia virus, which causes smallpox (×16,000)

Hygiene

Simple hygiene can help to prevent the spread of infectious diseases such as the common cold and athlete's foot.

e Imagine you have athlete's foot and a cold. Describe the measures you would take to prevent the diseases from spreading to other people.

Thinking further

■ 1 Explain the differences between a plant cell and a cell from a fungus.

◆ 2 If viruses are non-living, explain how they manage to reproduce.

KEY WORDS

athlete's foot • bacteria • fungi • hyphae • infectious • mycelium • tetanus • virus

A4.2 HIV, AIDS and parasites

Key points

- Human immunodeficiency virus (HIV) infects the white blood cells.
- AIDS is the ultimate effect of HIV infection.
- Parasites can be spread from person to person.

HIV – the human immunodeficiency virus

HIV is spread from person to person through sexual contact or by direct transfer of tissue fluid, such as occurs when drug users use other people's dirty needles.

Normally we are protected against viruses by our **white blood cells**, which produce antibodies to attack the **virus**. However, HIV attacks and invades the same white blood cells that try to protect us from infection (fig 9). For a while the virus may lay dormant in the white blood cells and all appears to be normal.
Gradually, however, the virus instructs the white blood cells to make more and more copies of the virus and eventually there are very few white blood cells left.

Once the number of white blood cells starts to fall, the body is left wide open to attack by other micro-organisms. This leads to **AIDS**.

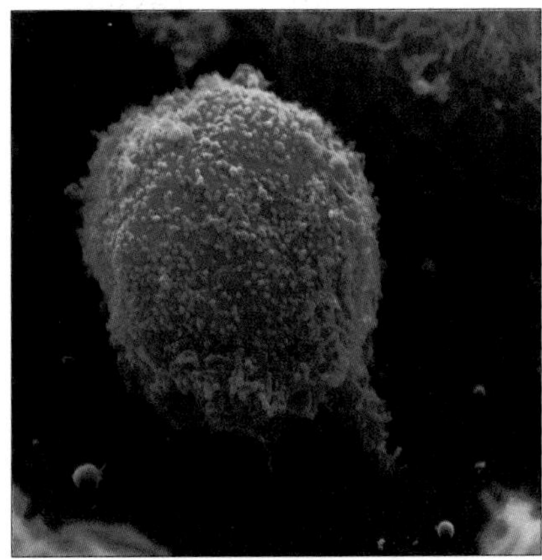

fig 9 Coloured scanning electron micrograph of a T lymphocyte (orange) infected with HIV (blue) (×3500)

AIDS – acquired immune deficiency syndrome

As the number of white blood cells decreases, the **immune system** gets weaker and weaker. The person starts to get a collection (or **syndrome**) of diseases that the immune system could usually prevent. Thus, a person who dies of AIDS is not killed directly by the HIV but by other diseases that they catch and cannot fight off because their immune system has been destroyed by HIV (fig 10). One example of a common disease caught by patients with AIDS is pneumonia, a serious lung infection.

a Explain why people with AIDS often die from pneumonia.

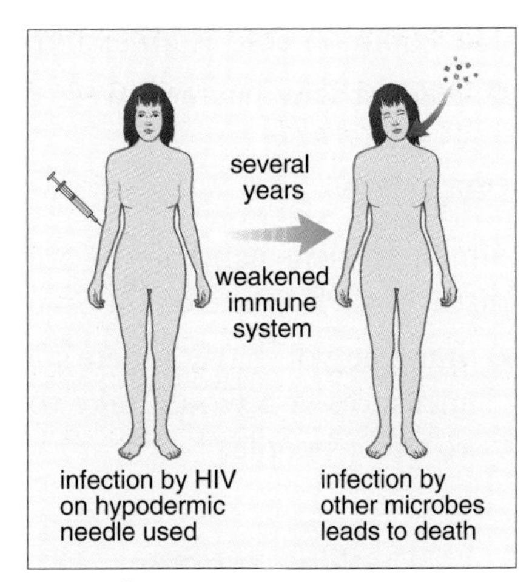

fig 10 Infection with HIV leads to the development of AIDS over many years as the immune system is gradually weakened by the virus

Preventing HIV infection and AIDS

Once a person has been infected with HIV, the rate of spread of the virus in the body can be slowed with drugs, but there is still no cure.

Spread of the HIV virus from person to person can be prevented by:

- safe sex – using a condom
- drug users using clean hypodermic needles rather than re-using dirty needles
- restricting the number of sexual partners.

Parasites

Parasites are larger than micro-organisms and can be seen with the naked eye. They live on, or in, another living organism and give nothing in return.

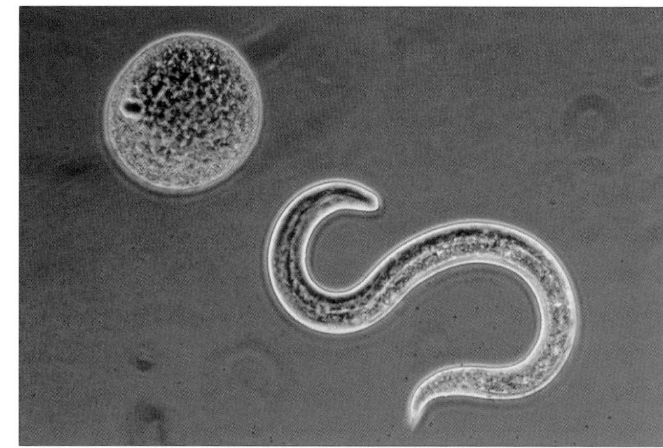

fig 11 | Light micrograph of the egg and first larval stage of the dog roundworm (*Toxocara canis*) (×64)

Toxocara (fig 11) is a small white worm. It usually lives in the gut of cats and dogs. Eggs from the worm pass out with the faeces. They may then be eaten by other cats and dogs. Sometimes children playing in parks may accidentally eat some of these eggs – if they get them on their hands, for example. The eggs hatch in the child's gut. The worms travel via the bloodstream to the back of the eye where they can cause serious damage.

b Suggest what we could do to prevent children catching toxocara from public places.

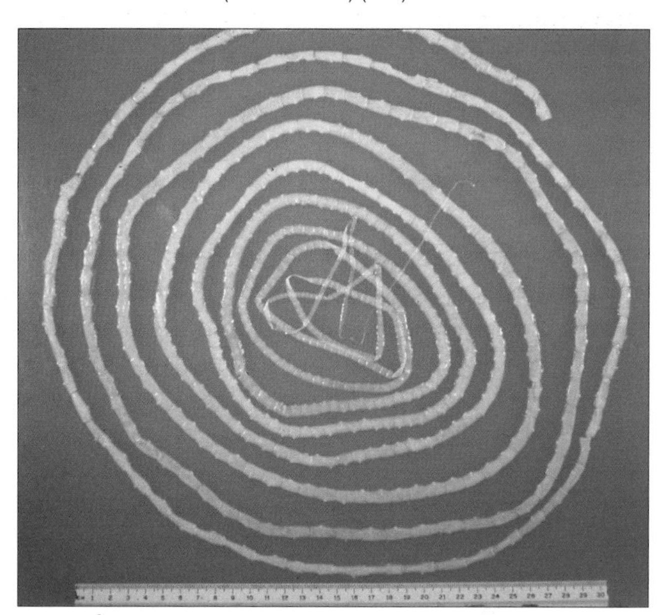

fig 12 | The beef tapeworm can be several metres in length – it is shown coiled here

Tapeworm (fig 12) is a parasite that can be caught by eating uncooked beef or pork. The worm is ribbon shaped and is several metres long. It lives in the gut. Eggs from the worm pass out with the faeces and can then infect another cow or pig through water or contaminated pasture. Fortunately, meat inspection and good sanitation mean that tapeworm infection is very rare in Europe.

c Suggest how the spread of tapeworm could be prevented.

Headlice (fig 13) are small lice that live in the hair on human heads. They cement their eggs to the base of a hair. These eggs are called nits. The lice spread by direct or very close contact, or by the sharing of hats. Lice prefer to live on clean heads and hair.

d Suggest how the spread of headlice can be prevented.

fig 13 | Coloured scanning electron micrograph of a head louse amongst human hair – it is 2–3.5 mm in length

Thinking further

■ **1** Explain why white blood cells are unable to destroy HIV.

◆ **2** Explain why HIV itself does not kill people but leads to AIDS, which does.

KEY WORDS

AIDS • HIV • immune system • parasite • syndrome • virus • white blood cells

A4.3 Antiseptics and antibiotics

Key points

- Antiseptics are chemicals that kill micro-organisms. They are used externally on the skin.
- Antibiotics are drugs that kill bacteria. They can be taken internally.

Antiseptics

Antiseptics are chemicals that are used to kill micro-organisms on the surface of the skin. They can be used to stop wounds becoming infected. However, it is not safe to drink antiseptics.

Antibiotics

Antibiotics are drugs that kill or slow down the growth of bacteria. They are swallowed (or injected) and kill the **bacteria** inside our bodies, especially in the bloodstream. Antibiotics do not kill viruses.

a Suggest why doctors will not gave an antibiotic to someone who is suffering from a viral infection.

Antibiotic resistance

Many strains of bacteria are becoming resistant to a wide range of antibiotics. **Antibiotic resistance** occurs in the following way (fig 14):

- Antibiotics are used to kill bacteria.
- A few bacteria have a natural resistance to the antibiotic.
- The antibiotic kills all the susceptible bacteria but leaves the few resistant ones unharmed.
- These resistant bacteria reproduce very rapidly because they do not have to compete with other bacteria for nutrients.
- Soon there is a large number of resistant bacteria.

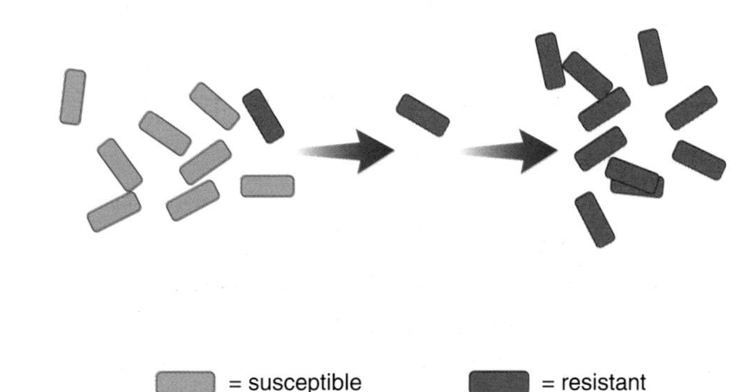

fig 14 | Development of antibiotic-resistant bacterial colonies

Antibiotic resistance can be reduced by:

- restricting the use of antibiotics – they are used too often for trivial illnesses and are also used to promote the growth of farm animals
- ensuring that patients complete a course of prescribed antibiotics – this ensures that any bacteria with a slight resistance to the antibiotic do not survive and multiply
- doctors prescribing combinations of antibiotics – this ensures that bacteria which are resistant to one antibiotic are killed by the other antibiotic and do not survive and multiply.

New drugs and techniques

As more and more strains of bacteria evolve antibiotic resistance, new antibiotics need to be discovered in order to keep one step ahead of the bacteria. Unfortunately this is very expensive and it takes a long time to get new drugs onto the market. Scientists are now looking for alternative solutions.

One solution is to chemically alter existing drugs so that bacteria no longer have resistance to them. Unfortunately, however, bacteria that are resistant to these modified drugs soon evolve.

Another solution is to use **phage** technology. Phages are **viruses** that attack bacteria and kill them (fig 15). Just as the bacteria evolve resistance to the phages, the phages also evolve so that they can still attack the bacteria.

b Where are the phages that would kill bacteria likely to be found?

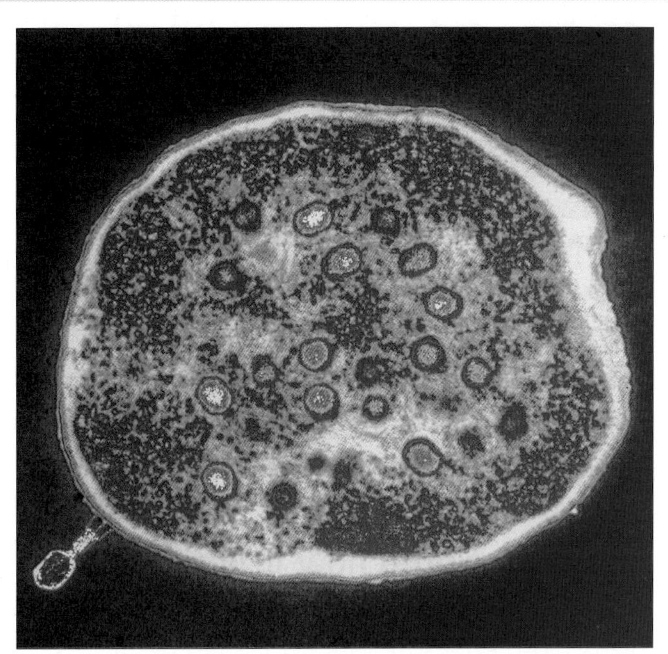

fig 15 False-colour transmission electron micrograph of a bacteriophage virus attacking and infecting a bacterium. The orange spheres are viruses that have reproduced inside the cell. A single virus sitting on the cell surface can be seen on the lower left of the bacterium (×143 000)

Sir Alexander Fleming and penicillin

Sir Alexander Fleming discovered penicillin in 1928. While working in a laboratory he noticed that some bacterial cultures had become contaminated with a mould (fig 16). Most people would have discarded the cultures and started again, but Fleming noticed that where the mould was growing, there were no bacteria.

His work with two other scientists called Florey and Chain led to the manufacture of the first antibiotic – penicillin. They were awarded the Nobel prize for medicine. Penicillin was regarded as a miracle drug because it saved the lives of many people who would otherwise have died from infection.

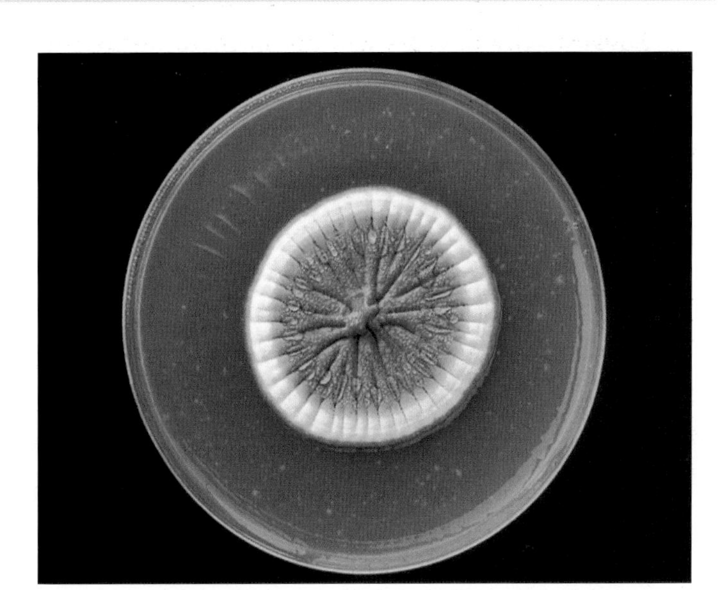

fig 16 A colony of the fungus *Penicillium notatum* growing on an agar plate. The fungus produces penicillin, which kills any bacteria growing near to it

Thinking further

■ **1** Suggest why drugs developed to kill viruses are also likely to be harmful to humans.

◆ **2** Suggest how phages might be isolated and used to treat bacterial infections.

KEY WORDS

antibiotic • antibiotic resistance • **antiseptic** • **bacteria** • phage • **virus**

A4.4 Immunisation

Key points

- The basis of immunisation is injecting dead or a mild form of the pathogen, against which the body makes antibodies.
- Some viruses such as the common cold can change their structure so that a vaccine is no longer effective.
- Edward Jenner produced the first vaccine against smallpox.
- Pathogens can be used to control pests.

Immunisation – how it works

Immunisation is a process in which the body is encouraged to make **antibodies** but without having the disease. The usual method (shown in fig 17) is to inject dead or a mild form of the **pathogen**. A pathogen is a micro-organism that causes disease.

The white blood cells react to the dead pathogen by making antibodies. When live **virulent** bacteria subsequently invade the body, the antibodies are already in the bloodstream and can destroy the harmful pathogen.

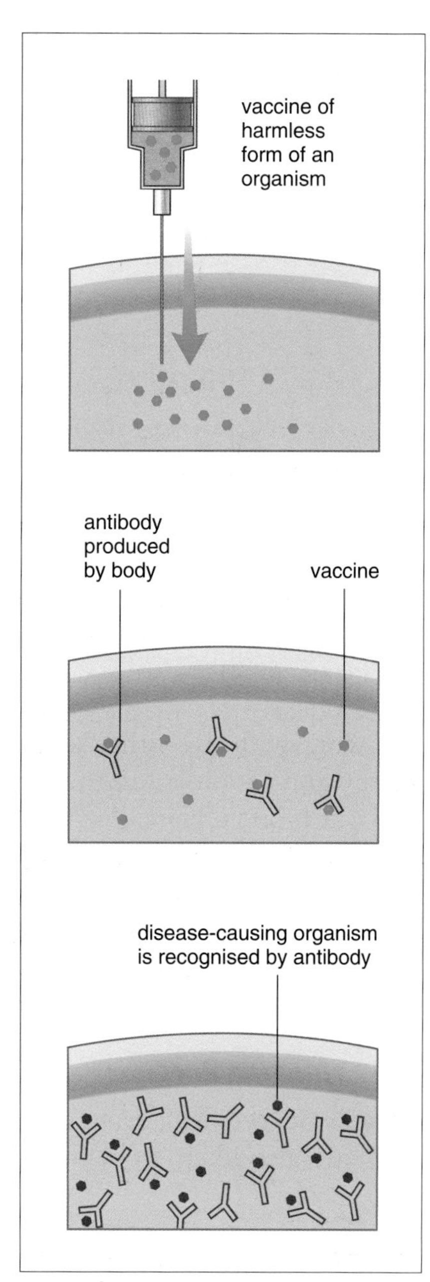

fig 17 | The process of immunisation

Active and passive immunity

Active immunity is acquired when a person makes their own antibodies to a pathogen. It happens when we are vaccinated, or when we come into contact with a disease-causing organism. The protection given by active immunity is usually long lasting.

Passive immunity is acquired when we are injected with ready-made antibodies from another source. Doctors do this when there is a danger that you already have the disease and there is no time to make your own antibodies. If you have never had a tetanus vaccination and you injure yourself, the doctor will probably give you an injection of ready-made tetanus antibodies which will prevent you from getting the disease. Although this gives instant protection, it does not last very long and you will also need to be vaccinated against tetanus so that you make your own antibodies.

a Suggest why passive immunity is not long lasting.

Risks

There is a very small risk that injecting dead or a mild form of a pathogen can cause harm, such as brain damage. However, the risk of catching and dying from the disease if you do not have the vaccination is usually much greater than the risk of being harmed by the immunisation.

The common cold

As yet it has been impossible to produce a vaccine against the common cold virus. This is because the cold virus can change the structure of its protein coat. This means that when it returns to re-infect us, our antibodies are unable to recognise it (fig 18). We then make new antibodies to fit the new structure but when the virus returns in a few months time it will have changed yet again and we get another cold.

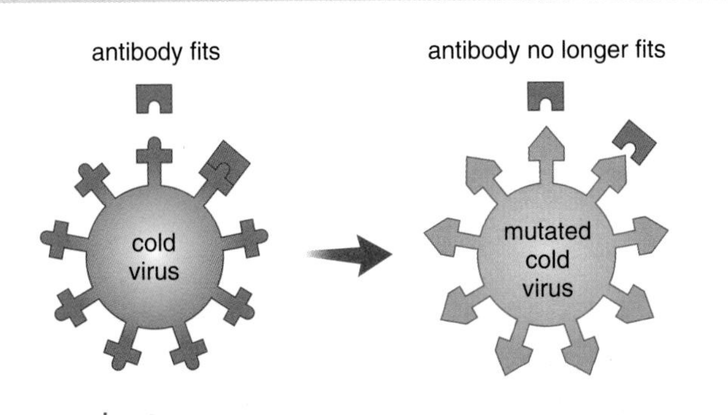

fig 18 | By mutating, the cold virus develops resistance to antibodies

Edward Jenner

Edward Jenner produced the world's first vaccine – against **smallpox.** He noticed that milk maids who caught cowpox (a mild disease) from cows never caught the more serious disease called smallpox. In 1796 Jenner experimented by injecting a young boy with cowpox, and a few weeks later injecting him with smallpox. If Jenner had been wrong, the young boy would probably have died. The boy did not die and Jenner had invented the first vaccine. It worked because the cowpox virus (shown in fig 8 on spread A4.1) was almost the same shape as the smallpox virus and antibodies made against the cowpox virus also worked against the smallpox virus.

b Suggest whether people who survived smallpox would also be immune to cowpox.

Louis Pasteur

Louis Pasteur developed a vaccine against **rabies.** He injected the virus into the brain of a rabbit. After a few days he removed the rabbit's brain and injected some of the tissue into another rabbit. He repeated this several times and then he dried the infected brain. This weakened the virus so that he was then able to inject the tissue into people as a vaccine. The longer the brain was dried, the weaker the virus became. Each day he injected the person with a vaccine that had been dried for a shorter time until after two weeks he could inject them with a virulent virus without ill effect. He saved the lives of many people who had been bitten by rabid animals and would otherwise have died.

Useful pathogens?

Pathogens have sometimes been used to control pest populations. In the wild, rabbits can breed very quickly and cause enormous damage to crops. Some rabbits were deliberately infected with the myxoma virus. This causes the disease **myxomatosis** which killed millions of rabbits. Now, however, rabbits have evolved immunity to the disease and it no longer seriously affects them.

Thinking further

■ **1** State three different ways of making a vaccine.

■ **2** Discuss the arguments for and against being vaccinated against a disease.

◆ **3** Examine the arguments for and against releasing pathogens into the environment in order to control pests.

KEY WORDS

active immunity • antibodies • immunisation • myxomatosis • passive immunity • pathogen • rabies • smallpox • virulent

A4.5 Plants and disease

Key points

- Infectious diseases can affect plants.
- The diseases can be controlled by selective breeding, chemical treatments and a variety of farming methods.

Potato blight

Potato blight is a **fungus** that attacks potatoes (fig 19). In 1846 it caused massive damage to the potato crop in Ireland and left many people starving. Large numbers of people left Ireland and travelled to America in order to find work and food.

The fungus attacks a potato plant when a tiny **spore** lands on the leaf. The spore germinates and enters the plant through the **stomata** (fig 20). The fungus then spreads rapidly through the plant, destroying cells and plant tissue. Spores are left in the soil and attack next year's crop once it has been planted.

fig 19 | Potato blight

Control of potato blight

Potato blight is now controlled by:

- **Breeding new resistant varieties** – modern varieties of potato are resistant to the blight.
- **Chemical treatment** – chemical sprays are an effective way of controlling the spread of most fungal diseases. Organic farming tries to control these diseases without using chemical sprays.

a Suggest what features of a modern variety of potato make it resistant to potato blight.

Crop rotation

Modern farming methods include crop rotation. This involves sowing different crops in a field each year.

b Explain why growing a different crop each year would help to prevent the spread of disease.

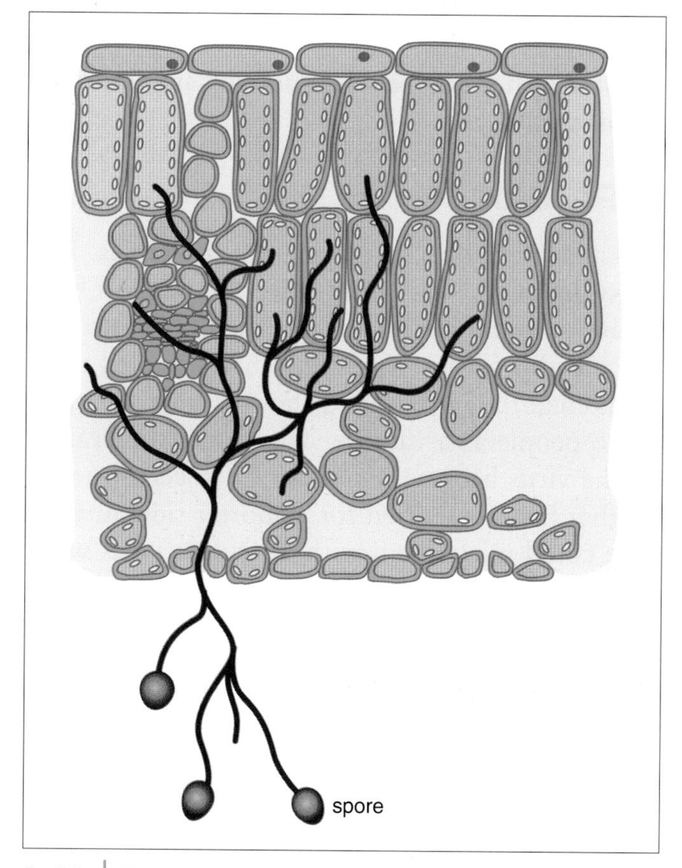

fig 20 | The potato blight fungal spores attack the leaf through the stomata

Changing sowing times

Farmers can vary the time of the year that they sow crops. This is an attempt to grow the crop at a time of the year when the disease is not active. This method of disease control is only partially successful.

fig 21 | Stems of a heavy-cropping apple variety can be grafted onto a disease-resistant root stock

Grafting

Heavy-cropping varieties that are susceptible to a particular disease can be grafted onto a **root stock** that is resistant to the disease (fig 21). The **graft** prevents the disease entering the plant through the roots from infected soil but still allows the farmer to grow heavy-cropping varieties.

Legislation

Laws have been passed to prevent certain susceptible varieties from being grown, and also to prevent the transport of infected material around the country.

c Suggest other laws that could be passed to prevent the spread of plant diseases.

Thinking further

■ 1 Find out about two other plants diseases and explain their effect on the plant and how they are spread.

■ 2 Explain how farmers can reduce the effects of plant diseases on their crops.

◆ 3 Explain how a farmer could undertake a programme of selective breeding to produce a variety of plant that would be resistant to a particular disease.

IDEAS AND EVIDENCE

◆ 4 Genetic engineering will enable scientists to produce varieties of plants that are resistant to most plant diseases. Explain whether you think that plants should be genetically modified in this way, or whether nature should be left to take care of itself.

KEY WORDS

fungus • graft • potato blight • root stock • spore • stomata

Questions on micro-organisms and disease

■ **1** Copy the passage below, using words from the following list to fill in the gaps. You may use each word once, more than once or not at all. *(4)*

asbestos • environment • infectious • haemophilia • viruses

Diseases have many causes. If a disease is caused by a micro-organism, it is __________ and can be passed from person to person. Different types of micro-organism include bacteria, __________ and fungi. Some diseases may be inherited and are passed from generation to generation. These include diseases such as __________ and cystic fibrosis. Yet others are a result of the __________ and may be caused by pollutants such as __________ and cigarette smoke.

■ **2** Jack goes to the doctor for a flu vaccination. He remembers that he had also had a flu vaccination the previous year. However, his teacher tells him that once the body makes antibodies to fight a disease, the antibodies last for a long time.

■ **a** Explain what will happen in Jack's body after he has been injected with the flu vaccine. *(2)*

◆ **b** Explain why Jack has to have another flu vaccination only a year after having had the previous one. *(2)*

■ **c** Jack knows that if he gets flu he should not ask the doctor for antibiotics. Explain why Jack is right. *(1)*

■ **d** Some months later, Jack gets tonsillitis, which is caused by a bacteria. Jack's doctor gives him antibiotics. Explain why the antibiotics should work against the tonsillitis, but not against the flu virus. *(1)*

◆ **e** The doctor tells Jack that he must finish the course of treatment, even if he begins to feel better. Explain why Jack must finish all the antibiotics. *(3)*

◆ **f** Jack also has athlete's foot. His doctor could give him some tablets but prefers Jack to use a cream that is spread on the affected area. Explain the advantages of using a cream, rather than taking a course of tablets. *(2)*

3 Viruses are sometimes regarded as non-living organisms because they do not carry out the normal functions of a living organism. Explain how viruses manage to:

● **a** spread from person to person *(1)*

■ **b** replicate. *(2)*

4 Peter has become infected with HIV after receiving contaminated blood products used to treat his haemophilia.

● **a** State and explain two other ways in which people can become HIV-positive. *(2)*

■ **b** Peter's friends think that he has caught AIDS. Peter tells them that they are wrong and that he does not have AIDS. Explain, giving reasons, who is right: Peter or his friends. *(1)*

■ **c** Explain why it is very difficult for Peter's immune system to combat the HIV. *(2)*

■ **d** Peter is told by his doctor that it may be many years before the HIV infection progresses to AIDS. Explain why. *(1)*

◆ **e** During the HIV infection the number of white blood cells that Peter has will fall. Explain why this is bad news for Peter. *(1)*

■ **f** Peter knows that some infections are a direct cause of death. However, people who die from AIDS are not killed directly by the HIV infection. Explain what Peter means by this. *(2)*

5 Wendy falls and grazes her knee. Her mother puts some antiseptic on the wound.

■ **a** Explain the difference between an antiseptic and an antibiotic. *(2)*

The graze gets infected while Wendy is playing outside. Her mother takes her to the doctor, who gives Wendy some antibiotic cream. The cream doesn't work. The doctor says that the bacteria are resistant to the antibiotic and gives her a different cream.

■ **b** Explain how the bacteria could have become resistant to the antibiotic. *(3)*

6 The Irish potato famine was caused by a fungus that attacks potatoes.

● **a** Explain how the fungus is spread from plant to plant. *(2)*

■ **b** Explain how modern farming techniques have ensured that the fungus is no longer the problem it once was. *(3)*

● **c** Explain how legislation has been used to prevent the spread of the disease. *(1)*

■ **7** Many hospitals have problems with a strain of bacteria called MRSA. MRSA is sometimes called a 'superbug' because it is resistant to almost all antibiotics. It is difficult to treat someone who has become infected with MRSA.

■ **a** Explain how bacteria can become resistant to an antibiotic. *(3)*

◆ **b** Suggest why these superbugs have appeared in hospitals, rather than in the general population. *(1)*

■ **c** State two actions that could be carried out in hospitals to ensure that patients do not become infected with the 'superbug'. *(2)*

One way of preventing the appearance of superbugs is to treat patients with a mixture of two antibiotics, rather than one.

◆ **d** Explain why this method of treatment is likely to prevent the appearance of superbugs. *(2)*

IDEAS AND EVIDENCE

■ **8** The first antibiotic was discovered by Sir Alexander Fleming. Explain how Fleming came to his discovery, even though his work did not involve looking for antibiotics. *(3)*

◆ **9** Neil cut himself in the garden. His doctor gave him an injection of ready-made tetanus antibodies. He told Neil to come back in a few days for a tetanus vaccination.

a Explain why the doctor first gave Neil an injection of ready-made antibodies, rather than giving him the tetanus vaccine straight away. *(2)*

b Explain why Neil still needed to have a tetanus vaccination a few days later. *(2)*

c Explain why it would have been too late for Neil to have his tetanus vaccination after he had cut himself. *(2)*

d Explain what will happen in Neil's blood when he has the tetanus vaccination. *(2)*

e Neil asked the doctor what was in the tetanus vaccine. Suggest and explain three possible things that could be in the tetanus vaccine. *(3)*

◆ **10** In 1796, a scientist called Edward Jenner developed a vaccine against smallpox. Describe how Jenner produced his vaccine and why he would not be allowed to use the same techniques today. *(5)*

■ **11** Babies are routinely vaccinated with the MMR vaccine to provide immunity against mumps, measles and rubella (German measles). These are very serious diseases, and in some cases can lead to permanent damage.
Some parents now think that giving the vaccine to their baby is risky. This is because it has been suggested that, in rare cases, the vaccine may cause a brain disease called autism. It is therefore very difficult for parents to decide whether to have their baby vaccinated.

a Suggest the issues that parents might consider when making this decision. *(2)*

b Explain how parents might get information to help them make their decision. *(2)*

c Suggest what would happen if doctors stopped using the MMR vaccine. *(2)*

d Explain what decision you would make if it were your baby. *(2)*

Glossary (TB 1–10)

Terms set in pink are higher tier material.

23 pairs (10.2) – the number of pairs of chromosomes found in a normal cell.

46 chromosomes (10.2) – the number of chromosomes found in a normal cell.

A

absorption (2.3) – movement of soluble food molecules from the digestive system into the bloodstream

acid rain (7.7) – rain that has a low pH due to dissolved sulphur dioxide and other impurities

active transport (1.3) – the movement of substances across a cell membrane using energy from respiration. This is usually against a concentration gradient. In some cases substances are transported down a diffusion gradient by active transport, speeding up movement that would be too slow by diffusion.

adaptation (7.2) – the characteristics of an organism that make it well suited to living in a particular environment.

ADH (9.3) – a hormone that regulates the water level in the body by increasing reabsorption in the renal tubules.

air movement (6.5) – the rate of transpiration increases as the speed of the air movement increases.

air spaces (5.1) – spaces within a leaf that allow air to move between the cells.

alcohol (3.2) – a substance produced by anaerobic respiration in yeast.

allele (10.7) – a genetic instruction received from one parent. Alleles from both parents form a gene.

alveoli (4.1) – small air sacs found in the lungs (singular = alveolus).

amylase (2.1) – an enzyme that digests starch to maltose.

anabolic steroids (8.5) – hormones that result in a build up of muscle tissue in the body.

anaerobic (3.2) – respiration without oxygen.

antibodies (6.3) – chemicals produced by the body's immune system to destroy foreign invading organisms.

aorta (6.2) – the main artery that carries blood from the heart, out to the body.

artery (6.1, 6.2) – blood vessel that carries blood away from the heart.

atrium (6.2) – the left and right atria are the two upper muscular chambers of the heart. They pump blood into the ventricles.

auxin (8.6) – a plant hormone that is produced in the growing points. It stimulates the growth of a shoot.

B

bases (10.1) – the four chemicals A, T, C and G that code for the instructions of life on DNA.

Benedict's solution (2.1) – a chemical reagent that is used to test for reducing sugars. It gives an orange colour when boiled with a reducing sugar.

bile (2.2) – a liquid produced iN the liver and stored in the gall bladder. It is released into the small intestine and contains bile salts.

bile salts (2.2) – chemicals found in bile that emulsify fats.

biological control (7.6) – the use of a living organism to control a pest population.

Biuret test (2.1) – a chemical test used to detect proteins. Solutions of sodium hydroxide and copper sulphate are used, and give a purple colour with proteins.

blind spot (8.1) – the area of the retina where the optic nerve leaves. This area does not contain light-sensitive cells.

blood (9.1) – a red liquid that transports nutrients, oxygen and other materials around the body.

blood pressure (6.1) – a measure of the pressure of the blood when the heart is contracting and when it is relaxing.

blood vessels (9.2) – tubes that carry blood around the body and back to the heart.

brain (8.3) – the enlarged front end of the CNS, responsible for much of the co-ordination in the body.

breathing rate (4.2) – the number of cycles of inhalation and exhalation in one minute.

bronchi (4.1) – two tubes that lead from the trachea into the lungs (singular = bronchus).

bronchioles (4.1) – small tubes in the lungs that lead from the bronchi to the alveoli.

bronchitis (4.3) – a disease caused by fluid collecting in the alveoli and becoming infected.

C

calorimeter (3.1) – a device for measuring the energy content of food. The units of measurement used to be calories but are now joules.

capillary (6.1) – tiny blood vessel that carries blood to the tissues of the body. A human being has thousands of miles of capillaries.

carbon cycle (7.5) – a scheme that describes how the element carbon is recycled in nature.

carbon dioxide (5.2) – a gas produced by respiration, in both plants and animals.

cell membrane (1.1) – a thin structure, made of protein and fat, that surrounds every cell.

cellulose (5.3) – a substance made by plants that forms the structure of their cell walls.

cell wall (1.1) – a tough protective structure made of cellulose that surround the cell membrane in plant cells.

chlorophyll (5.1, 5.3) – a green pigment produced by plants that is used to trap light energy for the process of photosynthesis.

chloroplasts (1.1, 5.1) – plant cell organelles that contain chlorophyll and are the site of photosynthesis.

chromosomes (10.1) – structures composed of DNA and found in the nuclei of cells.

cilia (4.3) – small hair-like structures on the surface of cells. They beat in a co-ordinated way in order to move the cell or move external substances.

ciliary muscle (8.1) a circular muscle that passes around the lens. It is composed of circular and longitudinal fibres and is used to change the shape of the lens. It is often referred to as the ciliary body.

clone (10.5) – two or more organisms that are genetically identical.

CNS (8.3) – the central nervous system, part of the nervous system, consisting of the brain and spinal cord.

community (7.1) – all the organisms that live in a particular habitat.

competition (7.2) – continual struggle that organisms have with each other for resources.

concentration gradient (1.3) – the variation in concentration of a substance in two different areas.

cones (8.1) – sensory cells in the retina of the eye that are sensitive to coloured light. Different cones are sensitive to different wavelengths.

conservation (7.8) – process of maintaining the environment in a natural state so that habitats and organisms can survive and flourish.

co-ordination (8.3) – process by which all the sensory information is monitored and responses initiated for the benefit of the organism as a whole.

cornea (8.1) – the transparent layer of tissue at the front of the eye that is responsible for most refraction of light in the eye.

cutting (8.7) – an artificial way of making genetically identical copies of plants by removing and planting sections of stems.

cystic fibrosis (10.4) – an inherited disease caused by a recessive allele. Only people with two recessive alleles have the disease.
It causes thick mucous secretions to be produced, leading to lung damage and digestion problems.

cytoplasm (1.1) – contents of a cell outside the nucleus, made up mainly of water with dissolved chemicals, and organelles.

D

decomposers (7.5) – organisms that feed on dead organic remains by secreting enzymes onto them and taking up the semi-digested food.

decomposition (7.5) – breakdown of dead organic material by decomposers.

denitrifying (7.5) – process by which nitrates are broken down to release nitrogen gas.

depressant (8.2) – drug that reduces the activity of the nervous system.

diabetes (9.1) – a disease in which a person does not produce enough insulin to control the level of sugar in the blood.

dialysis (9.3) – a technique similar to osmosis, used in kidney machines to filter the blood of impurities.

diaphragm (4.1) – sheet of muscle that separates the thorax from the abdomen.

diffuse/diffusion (1.3, 6.1) – net passive movement of particles from an area of high concentration to an area of low concentration.

DNA (10.1, 10.6) – the molecule that codes for all the instructions needed to make an organism, and is also capable of replication.

dominant (10.7) – an allele that expresses itself in the phenotype.

Down's syndrome (10.4) – a genetic disease caused by having an extra chromosome 21.

ductless (8.4) – characteristic of hormone-producing glands which lack ducts but release their secretions straight into the bloodstream.

E

electron microscope (1.1) – a device that magnifies structures to high resolution by using a beam of electrons.

emphysema (4.3) – a disease caused by breakdown of the walls of alveoli, thus reducing gaseous exchange.

emulsification (2.2) – the process of breaking down fat droplets into smaller ones.

energy (3.1, 5.1) – the ability to do work.

energy flow (7.4) – the transfer of energy through an ecosystem.

engulf (6.3) – to swallow up.

enzymes (9.2) – organic catalysts that speed up the rate of a reaction.

epithelium (4.3) – the layer of cells that covers surfaces inside and outside the body (plural = epithelia).

evolution (10.9) – adaptation of organisms to changes in the environment through natural selection.

extinct(ion) (7.8, 10.9) – failure of organisms to adapt to changes in the environment so that they die out.

F

F1 generation (10.7) – the first generations produced from two true-breeding parents.

F2 generation (10.7) – the generation produced from crossing two F1 individuals.

fermentation (3.2) – anaerobic respiration in organisms such as yeast.

fertilise/fertilisation (10.5) – the fusion of male and female sex cells.

filtered (9.3) – performed by renal tubules to remove urea from the blood.

flaccid (1.4) – situation in plant cells that have lost water by osmosis so that the cytoplasm does not push against the cell wall.

fossil (10.9) – the preserved remains of a dead organism.

fovea (8.1) – area of the retina that contains the highest concentration of light-sensitive cells (cones).

G

gamete (10.5) – a cell involved in reproduction, such as an ovum or a sperm.

gastric juice (2.2) – the acidic liquid that is secreted by the glands lining the stomach. It contains protein-digesting enzymes.

gene (10.1, 10.6) – a section of DNA that codes for one specific instruction.

genetic cloning (10.6) – a technique used to produce genetically identical organisms.

genotype (10.7) – a description of the two alleles that form a gene.

geotropism (8.6) – a growth response in plants either towards or away from gravity.

glucose (3.1, 5.3, 9.1, 9.3) – a substance that is produced by photosynthesis and used as an energy source in respiration.

glycogen (9.1) – a substance stored in the liver and formed when excess glucose is present in the blood.

goblet cells (4.3) – cells lining the various tubes in the lungs which secrete mucus.

greenhouse effect (7.7) – the process by which various gases in the Earth's atmosphere trap heat, thereby keeping the atmosphere warm.

guard cells (6.4) – two cells that control the opening and closing of a stoma.

habitat (7.1) – an area where organisms live, with specific environmental conditions.

hepatic portal vein (2.3) – the vein that takes blood, rich in dissolved food, from the small intestine to the liver.

heterozygous (10.7) – a gene that consists of two different alleles.

homozygous (10.7) – a gene that consists of two identical alleles.

hormones (8.4, 9.1) – chemical messengers released from various glands which reach their target organ(s) via the blood.

host (7.3) – a live organism that is fed upon by a parasite.

humidity (6.5) – a measure of the amount of water vapour in the atmosphere.

ileum (2.3) – the last part of the small intestine that is the site for most absorption of food into the bloodstream.

infertility (8.5) – the inability to conceive.

inherited (10.3) – passed from parent to child via the genes.

insecticides (7.6) – chemicals that kill insects.

insulin (8.4, 9.1) – a hormone, produced by the pancreas, that reduces the level of glucose in the blood.

intensive (7.6) – a system of farming that uses modern technology to produce maximum possible yields.

intercostal muscles (4.1) – two sets of muscles that move the ribs, allowing breathing to occur.

iodine solution (2.1) – a chemical consisting of iodine dissolved in potassium iodide. It is used to test for starch, turning a blue–black colour on contact.

iris (8.1) – the coloured area around the pupil of the eye. It contains muscles that change the diameter of the pupil according to the light conditions.

joule (3.1) – a unit for measuring energy.

kidneys (9.3) – organs that control the water level of the body and removes urea from the blood.

kidney tubules (9.3) – structures in the kidney that filter the blood.

lacteals (2.3) – lymphatic vessels that are found in villi. They absorb some of the products of digestion, particularly fats.

lactic acid (3.2) – a chemical produced by anaerobic respiration in humans; it causes muscle fatigue.

law of independent assortment (10.8) – Mendel's law which states that any allele from a gene of one parent can combine with any allele of the same gene from the other parent.

law of segregation (10.8) – Mendel's law which states that the two alleles of a gene will go into different gametes at meiosis.

leaf (5.1) – the plants 'green machine' that makes food by photosynthesis.

lens (8.1) – an elastic transparent structure in the eye that is responsible for the fine focusing of light.

light intensity (5.2) – one of the factors that can limit the rate of photosynthesis.

light microscope (1.1) – a device that uses light rays to produce a magnified image of an object.

limiting factor (5.2) – a factor that limits the rate of photosynthesis.

lipase (2.1) – an enzyme that digests fats to fatty acids and glycerol.

liver (9.1) – an organ of the body that stores glycogen and breaks down harmful toxins.

lung (6.2) – a respiratory surface found in mammals.

lung cancer (4.3) – a disease in which cells in the lungs divide in a rapid uncontrolled manner, forming a tumour.

M

magnesium (5.3) – a mineral salt required for the formation of chlorophyll.

meiosis (10.5) – cell division that occurs when gametes are produced; it reduces the number of chromosomes from 46 to 23.

Mendel (10.8) – Augustinian monk who was called 'the father of genetics'.

menstrual cycle (8.5) – the recurring pattern of changes in a woman's reproductive organs. Each cycle usually lasts about 28 days.

menstruation (8.5) – the breakdown and loss of the inner lining of the uterus.

micropropagation (10.5) – a way of using individual cells to produce lots of identical plants.

microvilli (2.3) – microscopic projections found on the surface of the villi in the small intestine.

mineral salts (6.4) – essential minerals that are required by living organisms.

mitochondria (1.1) – microscopic organelles found in the cytoplasm of plant and animal cells. They are the site of many of the reactions of respiration (singular = mitochondrion).

mitosis (10.5) – cell division that produces identical copies of cells.

motor neurone (8.3) – a nerve cell that carries impulses from the CNS to the effectors.

mucus (4.3) – a slimy liquid that is secreted by goblet cells to provide lubrication and trap foreign particles.

mutation (10.3) – a change in the structure of a gene or DNA, caused by such things as chemicals, X-rays or radiation.

mutualism (7.3) – a relationship between two organisms of different species in which both organisms gain.

N

nastic (8.6) – a growth response by plants to a non-directional stimulus.

natural selection (10.9) – a process in which organisms that are most suited to the environment survive and produce more offspring.

nerve (8.2) – a collection of neurones held together in a bundle by connective tissue.

nerve impulse (8.2) – an electro-chemical change that passes along a neurone.

neurone (8.2) – a single nerve cell. Many neurones make up a nerve.

neurotransmitter (8.2) – a chemical that is released at a synapse when a nerve impulse arrives. It diffuses across the synapse and starts an impulse in the next nerve cell.

nitrifying (7.5) – the process that converts ammonium compounds to nitrates.

nitrogen (5.3) – a highly unreactive gas found in the air and required for protein production.

nitrogen fixing (7.5) – the process in which nitrogen gas is converted into nitrates and other compounds of nitrogen that can be used by plants.

nucleus (1.1, 10.1) – the area of a cell that contains the genetic material and so controls all the processes occurring in the cell.

O

oestrogen (8.5) – a hormone secreted by the ovaries which controls the female secondary sex characteristics.

optic nerve (8.1) – a collection of nerve cells that send information from the eyes to the brain.

optimum (9.2) – the optimum conditions are those at which the rate of reaction is fastest.

organ (1.2) – a structure made up of different tissues working together to perform a particular function.

osmoregulation (9.3) – control of the body's water level by the kidneys.

osmosis (1.4, 6.4) – the movement of water molecules from a dilute solution to a concentrated solution, through a partially permeable membrane.

ovum (10.5) – a female sex cell (plural = ova).

oxygen debt (3.2) – caused by anaerobic respiration and the production of lactic acid. After exercise the debt has to be repaid in order to break down the lactic acid.

P

pancreas (9.1, 10.4) – the organ that produces the hormone insulin.

parasite (7.3) – an organism that lives on or in another living organism, causing it harm.

partially permeable (1.4) – allowing certain molecules through but not others.

passive (1.3) – a passive process does not require an input of energy from respiration.

persistent (7.6) – a chemical that breaks down very slowly in the environment.

phenotype (10.7) – the expression of the gene e.g. tall, short, blue eyes etc.

phloem (5.1) – plant tissue that transports dissolved food around the plant.

phosphorus (5.3) – an essential mineral salt required by plants and animals.

photosynthesis (3.1, 5.1) – the process by which plants convert water and carbon dioxide into oxygen and glucose, using energy from the Sun.

phototropism (8.6) – a growth response in plants either towards or away from a light source.

plasma (6.3) – a pale-yellow liquid that forms the fluid part of the blood.

platelets (6.3) – small fragments of cells found in the blood and involved in blood clotting.

population (7.1) – a group of organisms of one species living together in a habitat.

predator (7.3) – an animal that hunts and kills other animals for food.

prey (7.3) – an animal that is hunted and killed for food by a predator.

productivity (7.6) – the yield of a crop or livestock that is made in a certain time.

progesterone (8.5) – a hormone produced by the ovary after the ovum has been released. It maintains the wall of the uterus during pregnancy.

protease (2.1) – an enzyme that digests protein.

protein (5.3) – a large molecule made from a combination of amino acids.

pulmonary (6.2) – relating to the lungs, e.g. pulmonary artery and vein.

pupil (8.1) – the hole in the iris through which light enters the eye.

pyramid of biomass (7.4) – a diagram that represents the total mass at each trophic level of a food chain.

Q

quadrat (7.1) – a square frame that is used to estimate the number of organisms in a particular area.

R

rate (5.2) – how quickly something happens.

recessive (10.7) – an allele that does not express itself in the phenotype unless two are present in the gene.

red blood cells (6.3) – blood cells that contain the red pigment haemoglobin, which carries oxygen from the lungs around the body.

reflex (8.3) – a rapid response to a stimulus brought about without conscious thought in order to protect an individual from damage.

reflex arc (8.3) – the pathway along which nerve impulses pass in a simple reflex action.

relay neurone (8.3) – a nerve cell in the CNS that passes impulses between two neurones.

respiration (3.1, 5.3) – the breaking down of glucose to release energy.

retina (8.1) – the layer of light sensitive cells lining the back of the eye.

rods (8.1) – light-sensitive cells in the retina that work in dim light but cannot detect colour.

root hairs (6.4) – cells found on the surface of a root that absorb water from the soil.

root nodules (7.5) – small growths from the roots of plants in the pea and bean family. They contain nitrogen-fixing bacteria.

S

salt (9.3) – a compound (sodium chloride ; NaCl) that is taken in with food and is excreted by the kidneys.

seedless fruit (8.7) fruit that develop without fertilisation of a flower and so do not contain seeds.

selective breeding (10.6) – a way of improving stock by selecting and breeding from those animals and plants that have the desired characteristics.

selective weedkiller (8.7) – artificial plant hormones that kill some plants but not others.

sensory neurone (8.3) – a nerve cell that carries impulses from a receptor to the CNS.

sex chromosomes (10.2) – the two chromosomes that determine sex. They are usually referred to as X and Y.

shivering (9.2) – rapid muscular contractions that generate heat and help to maintain the body's temperature.

skin (9.2) – tissue which surrounds the body and acts as a barrier against invading microbes.

specialisation (1.2) – the process by which cells have become adapted to perform only a certain function and so have become more efficient.

species (10.9) – a group of organisms that breeds and produces fertile offspring.

specific (2.1) – the characteristic of an enzyme in which it will only act on a certain reaction.

sperm (10.5) – a male sex cell.

spinal cord (8.3) – a large collection of neurones that runs up the vertebral column and joins with the brain.

spirometer (4.2) – a machine that is used to measure a person's breathing rate and depth.

starch (5.3) – a food storage substance produced by plants.

stomata (5.1) – small pores on the underside of a leaf that regulate the release of water, and allow release of oxygen and the absorption of carbon dioxide (singular = stoma).

survival of the fittest (10.9) – organisms that are best adapted to their environment tend to produce successful offspring, thus ensuing their survival.

sustainable (7.7) – the use of the Earth's resources at a rate at which they can be replaced.

sweating (9.2) – the release of liquid onto the skin to cool the body by latent heat of evaporation.

synapse (8.2) – a minute gap between two neurones.

system (1.2) – a collection of organs working together to perform related functions.

T

temperature (5.2, 6.5, 9.2) – a scale to compare the intensity of heat of different objects. Normal body temperature is 37°C.

testosterone (8.5) – a hormone, produced in the testes, that controls the male's secondary sex characteristics.

thorax (4.1) – the cavity in the body above the diaphragm that contains the lungs and heart.

tidal volume (4.2) – the volume of air exchanged in each breath.

tissue (1.2) – a collection of similar cells that work together to perform a particular function.

tissue fluid (6.1) – plasma minus the large blood protein molecules that has leaked out of blood vessels and bathes all the body's cells.

trachea (4.1) – a tube, strengthened by cartilage, which carries air between the mouth and the bronchi.

transpiration pull (6.5) – the force that pulls water up from the roots to the leaves.

tropic (8.6) – the growth response in plants to a directional stimulus.

turgid (1.4) – the condition in plant cells when the cytoplasm pushes against the cell wall.

U

urea (9.3) – a waste material produced from the breakdown of unwanted amino acids.

urine (9.3) – a solution of urea in water which is stored in the bladder prior to elimination.

V

vacuole (1.1) – part of a cell that contains fluid enclosed in a membrane.

valve (6.1, 6.2) – structure that prevents blood flowing backwards. They are found in the heart and in veins.

variation (10.3, 10.9) – differences that exist between organisms.

vascular bundle (6.4) – a collection of xylem and phloem vessels that transport food and water around a plant.

vegetarian (7.6) – a person who does not eat meat.

vein (6.1, 6.2) – a blood vessel that returns blood to the heart.

vena cava (6.2) – the large vein that returns blood from the body to the heart.

ventricle (6.2) – the lower two muscular chambers of the heart. The left ventricle pumps blood around the body; the right ventricle pumps blood to the lungs.

villi (2.3) – small finger-like projections in the small intestine that increase the surface area for absorption (singular = villus).

vital capacity (4.2) – the maximum amount of air that can be exchanged in one breath.

voluntary action (8.3) – a response to a stimulus which involves conscious thought.

W

water (9.3) – a molecule that is essential to all living organisms, enabling life processes to be carried out. It is reabsorbed in large amounts by kidney tubules.

water potential (1.4) – a measure of the tendency of a cell to lose or gain water by osmosis.

waxy cuticle (6.4) – waterproof layer found on the upper surface of most leaves.

white blood cells (6.3) – found in the blood and form part of the body's defence mechanism. They produce antibodies and engulf bacteria.

wilt (1.4) – the drooping of a plant when its cells become flaccid.

XYZ

X (10.2) – a sex chromosome. Females have two X chromosomes; males have only one.

xylem (5.1, 6.4) – conductive tissue found in plants that carries water up from the roots to the leaves.

Y (10.2) – a sex chromosome found in males.

Glossary (TB A1–A4)

Terms set in pink are higher tier material.

A

Acetobacter (A3.2) – a bacteria that converts alcohol to vinegar.

active immunity (A4.4) – immunity that results from by the body making its own antibodies.

adrenaline (A1.3) – a hormone released from the adrenal glands.

AIDS (A4.2) – acquired immune deficiency syndrome – the collection of diseases that results from destruction of the immune system following infection with HIV.

amino acid (A1.1) – basic building block of protein.

anaemia (A1.1) – a disease resulting from a lack of red blood cells.

antibiotic (A4.3) – a drug that is used internally to kill bacteria. Antibiotics do not kill viruses.

antibiotic resistance (A4.3) – bacteria that are not killed by a particular antibiotic are described as antibiotic resistant.

antibodies (A4.4) – chemicals produced by the body that help to destroy foreign invading organisms.

antiseptic (A4.3) – a chemical that is used externally to kill micro-organisms.

arid (A2.2) – a dry habitat with little available water.

artificial system (A2.1) – a system that classifies organisms on the basis of a single characteristic.

athlete's foot (A4.1) – a fungal infection of the foot.

autotrophic (A2.2) – the production of food from simple molecules, usually by photosynthesis.

B

bacteria (A4.1, A4.3) – a type of microscopic organism (singular = bacterium).

bases (A3.4) – the four chemicals designated A, T, C and G that code for the instructions of life on DNA.

binomial system (A2.1) – a method of naming organisms using two names, the first being the genus, the second the species.

C

canning (A3.1) – the process of preserving food by sealing it in a tin.

catalyst (A3.3) – a chemical that increases the rate of reaction without being used up.

cerebellum (A1.5) – an area at the back of the brain responsible for the control of balance and co-ordinating movements.

cerebrum (A1.5) – the area at the top of the brain responsible for conscious thought.

chemical preservatives (A3.1) – chemicals that prevent the decay of food.

choice chamber (A2.3) – a device used to determine the preferred habitat of organisms.

cholesterol (A1.1) – a lipid-based molecule needed for the correct functioning of cell membranes. Excess cholesterol in the blood can block blood vessels, leading to coronary heart disease.

chymosin (A3.2, A3.5) – an enzyme that clots milk.

class (A2.1) – grouping of organisms in classification between phylum and order.

conditioned reflex (A1.5) – an automatic response that has been learnt and does not involve conscious thought.

contaminated (A3.1) – the presence of an unwanted substance or micro-organisms.

coronary arteries (A1.1) – the main blood vessels supplying the heart muscle with oxygenated blood.

curds (A3.2) – the semi-solid part of milk in the cheese-making process.

dental decay (A1.1) – the breakdown of the surface of the teeth, caused by acid produced by bacteria in the mouth.

dialysis machine (A1.4) – a device used by a person whose kidneys are not working to regulate the composition of the blood.

DNA (A3.4) – the molecule that codes for all the instructions needed to make an organism, and is also capable of replication.

dorsal root (A1.5) – the branch of a spinal nerve that carries sensory neurones into the spinal cord.

drying (A3.1) – removing water. Drying food prevents bacterial decay.

encoded (A3.5) – the sequence of bases that spells out the instructions in DNA.

end plate (A1.5) – a swelling at the end of a motor neurone that comes into close proximity to a muscle fibre. Transmitter substances are released from the end plate and stimulate the muscle fibre to contract.

enzyme (A3.3, A3.5) organic catalyst that speeds up the rate of a reaction.

external fertilisation (A2.3) – the fusing of gametes outside the female's body.

extrinsic sugars (A1.1) – sugars in food that are not held in cells.

family (A2.1) – grouping of organisms in classification between order and genus.

fermentation vessel (A3.5) – a container used in industry in which micro-organisms carry out anaerobic processes.

food (A3.1) – the source of nutrients and fuel for the body.

freezing (A3.1) – use of sub-zero temperatures to preserve food.

fungi (A3.1, A4.1, A4.5) – a type of microscopic organism (singular = fungus).

G

gene (A3.4) – a section of DNA that codes for one specific instruction.

genus (A2.1) – grouping of organisms in classification between family and species (plural = genera).

gill bar (A2.3) – the part of a gill that carries blood vessels and supports the gill filaments.

gill filaments (A2.3) – the part of a gill responsible for gaseous exchange.

gill rakers (A2.3) – the part of a gill that filters water.

gills (A2.3) – paired structures in fish responsible for gaseous exchange.

graft (A4.5) – the process of adding tissue, usually from a different organism.

growth spurt (A1.2) – a phase of rapid growth that occurs during puberty.

H

heterotrophic (A2.2) – the intake of food as complex organic molecules.

HIV (A4.2) – human immunodeficiency virus – the virus that infects white blood cells and ultimately leads to AIDS.

hyphae (A4.1) – thread-like structures that form a fungus.

I

immune system (A4.2) – the body's defence against foreign organisms.

immunisation (A4.4) – the process of stimulating the body to produce antibodies to a specific antigen.

infectious (A4.1) – a disease that can be passed from one person to another.

internal fertilisation (A2.3) – the fusing of male and female gametes inside the female's body.

irradiation (A3.1) – the process of bombarding a substance with radiation.

K

kinesis (A2.3) – a behaviour pattern that involves more rapid movement in areas where conditions are unfavourable.

kidney tubules (1.4) – structures in the kidney that filter the blood and modify the content of the filtrate.

kingdom (A2.1) – the first major grouping in classification. There are five kingdoms.

L

lactic acid (A3.2) – a chemical produced when *Lactobacillus* breaks down the milk sugar lactose. (It is also produced by anaerobic respiration in humans, and causes muscle fatigue.)

Lactobacillus (A3.2) – a bacteria that converts the milk sugar lactose into lactic acid.

larva(e) (A2.3) – a stage in many insect life cycles between the egg and pupa (plural = larvae).

M

medulla (A1.3) – an area at the base of the brain responsible for many reflex control mechanisms.

meninges (A1.5) – protective membranes enclosing the brain and spinal cord.

metamorphosis (A2.3) – a complete change in body form.

moisture (A3.1) – water; required by all living organisms.

Mucor mieleli (A3.5) – a species of fungus.

mycelium (A4.1) – a network of hyphae that make up a fungus.

mycoprotein (A3.2) – a protein produced by a fungus.

myxomatosis (A4.4) – a disease of rabbits caused by the myxoma virus.

N

natural system (A2.1) – a system in which organisms are classified on the basis of the maximum number of common characteristics.

nephron (A1.4) – the functional unit of the kidney, consisting of a kidney tubule and blood vessels. There are millions of nephrons in each kidney.

O

optimum (A3.3) – the optimum conditions are those at which the rate of reaction is fastest.

order (A2.1) – grouping of organisms in classification between class and family.

P

parasite (A4.2) – an organism that lives on or in another living organism, causing it harm.

passive immunity (A4.4) – temporary immunity produced by preformed antibodies (which are injected, or are passed from mother to baby).

pasteurised (A3.2) – the process of destroying harmful bacteria in milk so that it is safe to drink.

pathogen (A4.4) – an organism that causes disease.

pectinase (A3.5) – an enzyme that breaks down pectin.

peristalsis (A1.1) – muscular contractions that move food along the digestive system.

phage (A4.3) – a virus that attacks bacteria.

phylum (A2.1) – groupings of organisms in classification between kingdom and class (plural = phyla).

potato blight (A4.5) – a fungal disease that affects potato plants.

protein (A3.4) – a large molecule formed from a combination of amino acids.

rabies (A4.4) – a viral disease characterised by madness and convulsions.

recombinant (A3.4) – an alteration of the position or number of genes found in DNA.

reference nutrient intake (RNI) (A1.2) – the amount of a molecule in the diet that is needed per day by most people for normal health.

rickets (A1.1) – a disease characterised by weak bones, arising from lack of vitamin D.

RNA (A3.4) – a single-strand template of DNA.

root stock (A4.5) – the root to which a stem from another plant is grafted.

Salmonella (A3.1) – a species of bacteria that cause food poisoning.

saturated fatty acids (A1.1) – fatty acids that do not contain any double bonds.

scurvy (A1.1) – a disease characterised by bleeding gums, painful joints and slow healing of wounds, arising from lack of vitamin C.

skeletal muscles (A1.5) – muscles that bring about movement of the bones of the skeleton. These muscles are under conscious control.

smallpox (A4.4) – a disease characterised by fever and pustules, caused by a virus. It has been eradicated by a global immunisation programme.

species (A2.1) – a group of organisms that breeds and produces fertile offspring; the smallest grouping in classification.

specific (A3.3) – the characteristic of an enzyme in which it will only act on a certain reaction.

spore (A4.5) – a small reproductive body produced by fungi.

stomata (A4.5) – small pores on the underside of a leaf that regulate the release of water, and allow release of oxygen and the absorption of carbon dioxide (singular = stoma).

Streptococcus (A3.2) – a genus of bacteria.

stroke (A1.3) – a blockage or burst blood vessel in the brain, starving brain tissue of oxygen.

substrate (A3.3) – a substance acted upon by an enzyme.

syndrome (A4.2) – a collection of symptoms of a disease.

taxonomy (A2.1) – the process of classifying organisms in groups.

tetanus (A4.1) – a disease caused by bacteria, characterised by muscle spasm and rigidity.

ultra-heat treatment (A3.1) – brief heating of milk to a high temperature to kill micro-organisms.

unsaturated fatty acids (A1.1) – fatty acids that contain one or more double bonds.

vegan (A1.2) – someone who does not eat or use animal products.

vegetarian (A1.2) – a person who does not eat meat.

ventral root (A1.5) – the branch of a spinal nerve that carries sensory neurones out of the spinal cord.

virulent (A4.4) – able to cause disease.

virus (A4.1, A4.2, A4.3) – a small packet of DNA or RNA that reproduces by invading cells.

warmth (A3.1) – heat; required by all living organisms.

water potential (A3.1) – a measure of the tendency of a cell to loss or gain water by osmosis.

weaned (A1.2) – the process of introducing solid food into a baby's diet.

whey (A3.2) – the liquid part of milk that is produced in the cheese-making process.

white blood cells (A4.2) – found in the blood and form part of the body's defence mechanism. They produce antibodies and engulf bacteria.

yeast (A3.2) – a fungus, species of which are used in the production of bread and alcoholic drinks.

Improving your longer written answers

All GCSE science papers have questions that require an answer with a series of linked sentences. These questions are called **extended** and **continuous writing.** At least 25% of the marks in your examination are awarded for these questions that require longer answers.

Most candidates do less well on these questions than on other types of question. It is therefore well worth practising these answers so that you score better marks.

Below are examples of typical questions that require a longer written answer. Some help is given to show you how to answer the first one.

Describe how oxygen is placed in the atmosphere by the process of photosynthesis *[6 + 1]*

- First, think carefully about what the question is asking you to do. It asks you to *describe* how oxygen is produced by the process of photosynthesis. It does not ask you about respiration, osmosis, or even global warming.
- There are six marks for content (shown by the 6 in brackets). This means that you must make at least six different points. These points must be made in the correct order.
- Here are some points you might make. Some are wrong, some are correct but are not relevant to the question, and some would be needed in a good answer. Go through each of the statements and decide which should be included.
    - Plants make carbon dioxide.
    - The oxygen passes out through the stomata into the atmosphere.
    - Glucose and oxygen are produced.
    - Plants take in carbon dioxide through the stomata.
    - Photosynthesis only occurs during the day.
    - Xylem vessels are part of the vascular bundle.
    - Chlorophyll is a green pigment found in plants.
    - Chlorophyll absorbs light energy.
    - The glucose produced is a protein.
    - Plants lose their leaves in winter.
    - The process is known as respiration.
    - Nitrogen is needed to make glucose.

- To score well you must present the statements in the correct order – the statements should follow on logically from each other.

Sample answer

Photosynthesis is a process in which plants use the green pigment chlorophyll ✓ to absorb energy from sunlight. ✓ The energy is used to combine water and carbon dioxide ✓ to make glucose and oxygen. ✓ The carbon dioxide is taken in through the stomata ✓ and the oxygen produced diffuses out through the same stomata into the atmosphere. ✓

The percentage of carbon dioxide in the atmosphere has risen over the last one hundred years, due to the burning of fossil fuels. The percentage of oxygen in the air, however, remains constant. Explain. *[6 + 1]*

This time your answer must be an *explanation*, not just a description. You must explain why the level of carbon dioxide has increased, and why the level of oxygen has remained the same. The key word is explain.

Make a list of the relevant points and then write out your answer. There are six marks in total, but you should not assume that this means three marks for each part.

Marks for quality

Marks also awarded for the *quality of written communication* in this type of question. In each of the example questions above there are six marks for content. The examiner can add one more mark for the quality of written communication. This can be awarded for any of the following:

- The correct use of sentences with capital letter, verb and full stop.
- The correct use and spelling of scientific words.
- The correct use of scientific terms such as photosynthesis.
- Putting events in the correct and logical order to ensure communication.

Your longer answers will improve if you remember what you have done on this page.

Data handling

Line graphs

Line graphs are a useful way of presenting data.

- You can **extrapolate** from a graph – you can estimate what will happen beyond the range of your measurement by extending the line of the graph (see fig 1).
- You can also **interpolate** – you can estimate the reading between two known data points.

Many GCSE question papers have a question that requires you to draw and use line graphs. You will probably draw line graphs for your coursework.

On Foundation tier written papers, the axes and scales will have been drawn for you, and one or two points may already be plotted. All the data points will be on a straight line or a curve and there will be no points in the wrong place.

On Higher tier papers, or for coursework, you will have to choose the scales and axes.

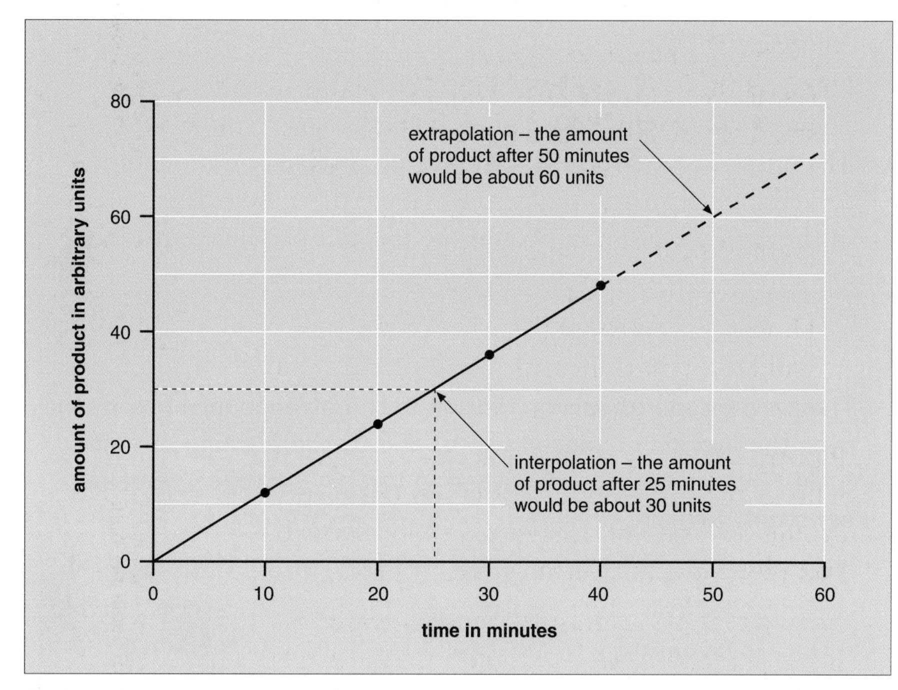

fig 1

amount of carbon dioxide in the air as a multiple of the normal concentration	0	0.5	1.0	1.5	2.0	2.5
rate of photosynthesis in grams of sugar per hour	0	1.2	2.2	3.6	3.8	3.8

fig 2

How to draw a line graph

- You will need a sharp pencil, a 30 cm ruler and a sheet of 2 mm graph paper.

  Here is some information from a data book (see fig 2).

- In this case, the rate of photosynthesis depends upon the level of carbon dioxide.
  - The dependent variable – which in this example is the rate of photosynthesis – is plotted on the vertical axis (called the *y* axis).

- The independent variable – which in this example is the level of carbon dioxide – is plotted on the horizontal axis (the x axis).

- Use a ruler to draw the axes and label them.
- Now choose suitable scales.
  - On the x axis, one large square (i.e. ten small squares) can be equivalent to a 0.5-fold increase in the carbon dioxide level.
  - On the y axis, one large square can be 1 gram of sugar per hour.
  - The axes do not have to start at zero. However, you should remember that you will lose a mark if your graph does not fill at least half the grid.
- Plot the points carefully, marking each point with a small cross or a dot with a circle around it. You will lose one or two marks if you plot the points incorrectly.
- Now you have to draw a line of best–fit. If the points are on a straight line, use a ruler to draw the line. Otherwise, draw the line of best fit freehand; do not just join the points together. Sometimes with experimental results there are anomalous points. These are points that do not appear to fit in with the rest of the data. Draw your best–fit line to miss these points.

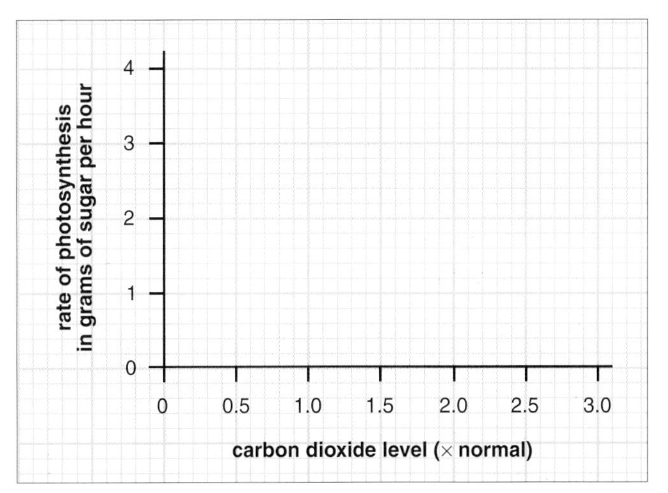

fig 3

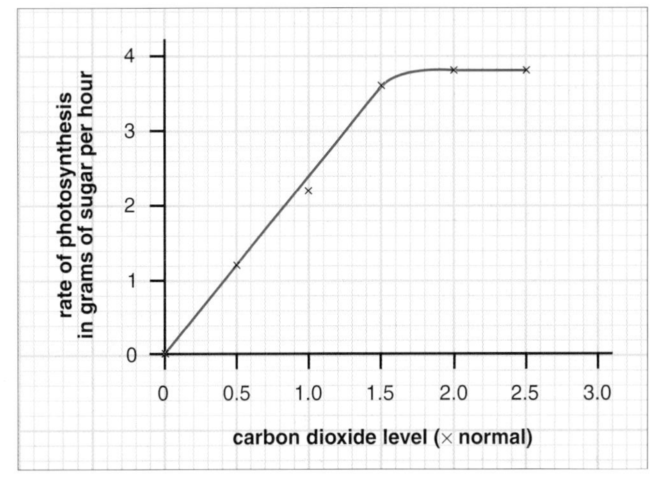

fig 4

Here is a set of results. Draw a graph of this data.

time in *s*	0	10	15	20	25	30	35	40	45
volume of gas collected in *cm³*	0	34	47	57	63	70	69	70	70

fig 5

Coursework

You will be expected to do some coursework during your two years of study. Your coursework is extremely important because it is worth 20% of your final mark. You should aim to do as well as you possibly can in your coursework because this will give you a good start when taking your final examinations. Pupils who produce good coursework usually get good GCSE grades.

Your teacher will assess the coursework. It is also possible that an external moderator will send for samples of work from your class. The moderator's job is to make sure that your work has been assessed correctly.

Your coursework will be assessed for four skills. These are:

- planning
- obtaining evidence – carrying out the experiment and collecting your results
- analysis – using your results to explain what you have found out
- evaluation – how well the experiment has worked and how it could be improved.

Each of the first three skills is marked out of eight marks. Evaluation is marked out of six marks. This gives a possible total of 30 marks. Make sure you give careful thought to your coursework so that you get as many of these marks as possible.

Coursework checklist

The following checklist will help you to make sure that you have covered all the points necessary when doing your coursework. As an example, we have used the experiment in which you measure the change in mass (or length) of potato chips in sugar solutions of different concentrations (see page 10).

Be warned ...

If you miss out any of the points in each skill, your teacher must stop marking. This means that even if you have done some excellent work later on, you cannot be credited for the higher level work because you have missed out a lower level part of the skill.

Planning

For **2** marks — ▶ Simple: just say what you are going to do.

For a further **2** marks (**4** in total) — ▶ Say what equipment you are going to use. It is a good idea to both write a list and draw a diagram. Say what evidence you are going to collect and what measurements you are going to take.

For a further **2** marks (**6** in total)

▶ Make a simple prediction: what you think is going to happen. Introduce some science into your planning by explaining your reasons for doing the experiment in the way that you describe. Use some science to justify your prediction. For example, you might say that you think the potato chips will gain mass when placed in water but lose mass when placed in a concentrated sugar solution, and that this is the result of the process of osmosis.

Say what variables you are going to control – which factors you are going to keep the same, and which single factor you will vary. Variables that occur in many experiments include temperature, time, concentration and surface area. Explain what measurement(s) you are going to take, how many times and what the range of your measurements will be.

For a further **2** marks (**8** in total)

▶ You must now use detailed scientific knowledge to justify your prediction. For example, you might explain how osmosis works and that when the potato neither gains nor loses mass, the solution and the cell sap will be in equilibrium. You can also explain that by plotting the results on a graph, you will be able to work out the water potential of the potato cell sap.

It is particularly important that you do some preliminary work. This means doing a simple experiment first to find out, for example, the range and concentrations of solutions that will work in your experiment. It is no good doing the whole experiment only to find that you have chosen the wrong concentrations!

Obtaining evidence

For **2** marks

▶ Explain how you will make sure that your experiment is safe. This might include ensuring that reagent bottle tops are replaced or that you will use eye protectors.

For a further **2** marks (**4** in total)

▶ You need to take a series of measurements that will enable you to make a sensible conclusion. You will need to write down your results, usually in the form of a table.

For a further **2** marks (**6** in total)

▶ You need to repeat your measurements and take an average of your results. For example, use three potato chips for each concentration and work out the average change in mass (or length). The measurements must be accurate, that is to the nearest two decimal places of a gram.

For a further **2** marks (**8** in total)

▶ Your measurements need to be taken accurately and with care. Your results should be recorded clearly and accurately and should be processed. For example, you could calculate the average percentage change in mass for the chips in each solution.

Analysis

For **2** marks

▶ Just write a simple explanation of your results.

For a further **2** marks (**4** in total)

▶ Draw a simple graph or chart of your results. Identify the trend or pattern that your results show. For example, potato chips gain mass at low sugar concentrations and lose mass at high sugar concentrations.

For a further **2** marks (**6** in total)

▶ You must show the line of best–fit on your graph, if appropriate, and you should used your graph to provide evidence for your conclusion. For example, you could determine the exact concentration of the potato cell sap from your graph.

You must then use scientific knowledge and understanding to explain your results. For example, you could draw a diagram to explain how osmosis works.

For a further **2** marks (**8** in total)

▶ You must use detailed scientific knowledge and processed evidence to explain your conclusion. For example, explain what happens when two solutions are isotonic and in equilibrium and show that this knowledge can be used to show that when there is no percentage change in the mass of the potato chips, the sugar solution must equal the concentration of the cell sap.

You must also use your results to explain whether your original conclusion was accurate or if it needs to be modified in light of your findings.

Evaluation

For **2** marks

▶ Write a simple comment about how well the experiment went.

For a further **2** marks (**4** in total)

▶ You need to comment on how accurate your measurements were and on any measurements that were not accurate. For example, if all the points plotted on the graph are close to the line of best–fit, then they are probably accurate. If one point is a long way from the line, it is probably an anomalous result and should be commented on.

You also need to suggest changes to your experiment that would improve the accuracy and reliability. For example, you could suggest that all the chips were of constant size or surface area.

For a further **2** marks (**6** in total)

▶ You need to explain whether your results are accurate enough to ensure that your conclusion is correct. It is possible that your results were not sufficiently accurate to do this, in which case you should say so.

You also need to suggest ways of extending and improving your investigation. For example, you might wish to test chips made from potatoes at different stages of development in order to find out the point at which starch is converted into sugar, thus changing the water potential of the cells. It is important to describe in detail how you would do this.

Index

D

E

F

G